A Casebook on the Hawthorne Question

A Casebook
on the
HAWTHORNE
QUESTION

Edited by

AGNES MC NEILL DONOHUE

Loyola University

THOMAS Y. CROWELL COMPANY

New York · Established 1834

First Printing, December, 1962
Second Printing, January, 1964
Third Printing, September, 1966
Fourth Printing, November, 1968
Fifth Printing, June, 1969
Sixth Printing, January, 1971
Seventh Printing, September, 1971

L.C. Card 63-8325
ISBN 0-690-17567-1

Designed by Laurel Wagner
Cover design by Orest Neimanis

Manufactured in the United States of America
by Vail-Ballou Press, Inc., Binghamton, N.Y.

for

L. *and* H. MC N., L. G., S. M. C., *and* D. W.

"the still small voice of gratitude"

Preface

The purpose of a *Casebook on the Hawthorne Question* is to stimulate the critical attention of the reader to an awareness of the many "questions" in Hawthorne. None of these questions involves the modern reader more meaningfully, or causes him to respond more equivocally, than that of Hawthorne's ambiguity. While maintaining a careful poise and an apparent detachment, and using traditional social history or theology as frames of reference, Hawthorne often summons up the most frightening dilemmas of human existence—and then withdraws into a rather conventional moral statement or an evasion.

The ten stories and sketches in the *Casebook* disclose a signal ambiguity in Hawthorne—his attitude toward man's moral nature. Sometimes he seems to assert the depravity of man while at the same time he dreams of an Adamic hero guileless in his prelapsarian Eden. He vacillates between trusting the human heart's intuitions as good and advancing his conviction that the heart is a "foul cavern" which must be destroyed in order to be purified.

Hawthorne's ambivalence about guilt and innocence can be seen as a lodestone that draws into its magnetic field other problems of human life. He writes of innocents initiated into shrewdness; secret sin and isolation; compulsive rituals of atonement and sacrifice; self righteousness becoming fanaticism; science confronting original sin; witchcraft and devil worship; carnal knowledge and guiltless love; the search for a home, a father, a self—in short, man's dark odyssey in an alien world.

The ambiguity in Hawthorne's stories is at once his triumph and, for some literalist critics, his failure. The tension it creates is a dramatic asset. Many of the tales, or romances as he thought of them, are multi-leveled, ironic explorations of the human psyche—capable of endless extensions of meaning and of stimulating repeated analysis and interpretation.

The often conflicting feelings that Hawthorne has about man's moral nature are expressed obliquely in allegory, myths, archetypes, symbols, and images. He uses recurrently the light and the dark, the red and the black, the forest and the clearing, the head and the heart, the garden and the labyrinth, the prison and the grave, the journey and return. Hawthorne avoids the literal by asking rhetorical questions or offering through various characters contradictory explanations of events.

Hawthorne is honest enough not to provide explicit landmarks for the human spirit because he himself is only too sensitively aware of the hidden unknown perils of the journey. He settles for remarkable evocations of the complexity and mystery of life.

The book is made up of four sections. In the first appear two sketches ("The Haunted Mind" and "Fancy's Show Box") and two stories ("The Maypole of Merry Mount" and "The Minister's Black Veil"), unaccompanied by critical articles. These may serve as an introduction to Hawthorne, and the student can write analyses of them unimpeded by other criticism. In the second section are six stories, each followed by two critical articles that the student will probably do well to turn to only after having first carefully read the story itself. He is then advised to reread the story critically as a test for the suggested interpretations. The third section, to provide a general background in Hawthorne, offers seven selections from "classical" Hawthorne criticism. The first two of these present without abridgment the appraisals of two famous contemporaries, Poe and Melville; following them are critical commentaries by Henry James, D. H. Lawrence, Yvor Winters, F. O. Matthiessen, and Q. D. Leavis. Spanning almost a century, all these selections are of value not only for their intrinsic literary interest, but also for the historical perspective within which they allow Hawthorne criticism to be viewed.

Various appendices constitute the final section of this casebook: a biographical sketch of Hawthorne; study questions on each of the stories; suggested topics for papers of various lengths—most based on materials in this book, but some requiring library work—and an extensive bibliography. Finally, I have included a few sections from the *American Notebooks;* these throw some light on Hawthorne's working habits and show that his random jottings often became the nuclei for later tales.

Throughout the book, bracketed numerals indicate the end of a page on which the selection appeared in the cited source. If the page of the original ended with a hyphenated word, the page number here follows the word. Omission of material in the source is indicated by a row of five ellipsis marks. In instances where material omitted is both at the bottom of one page of the source and at the top of the following page, I have inserted two lines of ellipsis marks, so that the precise place of the page break can be indicated. Brackets around footnotes denote my editorial insertions. Typographical errors have been corrected throughout, and spelling has been regularized in some instances.

AGNES MC NEILL DONOHUE

Lake Forest, Illinois
December, 1962

Contents

SKETCHES AND TALES

The Haunted Mind*

What a singular moment is the first one, when you have hardly begun to recollect yourself, after starting from midnight slumber? By unclosing your eyes so suddenly, you seem to have surprised the personages of your dream in full convocation round your bed, and catch one broad glance at them before they can flit into obscurity. Or, to vary the metaphor, you find yourself, for a single instant, wide awake in that realm of illusions, whither sleep has been the passport, and behold its ghostly inhabitants and wondrous scenery, with a perception of their strangeness such as you never attain while the dream is undisturbed. The distant sound of a church clock is borne faintly on the wind. You question with yourself, half seriously, whether it has stolen to your waking ear from some gray tower that stood within the precincts of your dream. While yet in suspense, another clock flings its heavy clang over the slumbering town, with so full and distinct a sound, and such a long murmur in the neighboring air, that you are certain it must proceed from the steeple at the nearest corner. You count the strokes—one—two, and there they cease, with a booming sound, like the gathering of a third stroke within the bell.

If you could choose an hour of wakefulness out of the whole night, it would be this. Since your sober bedtime, at eleven, you have had rest enough to take off the pressure of yesterday's fatigue; while before [343] you, till the sun comes from "far Cathay" to brighten your window, there is almost the space of a summer night, one hour to be spent in thought, with the mind's eye half shut, and two in pleasant dreams, and two in that strangest of enjoyments, the forgetfulness alike of joy and woe. The moment of rising belongs to another period of time, and appears so distant that the plunge out of a warm bed into the frosty air

* This sketch and all of the following Hawthorne stories are reprinted from the famous Riverside Edition of *The Complete Works of Nathaniel Hawthorne* with introductory notes by George Parsons Lathrop (12 vols.; Boston: Houghton Mifflin Company, 1883). "The Haunted Mind" first appeared in 1835 in *The Token*, an annual journal of American literature and engraving. It was later published in *Twice-Told Tales* (Second Series) in 1842.

cannot yet be anticipated with dismay. Yesterday has already vanished among the shadows of the past; to-morrow has not yet emerged from the future. You have found an intermediate space, where the business of life does not intrude; where the passing moment lingers, and becomes truly the present; a spot where Father Time, when he thinks nobody is watching him, sits down by the wayside to take breath. Oh, that he would fall asleep, and let mortals live on without growing older!

Hitherto you have lain perfectly still, because the slightest motion would dissipate the fragments of your slumber. Now, being irrevocably awake, you peep through the half-drawn window curtain, and observe that the glass is ornamented with fanciful devices in frostwork, and that each pane presents something like a frozen dream. There will be time enough to trace out the analogy while waiting the summons to breakfast. Seen through the clear portion of the glass, where the silvery mountain peaks of the frost scenery do not ascend, the most conspicuous object is the steeple; the white spire of which directs you to the wintry lustre of the firmament. You may almost distinguish the figures on the clock that has just told the hour. Such a frosty sky, and the snow-covered roofs, and the long vista of the frozen street, all white, and the distant [344] water hardened into rock, might make you shiver, even under four blankets and a woollen comforter. Yet look at that one glorious star! Its beams are distinguishable from all the rest, and actually cast the shadow of the casement on the bed, with a radiance of deeper hue than moonlight, though not so accurate an outline.

You sink down and muffle your head in the clothes, shivering all the while, but less from bodily chill than the bare idea of a polar atmosphere. It is too cold even for the thoughts to venture abroad. You speculate on the luxury of wearing out a whole existence in bed, like an oyster in its shell, content with the sluggish ecstasy of inaction, and drowsily conscious of nothing but delicious warmth, such as you now feel again. Ah! that idea has brought a hideous one in its train. You think how the dead are lying in their cold shrouds and narrow coffins, through the drear winter of the grave, and cannot persuade your fancy that they neither shrink nor shiver, when the snow is drifting over their little hillocks, and the bitter blast howls against the door of the tomb. That gloomy thought will collect a gloomy multitude, and throw its complexion over your wakeful hour.

In the depths of every heart there is a tomb and a dungeon, though the lights, the music, and revelry above may cause us to forget their existence, and the buried ones, or prisoners, whom they hide. But sometimes, and oftenest at midnight, these dark receptacles are flung wide open. In an hour like this, when the mind has a passive sensibility, but no active strength; when the imagination is a mirror, imparting vividness to all ideas, without the power of selecting or controlling them; then pray that your griefs may slumber,[345] and the brotherhood of remorse not break their chain. It is too late! A funeral train comes gliding by your bed, in which Passion and Feeling assume bodily shape, and things of the mind become dim spectres to the eye. There is your earliest Sorrow, a pale young mourner, wearing a sister's likeness to first love, sadly beautiful, with a hallowed sweetness in her melancholy features, and grace in the flow of her sable robe. Next appears a shade of ruined loveliness, with dust among her golden hair, and her bright garments all faded and defaced, stealing from your glance with drooping head, as fearful of reproach; she was your fondest Hope, but a delusive one; so call her Disappointment now. A sterner form succeeds, with a brow of wrinkles, a look and gesture of iron authority; there is no name for him unless it be Fatality, an emblem of the evil influence that rules your fortunes; a demon to whom you subjected yourself by some error at the outset of life, and were bound his slave forever, by once obeying him. See! those fiendish lineaments graven on the darkness, the writhed lip of scorn, the mockery of that living eye, the pointed finger, touching the sore place in your heart! Do you remember any act of enormous folly at which you would blush, even in the remotest cavern of the earth? Then recognize your Shame.

Pass, wretched band! Well for the wakeful one, if, riotously miserable, a fiercer tribe do not surround him, the devils of a guilty heart, that holds its hell within itself. What if Remorse should assume the features of an injured friend? What if the fiend should come in woman's garments, with a pale beauty amid sin and desolation, and lie down by your side? What if he should stand at your bed's foot, in the [346] likeness of a corpse, with a bloody stain upon the shroud? Sufficient, without such guilt, is this nightmare of the soul; this heavy, heavy sinking of the spirits; this wintry gloom about the heart; this indistinct horror of the mind, blending itself with the darkness of the chamber.

By a desperate effort you start upright, breaking from a sort of conscious sleep, and gazing wildly round the bed, as if the fiends were anywhere but in your haunted mind. At the same moment, the slumbering embers on the hearth send forth a gleam which palely illuminates the whole outer room, and flickers through the door of the bed-chamber, but cannot quite dispel its obscurity. Your eye searches for whatever may remind you of the living world. With eager minuteness you take note of the table near the fireplace, the book with an ivory knife between its leaves, the unfolded letter, the hat, and the fallen glove. Soon the flame vanishes, and with it the whole scene is gone, though its image remains an instant in your mind's eye, when darkness has swallowed the reality. Throughout the chamber there is the same obscurity as before, but not the same gloom within your breast. As your head falls back upon the pillow, you think—in a whisper be it spoken—how pleasant, in these night solitudes, would be the rise and fall of a softer breathing than your own, the slight pressure of a tenderer bosom, the quiet throb of a purer heart, imparting its peacefulness to your troubled one, as if the fond sleeper were involving you in her dream.

Her influence is over you, though she have no existence but in that momentary image. You sink down in a flowery spot, on the borders of sleep and wakefulness,[347] while your thoughts rise before you in pictures, all disconnected, yet all assimilated by a pervading gladsomeness and beauty. The wheeling of gorgeous squadrons that glitter in the sun is succeeded by the merriment of children round the door of a schoolhouse, beneath the glimmering shadow of old trees, at the corner of a rustic lane. You stand in the sunny rain of a summer shower, and wander among the sunny trees of an autumnal wood, and look upward at the brightest of all rainbows, overarching the unbroken sheet of snow, on the American side of Niagara. Your mind struggles pleasantly between the dancing radiance round the hearth of a young man and his recent bride, and the twittering flight of birds in spring about their new-made nest. You feel the merry bounding of a ship before the breeze, and watch the tuneful feet of rosy girls as they twine their last and merriest dance in a splendid ball-room, and find yourself in the brilliant circle of a crowded theatre as the curtain falls over a light and airy scene.

With an involuntary start you seize hold on consciousness, and prove yourself but half awake, by running a doubtful parallel between human life and the hour which has now elapsed. In both you emerge from mystery, pass through a vicissitude that you can but imperfectly control, and are borne onward to another mystery. Now comes the peal of the distant clock, with fainter and fainter strokes as you plunge farther into the wilderness of sleep. It is the knell of a temporary death. Your spirit has departed, and strays, like a free citizen, among the people of a shadowy world, beholding strange sights, yet without wonder or dismay. So calm, perhaps, will be the final change; so undisturbed, as if among familiar things the entrance of the soul to its Eternal home! [348]

Fancy's Show Box *

A Morality

What is Guilt? A stain upon the soul. And it is a point of vast interest whether the soul may contract such stains, in all their depth and flagrancy, from deeds which may have been plotted and resolved upon, but which, physically, have never had existence. Must the fleshly hand and visible frame of man set its seal to the evil designs of the soul, in order to give them their entire validity against the sinner? Or, while none but crimes perpetrated are cognizable before an earthly tribunal, will guilty thoughts —of which guilty deeds are no more than shadows—will these draw down the full weight of a condemning sentence, in the supreme court of eternity? In the solitude of a midnight chamber or in a desert, afar from men or in a church, while the body is kneeling, the soul may pollute itself even with those crimes which we are accustomed to deem altogether carnal. If this be true, it is a fearful truth.

Let us illustrate the subject by an imaginary example. A venerable gentleman, one Mr. Smith, who had long been regarded as a pattern of moral excellence, was warming his aged blood with a glass or two of generous wine. His children being gone forth about their worldly business, and his grandchildren at school, he sat alone, in a deep, luxurious arm-chair, with his feet beneath a richly-carved mahogany table. Some [250] old people have a dread of solitude, and when better company may not be had, rejoice even to hear the quiet breathing of a babe, asleep upon the carpet. But Mr. Smith, whose silver hair was the bright symbol of a life unstained, except by such spots as are inseparable from human nature, had no need of a babe to protect him by its purity, nor of a grown person to stand between him and his own soul. Nevertheless, either Manhood must converse with Age, or Womanhood must soothe him with gentle cares, or Infancy must sport around his chair, or his thoughts will stray into the misty region of the past, and the old man be chill and sad. Wine will not always cheer him. Such might have been the case with Mr. Smith, when, through the brilliant medium of his

* This sketch appeared first in *The Token* in 1837, later in *Twice-Told Tales* the same year.

glass of old Madeira, he beheld three figures entering the room. These were Fancy, who had assumed the garb and aspect of an itinerant show-man, with a box of pictures on her back; and Memory, in the likeness of a clerk, with a pen behind her ear, an inkhorn at her buttonhole, and a huge manuscript volume beneath her arm; and lastly, behind the other two, a person shrouded in a dusky mantle, which concealed both face and form. But Mr. Smith had a shrewd idea that it was Conscience.

How kind of Fancy, Memory, and Conscience to visit the old gentle-man, just as he was beginning to imagine that the wine had neither so bright a sparkle nor so excellent a flavor as when himself and the liquor were less aged! Through the dim length of the apartment, where crimson curtains muffled the glare of sunshine and created a rich obscurity, the three guests drew near the silver-haired old man. Memory, with a finger between the leaves of her huge volume,[251] placed herself at his right hand. Conscience, with her face still hidden in the dusky mantle, took her station on the left, so as to be next his heart; while Fancy set down her picture box upon the table, with the magnifying glass convenient to his eye. We can sketch merely the outlines of two or three out of the many pictures which, at the pulling of a string, successively peopled the box with the semblances of living scenes.

One was a moonlight picture: in the background, a lowly dwelling; and in front, partly shadowed by a tree, yet besprinkled with flakes of radiance, two youthful figures, male and female. The young man stood with folded arms, a haughty smile upon his lip, and a gleam of triumph in his eye, as he glanced downward at the kneeling girl. She was almost prostrate at his feet, evidently sinking under a weight of shame and anguish, which hardly allowed her to lift her clasped hands in supplica-tion. Her eyes she could not lift. But neither her agony, nor the lovely features on which it was depicted, nor the slender grace of the form which it convulsed, appeared to soften the obduracy of the young man. He was the personification of triumphant scorn. Now, strange to say, as old Mr. Smith peeped through the magnifying glass, which made the objects start out from the canvas with magical deception, he began to recognize the farm-house, the tree, and both the figures of the picture. The young man, in times long past, had often met his gaze within the looking-glass; the girl was the very image of his first love—his cottage love—his Martha Burroughs! Mr. Smith was scandalized. "O vile and slanderous picture!" he exclaims. "When have I triumphed over ruined innocence? Was not Martha wedded, in her teens, to David Tomkins, who won her girlish love,[252] and long enjoyed her affection as a wife?

And ever since his death she has lived a reputable widow!" Meantime, Memory was turning over the leaves of her volume, rustling them to and fro with uncertain fingers, until, among the earlier pages, she found one which had reference to this picture. She reads it, close to the old gentleman's ear; it is a record merely of sinful thought, which never was embodied in an act; but while Memory is reading, Conscience unveils her face, and strikes a dagger to the heart of Mr. Smith. Though not a death-blow, the torture was extreme.

The exhibition proceeded. One after another, Fancy displayed her pictures, all of which appeared to have been painted by some malicious artist on purpose to vex Mr. Smith. Not a shadow of proof could have been adduced, in any earthly court, that he was guilty of the slightest of those sins which were thus made to stare him in the face. In one scene there was a table set out, with several bottles, and glasses half filled with wine, which threw back the dull ray of an expiring lamp. There had been mirth and revelry, until the hand of the clock stood just at midnight, when murder stepped between the boon companions. A young man had fallen on the floor, and lay stone dead, with a ghastly wound crushed into his temple, while over him, with a delirium of mingled rage and horror in his countenance, stood the youthful likeness of Mr. Smith. The murdered youth wore the features of Edward Spencer! "What does this rascal of a painter mean?" cries Mr. Smith, provoked beyond all patience. "Edward Spencer was my earliest and dearest friend, true to me as I to him, through more than half a century. Neither I, nor any other, ever murdered him. Was he not alive within [253] five years, and did he not, in token of our long friendship, bequeath me his gold-headed cane and a mourning ring?" Again had Memory been turning over her volume, and fixed at length upon so confused a page that she surely must have scribbled it when she was tipsy. The purport was, however, that while Mr. Smith and Edward Spencer were heating their young blood with wine, a quarrel had flashed up between them, and Mr. Smith, in deadly wrath, had flung a bottle at Spencer's head. True, it missed its aim, and merely smashed a looking-glass; and the next morning, when the incident was imperfectly remembered, they had shaken hands with a hearty laugh. Yet, again, while Memory was reading, Conscience unveiled her face, struck a dagger to the heart of Mr. Smith, and quelled his remonstrance with her iron frown. The pain was quite excruciating.

Some of the pictures had been painted with so doubtful a touch, and in colors so faint and pale, that the subjects could barely be conjectured.

A dull, semi-transparent mist had been thrown over the surface of the canvas, into which the figures seemed to vanish, while the eye sought most earnestly to fix them. But in every scene, however dubiously portrayed, Mr. Smith was invariably haunted by his own lineaments, at various ages, as in a dusty mirror. After poring several minutes over one of these blurred and almost indistinguishable pictures, he began to see that the painter had intended to represent him, now in the decline of life, as stripping the clothes from the backs of three half-starved children. "Really, this puzzles me!" quoth Mr. Smith, with the irony of conscious rectitude. "Asking pardon of the painter, I pronounce him a fool, as well as a scandalous knave.[254] A man of my standing in the world to be robbing little children of their clothes! Ridiculous!" But while he spoke, Memory had searched her fatal volume, and found a page, which, with her sad, calm voice, she poured into his ear. It was not altogether inapplicable to the misty scene. It told how Mr. Smith had been grievously tempted by many devilish sophistries, on the ground of a legal quibble, to commence a lawsuit against three orphan children, joint heirs to a considerable estate. Fortunately, before he was quite decided, his claims had turned out nearly as devoid of law as justice. As Memory ceased to read, Conscience again thrust aside her mantle, and would have struck her victim with the envenomed dagger, only that he struggled and clasped his hands before his heart. Even then, however, he sustained an ugly gash.

Why should we follow Fancy through the whole series of those awful pictures? Painted by an artist of wondrous power, and terrible acquaintance with the secret soul, they embodied the ghosts of all the never perpetrated sins that had glided through the lifetime of Mr. Smith. And could such beings of cloudy fantasy, so near akin to nothingness, give valid evidence against him at the day of judgment? Be that the case or not, there is reason to believe that one truly penitential tear would have washed away each hateful picture, and left the canvas white as snow. But Mr. Smith, at a prick of Conscience too keen to be endured, bellowed aloud, with impatient agony, and suddenly discovered that his three guests were gone. There he sat alone, a silver-haired and highly-venerated old man, in the rich gloom of the crimson-curtained room, with no box of pictures on [255] the table, but only a decanter of most excellent Madeira. Yet his heart still seemed to fester with the venom of the dagger.

Nevertheless, the unfortunate old gentleman might have argued the matter with Conscience, and alleged many reasons wherefore she should not smite him so pitilessly. Were we to take up his cause, it should be somewhat in the following fashion: A scheme of guilt, till it be put in execution, greatly resembles a train of incidents in a projected tale. The latter, in order to produce a sense of reality in the reader's mind, must be conceived with such proportionate strength by the author as to seem, in the glow of fancy, more like truth, past, present, or to come, than purely fiction. The prospective sinner, on the other hand, weaves his plot of crime, but seldom or never feels a perfect certainty that it will be executed. There is a dreaminess diffused about his thoughts; in a dream, as it were, he strikes the death-blow into his victim's heart, and starts to find an indelible blood-stain on his hand. Thus a novel writer or a dramatist, in creating a villain of romance and fitting him with evil deeds, and the villain of actual life, in projecting crimes that will be perpetrated, may almost meet each other half-way between reality and fancy. It is not until the crime is accomplished that guilt clinches its gripe upon the guilty heart, and claims it for its own. Then, and not before, sin is actually felt and acknowledged, and, if unaccompanied by repentance, grows a thousand-fold more virulent by its self-consciousness. Be it considered, also, that men often over-estimate their capacity for evil. At a distance, while its attendant circumstances do not press upon their notice, and its results are dimly seen, they can [256] bear to contemplate it. They may take the steps which lead to crime, impelled by the same sort of mental action as in working out a mathematical problem, yet be powerless with compunction at the final moment. They knew not what deed it was that they deemed themselves resolved to do. In truth, there is no such thing in man's nature as a settled and full resolve, either for good or evil, except at the very moment of execution. Let us hope, therefore, that all the dreadful consequences of sin will not be incurred, unless the act have set its seal upon the thought.

Yet, with the slight fancy work which we have framed, some sad and awful truths are interwoven. Man must not disclaim his brotherhood, even with the guiltiest, since, though his hand be clean, his heart has surely been polluted by the flitting phantoms of iniquity. He must feel that, when he shall knock at the gate of heaven, no semblance of an unspotted life can entitle him to entrance there. Penitence must kneel, and Mercy come from the footstool of the throne, or that golden gate will never open! [257]

The Maypole of Merry Mount *

There is an admirable foundation for a philosophic romance in the
curious history of the early settlement of Mount Wollaston, or Merry
Mount. In the slight sketch here attempted, the facts, recorded on
the grave pages of our New England annalists, have wrought themselves, almost spontaneously, into a sort of allegory. The masques,
mummeries, and festive customs, described in the text, are in accordance with the manners of the age. Authority on these points may
be found in Strutt's Book of English Sports and Pastimes.

Bright were the days at Merry Mount, when the Maypole was the
banner staff of that gay colony! They who reared it, should their banner
be triumphant, were to pour sunshine over New England's rugged hills,
and scatter flower seeds throughout the soil. Jollity and gloom were
contending for an empire. Midsummer eve had come, bringing deep
verdure to the forest, and roses in her lap, of a more vivid hue than the
tender buds of Spring. But May, or her mirthful spirit, dwelt all the
year round at Merry Mount, sporting with the Summer months, and
revelling with Autumn, and basking in the glow of Winter's fireside.
Through a world of toil and care she flitted with a dreamlike smile, and
came hither to find a home among the lightsome hearts of Merry Mount.
     Never had the Maypole been so gayly decked as at sunset on mid-
summer eve. This venerated emblem was a pine-tree, which had preserved
the slender grace of youth, while it equalled the loftiest height of the
old wood monarchs. From its top streamed a silken banner, colored like
the rainbow. Down nearly to the [70] ground the pole was dressed with
birchen boughs, and others of the liveliest green, and some with silvery
leaves, fastened by ribbons that fluttered in fantastic knots of twenty
different colors, but no sad ones. Garden flowers, and blossoms of the
wilderness, laughed gladly forth amid the verdure, so fresh and dewy
that they must have grown by magic on that happy pine-tree. Where
this green and flowery splendor terminated, the shaft of the Maypole

* This story appeared in The Token in 1836 and in Twice-Told Tales in
1837.

was stained with the seven brilliant hues of the banner at its top. On the lowest green bough hung an abundant wreath of roses, some that had been gathered in the sunniest spots of the forest, and others, of still richer blush, which the colonists had reared from English seed. O, people of the Golden Age, the chief of your husbandry was to raise flowers!

But what was the wild throng that stood hand in hand about the Maypole? It could not be that the fauns and nymphs, when driven from their classic groves and homes of ancient fable, had sought refuge, as all the persecuted did, in the fresh woods of the West. These were Gothic monsters, though perhaps of Grecian ancestry. On the shoulders of a comely youth uprose the head and branching antlers of a stag; a second, human in all other points, had the grim visage of a wolf; a third, still with the trunk and limbs of a mortal man, showed the beard and horns of a venerable he-goat. There was the likeness of a bear erect, brute in all but his hind legs, which were adorned with pink silk stockings. And here again, almost as wondrous, stood a real bear of the dark forest, lending each of his fore paws to the grasp of a human hand, and as ready for the dance as any in that circle. His inferior nature rose half way, to [71] meet his companions as they stooped. Other faces wore the similitude of man or woman, but distorted or extravagant, with red noses pendulous before their mouths, which seemed of awful depth, and stretched from ear to ear in an eternal fit of laughter. Here might be seen the Salvage Man, well known in heraldry, hairy as a baboon, and girdled with green leaves. By his side, a noble figure, but still a counterfeit, appeared an Indian hunter, with feathery crest and wampum belt. Many of this strange company wore foolscaps, and had little bells appended to their garments, tinkling with a silvery sound, responsive to the inaudible music of their gleesome spirits. Some youths and maidens were of soberer garb, yet well maintained their places in the irregular throng by the expression of wild revelry upon their features. Such were the colonists of Merry Mount, as they stood in the broad smile of sunset round their venerated Maypole.

Had a wanderer, bewildered in the melancholy forest, heard their mirth, and stolen a half-affrighted glance, he might have fancied them the crew of Comus, some already transformed to brutes, some midway between man and beast, and the others rioting in the flow of tipsy jollity that foreran the change. But a band of Puritans, who watched the scene, invisible themselves, compared the masques to those devils and ruined souls with whom their superstition peopled the black wilderness.

Within the ring of monsters appeared the two airiest forms that had ever trodden on any more solid footing than a purple and golden cloud. One was a youth in glistening apparel, with a scarf of the rainbow pattern crosswise on his breast. His right hand held a gilded staff, the ensign of high dignity among [72] the revellers, and his left grasped the slender fingers of a fair maiden, not less gayly decorated than himself. Bright roses glowed in contrast with the dark and glossy curls of each, and were scattered round their feet, or had sprung up spontaneously there. Behind this lightsome couple, so close to the Maypole that its boughs shaded his jovial face, stood the figure of an English priest, canonically dressed, yet decked with flowers, in heathen fashion, and wearing a chaplet of the native vine leaves. By the riot of his rolling eye, and the pagan decorations of his holy garb, he seemed the wildest monster there, and the very Comus of the crew.

"Votaries of the Maypole," cried the flower-decked priest, "merrily, all day long, have the woods echoed to your mirth. But be this your merriest hour, my hearts! Lo, here stand the Lord and Lady of the May, whom I, a clerk of Oxford, and high priest of Merry Mount, am presently to join in holy matrimony. Up with your nimble spirits, ye morris-dancers, green men, and glee maidens, bears and wolves, and horned gentlemen! Come; a chorus now, rich with the old mirth of Merry England, and the wilder glee of this fresh forest; and then a dance, to show the youthful pair what life is made of, and how airily they should go through it! All ye that love the Maypole, lend your voices to the nuptial song of the Lord and Lady of the May!"

This wedlock was more serious than most affairs of Merry Mount, where jest and delusion, trick and fantasy, kept up a continual carnival. The Lord and Lady of the May, though their titles must be laid down at sunset, were really and truly to be partners for the dance of life, beginning the measure that same [73] bright eve. The wreath of roses, that hung from the lowest green bough of the Maypole, had been twined for them, and would be thrown over both their heads, in symbol of their flowery union. When the priest had spoken, therefore, a riotous uproar burst from the rout of monstrous figures.

"Begin you the stave, reverend Sir," cried they all; "and never did the woods ring to such a merry peal as we of the Maypole shall send up!"

Immediately a prelude of pipe, cithern, and viol, touched with practised minstrelsy, began to play from a neighboring thicket, in such a mirthful cadence that the boughs of the Maypole quivered to the sound. But the May Lord, he of the gilded staff, chancing to look into his Lady's eyes, was wonder struck at the almost pensive glance that met his own.

"Edith, sweet Lady of the May," whispered he reproachfully, "is yon wreath of roses a garland to hang above our graves, that you look so sad? O, Edith, this is our golden time! Tarnish it not by any pensive shadow of the mind; for it may be that nothing of futurity will be brighter than the mere remembrance of what is now passing."

"That was the very thought that saddened me! How came it in your mind too?" said Edith, in a still lower tone than he, for it was high treason to be sad at Merry Mount. "Therefore do I sigh amid this festive music. And besides, dear Edgar, I struggle as with a dream, and fancy that these shapes of our jovial friends are visionary, and their mirth unreal, and that we are no true Lord and Lady of the May. What is the mystery in my heart?"

Just then, as if a spell had loosened them, down came a little shower of withering rose leaves from the [74] Maypole. Alas, for the young lovers! No sooner had their hearts glowed with real passion than they were sensible of something vague and unsubstantial in their former pleasures, and felt a dreary presentiment of inevitable change. From the moment that they truly loved, they had subjected themselves to earth's doom of care and sorrow, and troubled joy, and had no more a home at Merry Mount. That was Edith's mystery. Now leave we the priest to marry them, and the masquers to sport round the Maypole, till the last sunbeam be withdrawn from its summit, and the shadows of the forest mingle gloomily in the dance. Meanwhile, we may discover who these gay people were.

Two hundred years ago, and more, the old world and its inhabitants became mutually weary of each other. Men voyaged by thousands to the West: some to barter glass beads, and such like jewels, for the furs of the Indian hunter; some to conquer virgin empires; and one stern band to pray. But none of these motives had much weight with the colonists of Merry Mount. Their leaders were men who had sported so long with life, that when Thought and Wisdom came, even these unwelcome guests were led astray by the crowd of vanities which they should have put to flight. Erring Thought and perverted Wisdom were made to put on masques, and play the fool. The men of whom we speak, after losing the heart's fresh gayety, imagined a wild philosophy of pleasure, and came hither to act out their latest day-dream. They gathered followers from all that giddy tribe whose whole life is like the festal days of soberer men. In their train were minstrels, not unknown in London streets: wandering players, whose theatres had been the halls [75] of noblemen; mummers, rope-dancers, and mountebanks, who would long be missed at wakes, church ales, and fairs; in a word, mirth makers of every sort, such as abounded in that age, but now began to be discountenanced by the rapid growth of Puritanism. Light had their footsteps been on land, and as lightly they came across the sea. Many had been maddened by their previous troubles into a gay despair; others were as madly gay in the flush of youth, like the May Lord and his Lady; but whatever might be the quality of their mirth, old and young were gay at Merry Mount. The young deemed themselves happy. The elder spirits, if they knew that mirth was but the counterfeit of happiness, yet followed the false shadow wilfully, because at least her garments glittered brightest. Sworn triflers of a lifetime, they would not venture among the sober truths of life not even to be truly blest.

All the hereditary pastimes of Old England were transplanted hither. The King of Christmas was duly crowned, and the Lord of Misrule bore potent sway. On the Eve of St. John, they felled whole acres of the forest to make bonfires, and danced by the blaze all night, crowned with garlands, and throwing flowers into the flame. At harvest time, though their crop was of the smallest, they made an image with the sheaves of Indian corn, and wreathed it with autumnal garlands, and bore it home triumphantly. But what chiefly characterized the colonists of Merry Mount was their veneration for the Maypole. It has made their true history a poet's tale. Spring decked the hallowed emblem with young blossoms and fresh green boughs; Summer brought roses of the deepest blush, and the perfected foliage of the forest; Autumn enriched [76] it with that red and yellow gorgeousness which converts each wildwood leaf into a painted flower; and Winter silvered it with sleet, and hung it round with icicles, till it flashed in the cold sunshine, itself a frozen sunbeam. Thus each alternate season did homage to the Maypole, and paid it a tribute of its own richest splendor. Its votaries danced round it, once, at least, in every month; sometimes they called it their religion, or their altar; but always, it was the banner staff of Merry Mount.

Unfortunately, there were men in the new world of a sterner faith than these Maypole worshippers. Not far from Merry Mount was a settlement of Puritans, most dismal wretches, who said their prayers before daylight, and then wrought in the forest or the cornfield till evening made it prayer time again. Their weapons were always at hand to shoot down the straggling savage. When they met in conclave, it was never to keep up the old English mirth, but to hear sermons three hours long, or to proclaim bounties on the heads of wolves and the scalps of Indians. Their festivals were fast days, and their chief pastime the singing of psalms. Woe to the youth or maiden who did but dream of a dance! The selectman nodded to the constable; and there sat the light-heeled reprobate in the stocks; or if he danced, it was round the whipping-post, which might be termed the Puritan Maypole.

A party of these grim Puritans, toiling through the difficult woods, each with a horseload of iron armor to burden his footsteps, would sometimes draw near the sunny precincts of Merry Mount. There were the silken colonists, sporting round their Maypole; perhaps teaching a bear to dance, or striving to communicate [77] their mirth to the grave Indian, or masquerading in the skins of deer and wolves, which they had hunted for that especial purpose. Often, the whole colony were playing at blindman's buff, magistrates and all, with their eyes bandaged, except a single scapegoat, whom the blinded sinners pursued by the tinkling of the bells at his garments. Once, it is said, they were seen following a flower-decked corpse, with merriment and festive music, to his grave. But did the dead man laugh? In their quietest times, they sang ballads and told tales, for the edification of their pious visitors; or preplexed them with juggling tricks; or grinned at them through horse collars; and when sport itself grew wearisome, they made game of their own stupidity, and began a yawning match. At the very least of these enormities, the men of iron shook their heads and frowned so darkly that the revellers looked up, imagining that a momentary cloud had overcast the sunshine, which was to be perpetual there. On the other hand, the Puritans affirmed that, when a psalm was pealing from their place of worship, the echo which the forest sent them back seemed often like the chorus of a jolly catch, closing with a roar of laughter. Who but the fiend, and his bond slaves, the crew of Merry Mount, had thus disturbed them? In due time, a feud arose, stern and bitter on one side, and as serious on the other as anything could be among such light spirits as had sworn allegiance to the Maypole. The future complexion of New England was involved in this important quarrel. Should the grizzly saints establish their jurisdiction over the gay sinners, then would their spirits darken all the clime, and make it a land of clouded visages, of hard toil, of sermon and psalm forever. But should the banner [78] staff of Merry Mount be fortunate, sunshine would break upon the hills, and flowers would beautify the forest, and late posterity do homage to the Maypole.

After these authentic passages from history, we return to the nuptials of the Lord and Lady of the May. Alas! we have delayed too long, and must darken our tale too suddenly. As we glance again at the Maypole, a solitary sunbeam is fading from the summit, and leaves only a faint, golden tinge blended with the hues of the rainbow banner. Even that dim light is now withdrawn, relinquishing the whole domain of Merry Mount to the evening gloom, which has rushed so instantaneously from the black surrounding woods. But some of these black shadows have rushed forth in human shape.

Yes, with the setting sun, the last day of mirth had passed from Merry Mount. The ring of gay masquers was disordered and broken; the stag lowered his antlers in dismay; the wolf grew weaker than a lamb; the bells of the morris-dancers tinkled with tremulous affright. The Puritans had played a characteristic part in the Maypole mummeries. Their darksome figures were intermixed with the wild shapes of their foes, and made the scene a picture of the moment, when waking thoughts start up amid the scattered fantasies of a dream. The leader of the hostile party stood in the centre of the circle, while the route of monsters cowered around him, like evil spirits in the presence of a dread magician. No fantastic foolery could look him in the face. So stern was the energy of his aspect, that the whole man, visage, frame, and soul, seemed wrought of iron, gifted with life and thought, yet all of one substance with his headpiece and breastplate. It was the Puritan of Puritans; it was Endicott himself! [79]

"Stand off, priest of Baal!" said he, with a grim frown, and laying no reverent hand upon the surplice. "I know thee, Blackstone! [1] Thou art the man who couldst not abide the rule even of thine own corrupted church, and hast come hither to preach iniquity, and to give example of it in thy life. But now shall it be seen that the Lord hath sanctified this wilderness for his peculiar people. Woe unto them that would defile it! And first, for this flower-decked abomination, the altar of thy worship!"

And with his keen sword Endicott assaulted the hallowed Maypole. Nor long did it resist his arm. It groaned with a dismal sound; it showered leaves and rosebuds upon the remorseless enthusiast; and finally, with all its green boughs and ribbons and flowers, symbolic of departed pleasures, down fell the banner staff of Merry Mount. As it sank, tradition says, the evening sky grew darker, and the woods threw forth a more sombre shadow.

[1] Did Governor Endicott speak less positively, we should suspect a mistake here. The Rev. Mr. Blackstone, though an eccentric, is not known to have been an immoral man. We rather doubt his identity with the priest of Merry Mount.

"There," cried Endicott, looking triumphantly on his work, "there lies the only Maypole in New England! The thought is strong within me that, by its fall, is shadowed forth the fate of light and idle mirth makers, amongst us and our posterity. Amen, saith John Endicott."

"Amen!" echoed his followers.

But the votaries of the Maypole gave one groan for their idol. At the sound, the Puritan leader glanced at the crew of Comus, each a figure of broad mirth, yet, at this moment, strangely expressive of sorrow and dismay.[80]

"Valiant captain," quoth Peter Palfrey, the Ancient of the band, "what order shall be taken with the prisoners?"

"I thought not to repent me of cutting down a Maypole," replied Endicott, "yet now I could find in my heart to plant it again, and give each of these bestial pagans one other dance round their idol. It would have served rarely for a whipping-post!"

"But there are pine-trees enow," suggested the lieutenant.

"True, good Ancient," said the leader. "Wherefore, bind the heathen crew, and bestow on them a small matter of stripes apiece, as earnest of our future justice. Set some of the rogues in the stocks to rest themselves, so soon as Prividence shall bring us to one of our own well-ordered settlements, where such accommodations may be found. Further penalties, such as branding and cropping of ears, shall be thought of hereafter."

"How many stripes for the priest?" inquired Ancient Palfrey.

"None as yet," answered Endicott, bending his iron frown upon the culprit. "It must be for the Great and General Court to determine, whether stripes and long imprisonment, and other grievous penalty, may atone for his transgressions. Let him look to himself! For such as violate our civil order, it may be permitted us to show mercy. But woe to the wretch that troubleth our religion!"

"And this dancing bear," resumed the officer. "Must he share the stripes of his fellows?"

"Shoot him through the head!" said the energetic Puritan. "I suspect witchcraft in the beast."

"Here be a couple of shining ones," continued [81] Peter Palfrey, pointing his weapon at the Lord and Lady of the May. "They seem to be of high station among these misdoers. Methinks their dignity will not be fitted with less than a double share of stripes."

Endicott rested on his sword, and closely surveyed the dress and aspect of the hapless pair. There they stood, pale, downcast, and apprehensive. Yet there was an air of mutual support, and of pure affection, seeking aid and giving it, that showed them to be man and wife, with the sanction of a priest upon their love. The youth, in the peril of the moment, had dropped his gilded staff, and thrown his arm about the Lady of the May, who leaned against his breast, too lightly to burden him, but with weight enough to express that their destinies were linked together, for good or evil. They looked first at each other, and then into the grim captain's face. There they stood, in the first hour of wedlock, while the idle pleasures, of which their companions were the emblems, had given place to the sternest cares of life, personified by the dark Puritans. But never had their youthful beauty seemed so pure and high as when its glow was chastened by adversity.

"Youth," said Endicott, "ye stand in an evil case thou and thy maiden wife. Make ready presently, for I am minded that ye shall both have a token to remember your wedding day!"

"Stern man," cried the May Lord, "how can I move thee? Were the means at hand, I would resist to the death. Being powerless, I entreat! Do with me as thou wilt, but let Edith go untouched!"

"Not so," replied the immitigable zealot. "We are not wont to show an idle courtesy to that sex, which requireth the stricter discipline. What sayest [82] thou, maid? Shall thy silken bridegroom suffer thy share of the penalty, besides his own?"

"Be it death," said Edith, "and lay it all on me!"

Truly, as Endicott had said, the poor lovers stood in a woful case. Their foes were triumphant, their friends captive and abased, their home desolate, the benighted wilderness around them, and a rigorous destiny, in the shape of the Puritan leader, their only guide. Yet the deepening twilight could not altogether conceal that the iron man was softened; he smiled at the fair spectacle of early love; he almost sighed for the inevitable blight of early hopes.

"The troubles of life have come hastily on this young couple," observed Endicott. "We will see how they comport themselves under their present trials ere we burden them with greater. If, among the spoil, there be any garments of a more decent fashion, let them be put upon this May Lord and his Lady, instead of their glistening vanities. Look to it, some of you."

"And shall not the youth's hair be cut?" asked Peter Palfrey, looking with abhorrence at the lovelock and long glossy curls of the young man.

"Crop it forthwith, and that in the true pumpkinshell fashion," answered the captain. "Then bring them along with us, but more gently than their fellows. There be qualities in the youth, which may make him valiant to fight, and sober to toil, and pious to pray; and in the maiden, that may fit her to become a mother in our Israel, bringing up babes in better nurture than her own hath been. Nor think ye, young ones, that they are the happiest, even in our lifetime of a moment, who misspend it in dancing round a Maypole!" [83]

And Endicott, the severest Puritan of all who laid the rock foundation of New England, lifted the wreath of roses from the ruin of the Maypole, and threw it, with his own gauntleted hand, over the heads of the Lord and Lady of the May. It was a deed of prophecy. As the moral gloom of the world overpowers all systematic gayety, even so was their home of wild mirth made desolate amid the sad forest. They returned to it no more. But as their flowery garland was wreathed of the brightest roses that had grown there, so, in the tie that united them, were intertwined all the purest and best of their early joys. They went heavenward, supporting each other along the difficult path which it was their lot to tread, and never wasted one regretful thought on the vanities of Merry Mount.[84]

The Minister's Black Veil *

A Parable [1]

The sexton stood in the porch of Milford meeting-house, pulling busily at the bell-rope. The old people of the village came stooping along the street. Children, with bright faces, tripped merrily beside their parents, or mimicked a graver gait, in the conscious dignity of their Sunday clothes. Spruce bachelors looked sidelong at the pretty maidens, and fancied that the Sabbath sunshine made them prettier than on week days. When the throng had mostly streamed into the porch, the sexton began to toll the bell, keeping his eye on the Reverend Mr. Hooper's door.

[1] Another clergyman in New England, Mr. Joseph Moody, of York, Maine, who died about eighty years since, made himself remarkable by the same eccentricity that is here related of the Reverend Mr. Hooper. In his case, however, the symbol had a different import. In early life he had accidentally killed a beloved friend; and from that day till the hour of his own death, he hid his face from men.
* This story appeared in *The Token* in 1836 and in *Twice-Told Tales* in 1837.

The first glimpse of the clergyman's figure was the signal for the bell to cease its summons.

"But what has good Parson Hooper got upon his face?" cried the sexton in astonishment.

All within hearing immediately turned about, and beheld the semblance of Mr. Hooper, pacing slowly his meditative way towards the meeting-house. With one accord they started, expressing more wonder than if some strange minister were coming to dust the cushions of Mr. Hooper's pulpit.[52]

"Are you sure it is our parson?" inquired Goodman Gray of the sexton.

"Of a certainty it is good Mr. Hooper," replied the sexton. "He was to have exchanged pulpits with Parson Shute, of Westbury; but Parson Shute sent to excuse himself yesterday, being to preach a funeral sermon."

The cause of so much amazement may appear sufficiently slight. Mr. Hooper, a gentlemanly person, of about thirty, though still a bachelor, was dressed with due clerical neatness, as if a careful wife had starched his band, and brushed the weekly dust from his Sunday's garb. There was but one thing remarkable in his appearance. Swathed about his forehead, and hanging down over his face, so low as to be shaken by his breath, Mr. Hooper had on a black veil. On a nearer view it seemed to consist of two folds of crape, which entirely concealed his features, except the mouth and chin, but probably did not intercept his sight, further than to give a darkened aspect to all living and inanimate things. With this gloomy shade before him, good Mr. Hooper walked onward, at a slow and quiet pace, stooping somewhat, and looking on the ground, as is customary with abstracted men, yet nodding kindly to those of his parishioners who still waited on the meeting-house steps. But so wonder-struck were they that his greeting hardly met with a return.

"I can't really feel as if good Mr. Hooper's face was behind that piece of crape," said the sexton.

"I don't like it," muttered an old woman, as she hobbled into the meeting-house. "He has changed himself into something awful, only by hiding his face."

"Our parson has gone mad!" cried Goodman Gray, following him across the threshold.[53]

A rumor of some unaccountable phenomenon had preceded Mr. Hooper into the meeting-house, and set all the congregation astir. Few could refrain from twisting their heads towards the door; many stood upright, and turned directly about; while several little boys clambered upon the seats, and came down again with a terrible racket. There was a general bustle, a rustling of the women's gowns and shuffling of the men's feet, greatly at variance with that hushed repose which should attend the entrance of the minister. But Mr. Hooper appeared not to notice the perturbation of his people. He entered with an almost noiseless step, bent his head mildly to the pews on each side, and bowed as he passed his oldest parishioner, a white-haired great-grandsire, who occupied an arm-chair in the centre of the aisle. It was strange to observe how slowly this venerable man became conscious of something singular in the appearance of his pastor. He seemed not fully to partake of the prevailing wonder, till Mr. Hooper had ascended the stairs, and showed himself in the pulpit, face to face with his congregation, except for the black veil. That mysterious emblem was never once withdrawn. It shook with his measured breath, as he gave out the psalm; it threw its obscurity between him and the holy page, as he read the Scriptures; and while he prayed, the veil lay heavily on his uplifted countenance. Did he seek to hide it from the dread Being whom he was addressing?

Such was the effect of this simple piece of crape, that more than one woman of delicate nerves was forced to leave the meeting-house. Yet perhaps the pale-faced congregation was almost as fearful a sight to the minister, as his black veil to them.[54]

Mr. Hooper had the reputation of a good preacher, but not an energetic one: he strove to win his people heavenward by mild, persuasive influences, rather than to drive them thither by the thunders of the Word. The sermon which he now delivered was marked by the same characteristics of style and manner as the general series of his pulpit oratory. But there was something, either in the sentiment of the discourse itself, or in the imagination of the auditors, which made it greatly the most powerful effort that they had ever heard from their pastor's lips. It was tinged, rather more darkly than usual, with the gentle gloom of Mr. Hooper's temperament. The subject had reference to secret sin, and those sad mysteries which we hide from our nearest and dearest, and would fain conceal from our own consciousness, even forgetting that the Omniscient can detect them. A subtle power was breathed into his words. Each member of the congregation, the most innocent girl, and the man of hardened breast, felt as if the preacher had crept upon them, behind his awful veil, and discovered their hoarded iniquity of deed or thought. Many spread their clasped hands on their bosoms. There was nothing terrible in what Mr. Hooper said, at least, no violence; and yet, with every tremor of his melancholy voice, the hearers quaked. An unsought pathos came hand in hand with awe. So sensible were the audience of some unwonted attribute in their minister, that they longed for a breath of wind to blow aside the veil, almost believing that a stranger's visage would be discovered, though the form, gesture, and voice were those of Mr. Hooper.

At the close of the services, the people hurried out with indecorous confusion, eager to communicate their [55] pent-up amazement, and conscious of lighter spirits the moment they lost sight of the black veil. Some gathered in little circles, huddled closely together, with their mouths all whispering in the centre; some went homeward alone, wrapt in silent meditation; some talked loudly, and profaned the Sabbath day with ostentatious laughter. A few shook their sagacious heads, intimating that they could penetrate the mystery; while one or two affirmed that there was no mystery at all, but only that Mr. Hooper's eyes were so weakened by the midnight lamp, as to require a shade. After a brief interval, forth came good Mr. Hooper also, in the rear of his flock. Turning his veiled face from one group to another, he paid due reverence to the hoary heads, saluted the middle aged with kind dignity as their friend and spiritual guide, greeted the young with mingled authority and love, and laid his hands on the little children's heads to bless them. Such was always his custom on the Sabbath day. Strange and bewildered looks repaid him for his courtesy. None, as on former occasions, aspired to the honor of walking by their pastor's side. Old Squire Saunders, doubtless by an accidental lapse of memory, neglected to invite Mr. Hooper to his table, where the good clergyman had been wont to bless the food, almost every Sunday since his settlement. He returned, therefore, to the parsonage, and, at the moment of closing the door, was observed to look back upon the people, all of whom had their eyes fixed upon the minister. A sad smile gleamed faintly from beneath the black veil, and flickered about his mouth, glimmering as he disappeared.

"How strange," said a lady, "that a simple black veil, such as any woman might wear on her bonnet,[56] should become such a terrible thing on Mr. Hooper's face!"

"Something must surely be amiss with Mr. Hooper's intellects," observed her husband, the physician of the village. "But the strangest part of the affair is the effect of this vagary, even on a sober-minded man like myself. The black veil, though it covers only our pastor's face, throws its influence over his whole person, and makes him ghostlike from head to foot. Do you not feel it so?"

"Truly do I," replied the lady; "and I would not be alone with him for the world. I wonder he is not afraid to be alone with himself!"

"Men sometimes are so," said her husband.

The afternoon service was attended with similar circumstances. At its conclusion, the bell tolled for the funeral of a young lady. The relatives and friends were assembled in the house, and the more distant acquaintances stood about the door, speaking of the good qualities of the deceased, when their talk was interrupted by the appearance of Mr. Hooper, still covered with his black veil. It was now an appropriate emblem. The clergyman stepped into the room where the corpse was laid, and bent over the coffin, to take a last farewell of his deceased parishioner. As he stooped, the veil hung straight down from his forehead, so that, if her eyelids had not been closed forever, the dead maiden might have seen his face. Could Mr. Hooper be fearful of her glance, that he so hastily caught back the black veil? A person who watched the interview between the dead and living, scrupled not to affirm, that, at the instant when the clergyman's features were disclosed, the corpse had slightly shuddered, rustling the shroud and muslin cap, though [57] the countenance retained the composure of death. A superstitious old woman was the only witness of this prodigy. From the coffin Mr. Hooper passed into the chamber of the mourners, and thence to the head of the staircase, to make the funeral prayer. It was a tender and heart-dissolving prayer, full of sorrow, yet so imbued with celestial hopes, that the music of a heavenly harp, swept by the fingers of the dead, seemed faintly to be heard among the saddest accents of the minister. The people trembled, though they but darkly understood him when he prayed that they, and himself, and all of mortal race, might be ready, as he trusted this young maiden had been, for the dreadful hour that should snatch the veil from their faces. The bearers went heavily forth, and the mourners followed, saddening all the street, with the dead before them, and Mr. Hooper in his black veil behind.

"Why do you look back?" said one in the procession to his partner.

"I had a fancy," replied she, "that the minister and the maiden's spirit were walking hand in hand."

"And so had I, at the same moment," said the other.

That night, the handsomest couple in Milford village were to be joined in wedlock. Though reckoned a melancholy man, Mr. Hooper had a placid cheerfulness for such occasions, which often excited a sympathetic smile where livelier merriment would have been thrown away. There was no quality of his disposition which made him more beloved than this. The company at the wedding awaited his arrival with impatience, trusting that the strange awe, which had gathered over him throughout the day, would now be dispelled. But such was not the result. When Mr. Hooper came, the [58] first thing that their eyes rested on was the same horrible black veil, which had added deeper gloom to the funeral, and could portend nothing but evil to the wedding. Such was its immediate effect on the guests that a cloud seemed to have rolled duskily from beneath the black crape, and dimmed the light of the candles. The bridal pair stood up before the minister. But the bride's cold fingers quivered in the tremulous hand of the bridegroom, and her deathlike paleness caused a whisper that the maiden who had been buried a few hours before was come from her grave to be married. If ever another wedding were so dismal, it was that famous one where they tolled the wedding knell. After performing the ceremony, Mr. Hooper raised a glass of wine to his lips, wishing happiness to the new-married couple in a strain of mild pleasantry that ought to have brightened the features of the guests, like a cheerful gleam from the hearth. At that instant, catching a glimpse of his figure in the looking-glass, the black veil involved his own spirit in the horror with which it overwhelmed all others. His frame shuddered, his lips grew white, he spilt the untasted wine upon the carpet, and rushed forth into the darkness. For the Earth, too, had on her Black Veil.

The next day, the whole village of Milford talked of little else than Parson Hooper's black veil. That, and the mystery concealed behind it, supplied a topic for discussion between acquaintances meeting in the street, and good women gossiping at their open windows. It was the first item of news that the tavernkeeper told to his guests. The children babbled of it on their way to school. One imitative little imp covered his face with an old black handkerchief, thereby [59] so affrighting his playmates that the panic seized himself, and he well-nigh lost his wits by his own waggery.

It was remarkable that of all the busybodies and impertinent people in the parish, not one ventured to put the plain question to Mr. Hooper, wherefore he did this thing. Hitherto, whenever there appeared the slightest call for such interference, he had never lacked advisers, nor shown himself averse to be guided by their judgment. If he erred at all, it was by so painful a degree of self-distrust, that even the mildest censure would lead him to consider an indifferent action as a crime. Yet, though so well acquainted with this amiable weakness, no individual among his parishioners chose to make the black veil a subject of friendly remonstrance. There was a feeling of dread, neither plainly confessed nor carefully concealed, which caused each to shift the responsibility upon another, till at length it was found expedient to send a deputation of the church, in order to deal with Mr. Hooper about the mystery, before it should grow into a scandal. Never did an embassy so ill discharge its duties. The minister received them with friendly courtesy, but became silent, after they were seated, leaving to his visitors the whole burden of introducing their important business. The topic, it might be supposed, was obvious enough. There was the black veil swathed round Mr. Hooper's forehead, and concealing every feature above his placid mouth, on which, at times, they could perceive the glimmering of a melancholy smile. But that piece of crape, to their imagination, seemed to hang down before his heart, the symbol of a fearful secret between him and them. Were the veil but cast aside, they might speak freely of it, but not till then. Thus they sat a considerable time, speechless, confused,[60] and shrinking uneasily from Mr. Hooper's eye, which they felt to be fixed upon them with an invisible glance. Finally, the deputies returned abashed to their constituents, pronouncing the matter too weighty to be handled, except by a council of the churches, if, indeed, it might not require a general synod.

But there was one person in the village unappalled by the awe with which the black veil had impressed all beside herself. When the deputies returned without an explanation, or even venturing to demand one, she, with the calm energy of her character, determined to chase away the strange cloud that appeared to be settling round Mr. Hooper, every moment more darkly than before. As his plighted wife, it should be her privilege to know what the black veil concealed. At the minister's first visit, therefore, she entered upon the subject with a direct simplicity, which made the task easier both for him and her. After he had seated himself, she fixed her eyes steadfastly upon the veil, but could discern nothing of the dreadful gloom that had so overawed the multitude: it was but a double fold of crape, hanging down from his forehead to his mouth, and slightly stirring with his breath.

"No," said she aloud, and smiling, "there is nothing terrible in this piece of crape, except that it hides a face which I am always glad to look upon. Come, good sir, let the sun shine from behind the cloud. First lay aside your black veil: then tell me why you put it on."

Mr. Hooper's smile glimmered faintly.

"There is an hour to come," said he, "when all of us shall cast aside our veils. Take it not amiss, beloved friend, if I wear this piece of crape till then."

"Your words are a mystery, too," returned the [61] young lady. "Take away the veil from them, at least."

"Elizabeth, I will," said he, "so far as my vow may suffer me. Know, then, this veil is a type and a symbol, and I am bound to wear it ever, both in light and darkness, in solitude and before the gaze of multitudes, and as with strangers, so with my familiar friends. No mortal eye will see it withdrawn. This dismal shade must separate me from the world: even you, Elizabeth, can never come behind it!"

"What grievous affliction hath befallen you," she earnestly inquired, "that you should thus darken your eyes forever?"

"If it be a sign of mourning," replied Mr. Hooper, "I, perhaps, like most other mortals, have sorrows dark enough to be typified by a black veil."

"But what if the world will not believe that it is the type of an innocent sorrow?" urged Elizabeth. "Beloved and respected as you are, there may be whispers that you hide your face under the consciousness of secret sin. For the sake of your holy office, do away this scandal!"

The color rose into her cheeks as she intimated the nature of the rumors that were already abroad in the village. But Mr. Hooper's mildness did not forsake him. He even smiled again—that same sad smile, which always appeared like a faint glimmering of light, proceeding from the obscurity beneath the veil.

"If I hide my face for sorrow, there is cause enough," he merely replied; "and if I cover it for secret sin, what mortal might not do the same?"

And with this gentle, but unconquerable obstinacy did he resist all her entreaties. At length Elizabeth sat silent. For a few moments she appeared lost [62] in thought, considering, probably, what new methods might be tried to withdraw her lover from so dark a fantasy, which, if it had no other meaning, was perhaps a symptom of mental disease. Though of a firmer character than his own, the tears rolled down her cheeks. But, in an instant, as it were, a new feeling took the place of sorrow: her eyes were fixed insensibly on the black veil, when, like a sudden twilight in the air, its terrors fell around her. She arose, and stood trembling before him.

"And do you feel it then, at last?" said he mournfully.

She made no reply, but covered her eyes with her hand, and turned to leave the room. He rushed forward and caught her arm.

"Have patience with me, Elizabeth!" cried he, passionately. "Do not desert me, though this veil must be between us here on earth. Be mine, and hereafter there shall be no veil over my face, no darkness between our souls! It is but a mortal veil—it is not for eternity! O! you know not how lonely I am, and how frightened, to be alone behind my black veil. Do not leave me in this miserable obscurity forever!"

"Lift the veil but once, and look me in the face," said she.

"Never! It cannot be!" replied Mr. Hooper.

"Then farewell!" said Elizabeth.

She withdrew her arm from his grasp, and slowly departed, pausing at the door, to give one long shuddering gaze, that seemed almost to penetrate the mystery of the black veil. But, even amid his grief, Mr. Hooper smiled to think that only a material emblem had separated him from happiness, though the horrors [63], which it shadowed forth, must be drawn darkly between the fondest of lovers.

From that time no attempts were made to remove Mr. Hooper's black veil, or, by a direct appeal, to discover the secret which it was supposed to hide. By persons who claimed a superiority to popular prejudice, it was reckoned merely an eccentric whim, such as often mingles with the sober actions of men otherwise rational, and tinges them all with its own semblance of insanity. But with the multitude, good Mr. Hooper was irreparably a bugbear. He could not walk the street with any peace of mind, so conscious was he that the gentle and timid would turn aside to avoid him, and that others would make it a point of hardihood to throw themselves in his way. The impertinence of the latter class compelled him to give up his customary walk at sunset to the burial ground; for when he leaned pensively over the gate, there would always be faces behind the gravestones, peeping at his black veil. A fable went the rounds that the stare of the dead people drove him thence. It grieved him, to the very depth of his kind heart, to observe how the children fled from his approach, breaking up their merriest sports, while his melancholy figure was yet afar off. Their instinctive dread caused him to feel more strongly than aught else, that a preternatural horror was interwoven with the threads of the black crape. In truth, his own antipathy to the veil was known to be so great, that he never willingly passed before a mirror, nor stooped to drink at a still fountain, lest, in its peaceful bosom, he should be affrighted by himself. This was what gave plausibility to the whispers, that Mr. Hooper's conscience tortured him for some great crime too horrible to be [64] entirely concealed, or otherwise than so obscurely intimated. Thus, from beneath the black veil, there rolled a cloud into the sunshine, an ambiguity of sin or sorrow, which enveloped the poor minister, so that love or sympathy could never reach him. It was said that ghost and fiend consorted with him there. With self-shudderings and outward terrors, he walked continually in its shadow, groping darkly within his own soul, or gazing through a medium that saddened the whole world. Even the lawless wind, it was believed, respected his dreadful secret, and never blew aside the veil. But still good Mr. Hooper sadly smiled at the pale visages of the worldly throng as he passed by.

Among all its bad influences, the black veil had the one desirable effect, of making its wearer a very efficient clergyman. By the aid of his mysterious emblem—for there was no other apparent cause—he became a man of awful power over souls that were in agony for sin. His converts always regarded him with a dread peculiar to themselves, affirming, though but figuratively, that, before he brought them to celestial light, they had been with him behind the black veil. Its gloom, indeed, enabled him to sympathize with all dark affections. Dying sinners cried aloud for Mr. Hooper, and would not yield their breath till he appeared; though ever, as he stooped to whisper consolation, they shuddered at the veiled face so near their own. Such were the terrors of the black veil, even when Death had bared his visage! Strangers came long distances to attend service at his church, with the mere idle purpose of gazing at his figure, because it was forbidden them to behold his face. But many were made to quake ere they departed! Once, during Governor Belcher's administration, Mr. Hooper was [65] appointed to preach the election sermon. Covered with his black veil, he stood before the chief magistrate, the council, and the representatives, and wrought so deep an impression, that the legislative measures of that year were characterized by all the gloom and piety of our earliest ancestral sway.

In this manner Mr. Hooper spent a long life, irreproachable in outward act, yet shrouded in dismal suspicions; kind and loving, though unloved, and dimly feared; a man apart from men, shunned in their health and joy, but ever summoned to their aid in mortal anguish. As years wore on, shedding their snows above his sable veil, he acquired a name throughout the New England churches, and they called him Father Hooper. Nearly all his parishioners, who were of mature age when he was settled, had been borne away by many a funeral: he had one congregation in the church, and a more crowded one in the churchyard; and having wrought so late into the evening, and done his work so well, it was now good Father Hooper's turn to rest.

Several persons were visible by the shaded candlelight, in the death chamber of the old clergyman. Natural connections he had none. But there was the decorously grave, though unmoved physician, seeking only to mitigate the last pangs of the patient whom he could not save. There were the deacons, and other eminently pious members of his church. There, also, was the Reverend Mr. Clark, of Westbury, a young and zealous divine, who had ridden in haste to pray by the bedside of the expiring minister. There was the nurse, no hired handmaiden of death, but one whose calm affection had endured thus long in secrecy, in solitude, amid the chill of age, and would not perish,[66] even at the dying hour. Who, but Elizabeth! And there lay the hoary head of good Father Hooper upon the death pillow, with the black veil still swathed about his brow, and reaching down over his face, so that each more difficult gasp of his faint breath caused it to stir. All through life that piece of crape had hung between him and the world: it had separated him from cheerful brotherhood and woman's love, and kept him in that saddest of all prisons, his own heart; and still it lay upon his face, as if to deepen the gloom of his darksome chamber, and shade him from the sunshine of eternity.

For some time previous, his mind had been confused, wavering doubtfully between the past and the present, and hovering forward, as it were, at intervals, into the indistinctness of the world to come. There had been feverish turns, which tossed him from side to side, and wore away what little strength he had. But in his most convulsive struggles, and in the wildest vagaries of his intellect, when no other thought retained its sober influence, he still showed an awful solicitude lest the black veil should slip aside. Even if his bewildered soul could have forgotten, there was a faithful woman at his pillow, who, with averted eyes, would have covered that aged face, which she had last beheld in the comeliness of manhood. At length the death-stricken old man lay quietly in the torpor of mental and bodily exhaustion, with an imperceptible pulse, and breath that grew fainter and fainter, except when a long, deep, and irregular inspiration seemed to prelude the flight of his spirit.

The minister of Westbury approached the bedside.

"Venerable Father Hooper," said he, "the moment of your release is at hand. Are you ready for the lifting of the veil that shuts in time from eternity?" [67]

Father Hooper at first replied merely by a feeble motion of his head; then, apprehensive, perhaps, that his meaning might be doubtful, he exerted himself to speak.

"Yea," said he, in faint accents, "my soul hath a patient weariness until that veil be lifted."

"And is it fitting," resumed the Reverend Mr. Clark, "that a man so given to prayer, of such a blameless example, holy in deed and thought, so far as mortal judgment may pronounce; is it fitting that a father in the church should leave a shadow on his memory, that may seem to blacken a life so pure? I pray you, my venerable brother, let not this thing be! Suffer us to be gladdened by your triumphant aspect as you go to your reward. Before the veil of eternity be lifted, let me cast aside this black veil from your face!"

And thus speaking, the Reverend Mr. Clark bent forward to reveal the mystery of so many years. But, exerting a sudden energy, that made all the beholders stand aghast, Father Hooper snatched both his hands from beneath the bedclothes, and pressed them strongly on the black veil, resolute to struggle, if the minister of Westbury would contend with a dying man.

"Never!" cried the veiled clergyman. "On earth, never!"

"Dark old man!" exclaimed the affrighted minister, "with what horrible crime upon your soul are you now passing to the judgment?"

Father Hooper's breath heaved; it rattled in his throat; but, with a mighty effort, grasping forward with his hands, he caught hold of life, and held it back till he should speak. He even raised himself in bed; and there he sat, shivering with the arms of death [68] around him, while the black veil hung down, awful, at that last moment, in the gathered terrors of a lifetime. And yet the faint, sad smile, so often there, now seemed to glimmer from its obscurity, and linger on Father Hooper's lips.

"Why do you tremble at me alone?" cried he, turning his veiled face round the circle of pale spectators. "Tremble also at each other! Have men avoided me, and women shown no pity, and children screamed and fled, only for my black veil? What, but the mystery which it obscurely typifies, has made this piece of crape so awful? When the friend shows his inmost heart to his friend; the lover to his best beloved; when man does not vainly shrink from the eye of his Creator, loathsomely treasuring up the secret of his sin; then deem me a monster, for the symbol beneath which I have lived, and die! I look around me, and, lo! on every visage a Black Veil!"

While his auditors shrank from one another, in mutual affright, Father Hooper fell back upon his pillow, a veiled corpse, with a faint smile lingering on the lips. Still veiled, they laid him in his coffin, and a veiled corpse they bore him to the grave. The grass of many years has sprung up and withered on that grave, the burial stone is moss-grown, and good Mr. Hooper's face is dust; but awful is still the thought that it mouldered beneath the Black Veil! [69]

TALES AND INTERPRETATIONS

My Kinsman, Major Molineux*

After the kings of Great Britain had assumed the right of appointing the colonial governors, the measures of the latter seldom met with the ready and general approbation which had been paid to those of their predecessors, under the original charters. The people looked with most jealous scrutiny to the exercise of power which did not emanate from themselves, and they usually rewarded their rulers with slender gratitude for the compliances by which, in softening their instructions from beyond the sea, they had incurred the reprehension of those who gave them. The annals of Massachusetts Bay will inform us, that of six governors in the space of about forty years from the surrender of the old charter, under James II., two were imprisoned by a popular insurrection; a third, as Hutchinson inclines to believe, was driven from the province by the whizzing of a musket-ball; a fourth, in the opinion of the same historian, was hastened to his grave by continual bickerings with the House of Representatives; and the remaining two, as well as their successors, till the Revolution, were favored with few and brief intervals of peaceful sway. The inferior members of the court party, in times of high political excitement, led scarcely a more desirable life. These remarks may serve as a preface to the following adventures, which chanced upon a summer night, not far from a hundred years ago. The reader, in order to avoid a long and dry detail of colonial affairs,[616] is requested to dispense with an account of the train of circumstances that had caused much temporary inflammation of the popular mind.

It was near nine o'clock of a moonlight evening, when a boat crossed the ferry with a single passenger, who had obtained his conveyance at that unusual hour by the promise of an extra fare. While he stood on the landing-place, searching in either pocket for the means of fulfilling his agreement, the ferryman lifted a lantern, by the aid of which, and the newly risen moon, he took a very accurate survey of the stranger's figure. He was a youth of barely eighteen years, evidently country-bred,

* This story appeared in *The Token* in 1832 and in *The Snow Image and Other Tales* in 1852 (English edition in 1851).

and now, as it should seem, upon his first visit to town. He was clad in a coarse gray coat, well worn, but in excellent repair; his under garments were durably constructed of leather, and fitted tight to a pair of seviceable and well-shaped limbs; his stockings of blue yarn were the incontrovertible work of a mother or a sister; and on his head was a three-cornered hat, which in its better days had perhaps sheltered the graver brow of the lad's father. Under his left arm was a heavy cudgel formed of an oak sapling, and retaining a part of the hardened root; and his equipment was completed by a wallet, not so abundantly stocked as to incommode the vigorous shoulders on which it hung. Brown, curly hair, well-shaped features, and bright, cheerful eyes were nature's gifts, and worth all that art could have done for his adornment.

The youth, one of whose names was Robin, finally drew from his pocket the half of a little province bill of five shillings, which, in the depreciation in that sort of currency, did but satisfy the ferryman's demand, with the surplus of a sexangular piece of parchment,[617] valued at three pence. He then walked forward into the town, with as light a step as if his day's journey had not already exceeded thirty miles, and with as eager an eye as if he were entering London city, instead of the little metropolis of a New England colony. Before Robin had proceeded far, however, it occurred to him that he knew not whither to direct his steps; so he paused, and looked up and down the narrow street, scrutinizing the small and mean wooden buildings that were scattered on either side.

"This low hovel cannot be my kinsman's dwelling," thought he, "nor yonder old house, where the moonlight enters at the broken casement; and truly I see none hereabouts that might be worthy of him. It would have been wise to inquire my way of the ferryman, and doubtless he would have gone with me, and earned a shilling from the Major for his pains. But the next man I meet will do as well."

He resumed his walk, and was glad to perceive that the street now became wider, and the houses more respectable in their appearance. He soon discerned a figure moving on moderately in advance, and hastened his steps to overtake it. As Robin drew nigh, he saw that the passenger was a man in years, with a full periwig of gray hair, a wide-skirted coat of dark cloth, and silk stockings rolled above his knees. He carried a long and polished cane, which he struck down perpendicularly before him at every step; and at regular intervals he uttered two successive hems, of a peculiarly solemn and sepulchral intonation. Having made these observations, Robin laid hold of the skirt of the old man's coat, just when the light from the open door and windows of a barber's shop fell upon both their figures.[618]

"Good evening to you, honored sir," said he, making a low bow, and still retaining his hold of the skirt. "I pray you tell me whereabouts is the dwelling of my kinsman, Major Molineux."

The youth's question was uttered very loudly; and one of the barbers, whose razor was descending on a well-soaped chin, and another who was dressing a Ramillies wig, left their occupations, and came to the door. The citizen, in the mean time, turned a long-favored countenance upon Robin, and answered him in a tone of excessive anger and annoyance. His two sepulchral hems, however, broke into the very centre of his rebuke, with most singular effect, like a thought of the cold grave obtruding among wrathful passions.

"Let go my garment, fellow! I tell you, I know not the man you speak of. What! I have authority, I have—hem, hem—authority; and if this be the respect you show for your betters, your feet shall be brought acquainted with the stocks by daylight, tomorrow morning!"

Robin released the old man's skirt, and hastened away, pursued by an ill-mannered roar of laughter from the barber's shop. He was at first considerably surprised by the result of his question, but, being a shrewd youth, soon thought himself able to account for the mystery.

"This is some country representative," was his conclusion, "who has never seen the inside of my kinsman's door, and lacks the breeding to answer a stranger civilly. The man is old, or verily—I might be tempted to turn back and smite him on the nose. Ah, Robin, Robin! even the barber's boys laugh at you for choosing such a guide! You will be wiser in time, friend Robin." [619]

He now became entangled in a succession of crooked and narrow streets, which crossed each other, and meandered at no great distance from the water-side. The smell of tar was obvious to his nostrils, the masts of vessels pierced the moonlight above the tops of the buildings, and the numerous signs, which Robin paused to read, informed him that he was near the centre of business. But the streets were empty, the shops were closed, and lights were visible only in the second stories of a few dwelling-houses. At length, on the corner of a narrow lane, through which he was passing, he beheld the broad countenance of a British hero swinging before the door of an inn, whence proceeded the voices of many guests. The casement of one of the lower windows was thrown back, and a very thin curtain permitted Robin to distinguish a party at supper, round a well-furnished table. The fragrance of the good cheer steamed forth into the outer air, and the youth could not fail to recollect that the last remnant of his travelling stock of provision had yielded to his morning appetite, and that noon had found and left him dinnerless.

"Oh, that a parchment three-penny might give me a right to sit down at yonder table!" said Robin, with a sigh. "But the Major will make me welcome to the best of his victuals; so I will even step boldly in, and inquire my way to his dwelling."

He entered the tavern, and was guided by the murmur of voices and the fumes of tobacco to the public-room. It was a long and low apartment, with oaken walls, grown dark in the continual smoke, and a floor which was thickly sanded, but of no immaculate purity. A number of persons—the larger part of whom appeared to be mariners, or in some way connected [620] with the sea—occupied the wooden benches, or leather-bottomed chairs, conversing on various matters, and occasionally lending their attention to some topic of general interest. Three or four little groups were draining as many bowls of punch, which the West India trade had long since made a familiar drink in the colony. Others, who had the appearance of men who lived by regular and laborious handicraft, preferred the insulated bliss of an unshared potation, and became more taciturn under its influence. Nearly all, in short, evinced a predilection for the Good Creature in some of its various shapes, for this is a vice to which, as Fast Day sermons of a hundred years ago will testify, we have a long hereditary claim. The only guests to whom Robin's sympathies inclined him were two or three sheepish countrymen, who were using the inn somewhat after the fashion of a Turkish caravansary; they had gotten themselves into the darkest corner of the room, and heedless of the Nicotian atmosphere, were supping on the bread of their own ovens, and the bacon cured in their own chimney-smoke. But though Robin felt a sort of brotherhood with these strangers, his eyes were attracted from them to a person who stood near the door, holding whispered conversation with a group of ill-dressed associates. His features were separately striking almost to grotesqueness, and the whole face left a deep impression on the memory. The forehead bulged out into a double prominence, with a vale between; the nose came boldly forth in an irregular curve, and its bridge was of more than a finger's breadth; the eyebrows were deep and shaggy, and the eyes glowed beneath them like fire in a cave.

While Robin deliberated of whom to inquire respecting his kinsman's dwelling, he was accosted by [621] the innkeeper, a little man in a stained white apron, who had come to pay his professional welcome to the stranger. Being in the second generation from a French Protestant, he seemed to have inherited the courtesy of his parent nation; but no variety of circumstances was ever known to change his voice from the one shrill note in which he now addressed Robin.

"From the country, I presume, sir?" said he, with a profound bow. "Beg leave to congratulate you on your arrival, and trust you intend a long stay with us. Fine town here, sir, beautiful buildings, and much that may interest a stranger. May I hope for the honor of your commands in respect to supper?"

"The man sees a family likeness! the rogue has guessed that I am related to the Major!" thought Robin, who had hitherto experienced little superfluous civility.

All eyes were now turned on the country lad, standing at the door, in his worn three-cornered hat, gray coat, leather breeches, and blue yarn stockings, leaning on an oaken cudgel, and bearing a wallet on his back.

Robin replied to the courteous innkeeper, with such an assumption of confidence as befitted the Major's relative. "My honest friend," he said, "I shall make it a point to patronize your house on some occasion, when" —here he could not help lowering his voice—"when I may have more than a parchment three-pence in my pocket. My present business," continued he, speaking with lofty confidence, "is merely to inquire my way to the dwelling of my kinsman, Major Molineux."

There was a sudden and general movement in the room, which Robin interpreted as expressing the eagerness [622] of each individual to become his guide. But the innkeeper turned his eyes to a written paper on the wall, which he read, or seemed to read, with occasional recurrences to the young man's figure.

"What have we here?" said he, breaking his speech into little dry fragments. " 'Left the house of the subscriber, bounden servant, Hezekiah Mudge,—had on, when he went away, gray coat, leather breeches, master's third-best hat. One pound currency reward to whosoever shall lodge him in any jail of the province.' Better trudge, boy; better trudge!"

Robin had begun to draw his hand towards the lighter end of the oak cudgel, but a strange hostility in every countenance induced him to relinquish his purpose of breaking the courteous innkeeper's head. As he turned to leave the room, he encountered a sneering glance from the bold-featured personage whom he had before noticed; and no sooner was he beyond the door, than he heard a general laugh, in which the inn-keeper's voice might be distinguished, like the dropping of small stones into a kettle.

"Now, is it not strange," thought Robin, with his usual shrewdness,— "is it not strange that the confession of an empty pocket should outweigh the name of my kinsman, Major Molineux? Oh, if I had one of those grinning rascals in the woods, where I and my oak sapling grew up together, I would teach him that my arm is heavy though my purse be light!"

On turning the corner of the narrow lane, Robin found himself in a spacious street, with an unbroken line of lofty houses on each side, and a steepled building at the upper end, whence the ringing of a bell announced the hour of nine. The light of the moon, and the lamps from the numerous shop-windows, discovered [623] people promenading on the pavement, and amongst them Robin hoped to recognize his hitherto inscrutable relative. The result of his former inquiries made him unwilling to hazard another, in a scene of such publicity, and he determined to walk slowly and silently up the street, thrusting his face close to that of every elderly gentleman, in search of the Major's lineaments. In his progress, Robin encountered many gay and gallant figures. Embroidered garments of showy colors, enormous periwigs, gold-laced hats, and silver-hilted swords glided past him and dazzled his optics. Travelled youths, imitators of the European fine gentlemen of the period, trod jauntily along, half dancing to the fashionable tunes which they hummed, and making poor Robin ashamed of his quiet and natural gait. At length, after many pauses to examine the gorgeous display of goods in the shop-windows, and after suffering some rebukes for the impertinence of his scrutiny into people's faces, the Major's kinsman found himself near the steepled building, still unsuccessful in his search. As yet, however, he had seen only one side of the thronged street; so Robin crossed, and continued the same sort of inquisition down the opposite pavement, with stronger hopes than the philosopher seeking an honest man, but with no better fortune. He had arrived about midway towards the lower end, from which his course began, when he overheard the approach of some one who struck down a cane on the flag-stones at every step, uttering, at regular intervals, two sepulchral hems.

"Mercy on us!" quoth Robin, recognizing the sound.

Turning a corner, which chanced to be close at his right hand, he hastened to pursue his researches in [624] some other part of the town. His patience now was wearing low, and he seemed to feel more fatigue from his rambles since he crossed the ferry, than from his journey of several days on the other side. Hunger also pleaded loudly within him, and Robin began to balance the propriety of demanding, violently, and with lifted cudgel, the necessary guidance from the first solitary passenger whom he should meet. While a resolution to this effect was gaining strength, he entered a street of mean appearance, on either side of which a row of ill-built houses was straggling towards the harbor. The moonlight fell upon no passenger along the whole extent, but in the third domicile which Robin passed there was a half-opened door, and his keen glance detected a woman's garment within.

"My luck may be better here," said he to himself.

Accordingly, he approached the door, and beheld it shut closer as he did so; yet an open space remained, sufficing for the fair occupant to observe the stranger, without a corresponding display on her part. All that Robin could discern was a strip of scarlet petticoat, and the occasional sparkle of an eye, as if the moonbeams were trembling on some bright thing.

"Pretty mistress," for I may call her so with a good conscience, thought the shrewd youth, since I know nothing to the contrary,—"my sweet pretty mistress, will you be kind enough to tell me whereabouts I must seek the dwelling of my kinsman, Major Molineux?"

Robin's voice was plaintive and winning, and the female, seeing nothing to be shunned in the handsome country youth, thrust open the door, and came forth into the moonlight. She was a dainty little figure, with a white neck, round arms, and a slender waist,[625] at the extremity of which her scarlet petticoat jutted out over a hoop, as if she were standing in a balloon. Moreover, her face was oval and pretty, her hair dark beneath the little cap, and her bright eyes possessed a sly freedom, which triumphed over those of Robin.

"Major Molineux dwells here," said this fair woman.

Now, her voice was the sweetest Robin had heard that night, the airy counterpart of a stream of melted silver; yet he could not help doubting whether that sweet voice spoke Gospel truth. He looked up and down the mean street, and then surveyed the house before which they stood. It was a small, dark edifice of two stories, the second of which projected over the lower floor, and the front apartment had the aspect of a shop for petty commodities.

"Now, truly, I am in luck," replied Robin, cunningly, "and so indeed is my kinsman, the Major, in having so pretty a housekeeper. But I prithee trouble him to step to the door; I will deliver him a message from his friends in the country, and then go back to my lodgings at the inn."

"Nay, the Major has been abed this hour or more," said the lady of the scarlet petticoat; "and it would be to little purpose to disturb him to-night, seeing his evening draught was of the strongest. But he is a kind-hearted man, and it would be as much as my life's worth to let a kinsman of his turn away from the door. You are the good old gentleman's very picture, and I could swear that was his rainy-weather hat. Also he has garments very much resembling those leather small-clothes. But come in, I pray, for I bid you hearty welcome in his name."

So saying, the fair and hospitable dame took our [626] hero by the hand; and the touch was light, and the force was gentleness, and though Robin read in her eyes what he did not hear in her words, yet the slender-waisted woman in the scarlet petticoat proved stronger than the athletic country youth. She had drawn his half-willing footsteps nearly to the threshold, when the opening of a door in the neighborhood startled the Major's housekeeper, and, leaving the Major's kinsman, she vanished speedily into her own domicile. A heavy yawn preceded the appearance of a man, who, like the Moonshine of Pyramus and Thisbe, carried a lantern, needlessly aiding his sister luminary in the heavens. As he walked sleepily up the street, he turned his broad, dull face on Robin, and displayed a long staff, spiked at the end.

"Home, vagabond, home!" said the watchman, in accents that seemed to fall asleep as soon as they were uttered. "Home, or we'll set you in the stocks by peep of day!"

"This is the second hint of the kind," thought Robin. "I wish they would end my difficulties, by setting me there to-night."

Nevertheless, the youth felt an instinctive antipathy towards the guardian of midnight order, which at first prevented him from asking his usual question. But just when the man was about to vanish behind the corner, Robin resolved not to lose the opportunity, and shouted lustily after him,—

"I say, friend! will you guide me to the house of my kinsman, Major Molineux?"

The watchman made no reply, but turned the corner and was gone; yet Robin seemed to hear the sound of drowsy laughter stealing along the solitary street. At that moment, also, a pleasant titter saluted [627] him from the open window above his head; he looked up, and caught the sparkle of a saucy eye; a round arm beckoned to him, and next he heard light footsteps descending the staircase within. But Robin, being of the household of a New England clergyman, was a good youth, as well as a shrewd one; so he resisted temptation, and fled away.

He now roamed desperately, and at random, through the town, almost ready to believe that a spell was on him, like that by which a wizard of his country had once kept three pursuers wandering, a whole winter night, within twenty paces of the cottage which they sought. The streets lay before him, strange and desolate, and the lights were extinguished in almost every house. Twice, however, little parties of men, among whom Robin distinguished individuals in outlandish attire, came hurrying along; but, though on both occasions they paused to address him, such intercourse did not at all enlighten his perplexity. They did but utter a few words in some language of which Robin knew nothing, and perceiving his inability to answer, bestowed a curse upon him in plain English and hastened away. Finally, the lad determined to knock at the door of every mansion that might appear worthy to be occupied by his kinsman, trusting that perseverance would overcome the fatality that had hitherto thwarted him. Firm in this resolve, he was passing beneath the walls of a church, which formed the corner of two streets, when, as he turned into the shade of its steeple, he encountered a bulky stranger, muffled in a cloak. The man was proceeding with the speed of earnest business, but Robin planted himself full before him, holding the oak cudgel with both hands across his body as a bar to further passage.[628]

"Halt, honest man, and answer me a question," said he, very resolutely. "Tell me, this instant, whereabouts is the dwelling of my kinsman, Major Molineux!"

"Keep your tongue between your teeth, fool, and let me pass!" said a deep, gruff voice, which Robin partly remembered. "Let me pass, I say, or I'll strike you to the earth!"

"No, no, neighbor!" cried Robin, flourishing his cudgel, and then thrusting its larger end close to the man's muffled face. "No, no, I'm not the fool you take me for, nor do you pass till I have an answer to my question. Whereabouts is the dwelling of my kinsman, Major Molineux?"

The stranger, instead of attempting to force his passage, stepped back into the moonlight, unmuffled his face, and stared full into that of Robin.

"Watch here an hour, and Major Molineux will pass by," said he.

Robin gazed with dismay and astonishment on the unprecedented physiognomy of the speaker. The forehead with its double prominence, the broad hooked nose, the shaggy eyebrows, and fiery eyes were those which he had noticed at the inn, but the man's complexion had undergone a singular, or, more properly, a twofold change. One side of the face blazed an intense red, while the other was black as midnight, the division line being in the broad bridge of the nose; and a mouth which seemed to extend from ear to ear was black or red, in contrast to the color of the cheek. The effect was as if two individual devils, a fiend of fire and a fiend of darkness, had united themselves to form this infernal visage. The stranger grinned in Robin's face, muffled his parti-colored features, and was out of sight in a moment.[629]

"Strange things we travellers see!" ejaculated Robin.

He seated himself, however, upon the steps of the church-door, resolving to wait the appointed time for his kinsman. A few moments were consumed in philosophical speculations upon the species of man who had just left him; but having settled this point shrewdly, rationally, and satisfactorily, he was compelled to look elsewhere for his amusement. And first he threw his eyes along the street. It was of more respectable appearance than most of those into which he had wandered; and the moon, creating, like the imaginative power, a beautiful strangeness in familiar objects, gave something of romance to a scene that might not have possessed it in the light of day. The irregular and often quaint architecture of the houses, some of whose roofs were broken into numerous little peaks, while others ascended, steep and narrow, into a single point, and others again were square; the pure snow-white of some of their complexions, the aged darkness of others, and the thousand sparklings, reflected from bright substances in the walls of many; these matters engaged Robin's attention for a while, and then began to grow wearisome. Next he endeavored to define the forms of distant objects, starting away, with almost ghostly indistinctness, just as his eye appeared to grasp them; and finally he took a minute survey of an edifice which stood on the opposite side of the street, directly in front of the church-door, where he was stationed. It was a large, square mansion, distinguished from its neighbors by a balcony, which rested on tall pillars, and by an elaborate Gothic window, communicating therewith.

"Perhaps this is the very house I have been seeking," thought Robin.[630]

Then he strove to speed away the time, by listening to a murmur which swept continually along the street, yet was scarcely audible, except to an unaccustomed ear like his; it was a low, dull, dreamy sound, compounded of many noises, each of which was at too great a distance to be separately heard. Robin marvelled at this snore of a sleeping town, and marvelled more whenever its continuity was broken by now and then a distant shout, apparently loud where it originated. But altogether it was a sleep-inspiring sound, and, to shake off its drowsy influence, Robin arose, and climbed a window-frame, that he might view the interior of the church. There the moonbeams came trembling in, and fell down upon the deserted pews, and extended along the quiet aisles. A fainter yet more awful radiance was hovering around the pulpit, and one solitary ray had dared to rest upon the open page of the great Bible. Had nature, in that deep hour, become a worshipper in the house which man had builded? Or was that heavenly light the visible sanctity of the place,—visible because no earthly and impure feet were within the walls? The scene made Robin's heart shiver with a sensation of loneliness stronger than he had ever felt in the remotest depths of his native woods; so he turned away and sat down again before the door. There were graves around the church, and now an uneasy thought obtruded into Robin's breast. What if the object of his search, which had been so often and so strangely thwarted, were all the time mouldering in his shroud? What if his kinsman should glide through yonder gate, and nod and smile to him in dimly passing by?

"Oh that any breathing thing were here with me!" said Robin.[631]

Recalling his thoughts from this uncomfortable track, he sent them over forest, hill, and stream, and attempted to imagine how that evening of ambiguity and weariness had been spent by his father's household. He pictured them assembled at the door, beneath the tree, the great old tree, which had been spared for its huge twisted trunk and venerable shade, when a thousand leafy brethren fell. There, at the going down of the summer sun, it was his father's custom to perform domestic worship, that the neighbors might come and join with him like brothers of the family, and that the wayfaring man might pause to drink at that fountain, and keep his heart pure by freshening the memory of home. Robin distinguished the seat of every individual of the little audience; he saw the good man in the midst, holding the Scriptures in the golden light that fell from the western clouds; he beheld him close the book and all rise up to pray. He heard the old thanksgiving for daily mercies, the old supplications for their continuance, to which he had so often listened in weariness, but which were now among his dear remembrances. He perceived the slight inequality of his father's voice when he came to speak of the absent one; he noted how his mother turned her face to the broad and knotted trunk; how his elder brother scorned, because the beard was rough upon his upper lip, to permit his features to be moved; how the younger sister drew down a low hanging branch before her eyes; and how the little one of all, whose sports had hitherto broken the decorum of the scene, understood the prayer for her playmate, and burst into clamorous grief. Then he saw them go in at the door; and when Robin would have entered also, the latch tinkled into its place, and he was excluded from his home.[632]

"Am I here, or there?" cried Robin, starting; for all at once, when his thoughts had become visible and audible in a dream, the long, wide, solitary street shone out before him.

He aroused himself, and endeavored to fix his attention steadily upon the large edifice which he had surveyed before. But still his mind kept vibrating between fancy and reality; by turns, the pillars of the balcony lengthened into the tall, bare stems of pines, dwindled down to human figures, settled again into their true shape and size, and then commenced a new succession of changes. For a single moment, when he deemed himself awake, he could have sworn that a visage—one which he seemed to remember, yet could not absolutely name as his kinsman's—was looking towards him from the Gothic window. A deeper sleep wrestled with and nearly overcame him, but fled at the sound of footsteps along the opposite pavement. Robin rubbed his eyes, discerned a man passing at the foot of the balcony, and addressed him in a loud, peevish, and lamentable cry.

"Hallo, friend! must I wait here all night for my kinsman, Major Molineux?"

The sleeping echoes awoke, and answered the voice; and the passenger, barely able to discern a figure sitting in the oblique shade of the steeple, traversed the street to obtain a nearer view. He was himself a gentleman in his prime, of open, intelligent, cheerful, and altogether prepossessing countenance. Perceiving a country youth, apparently homeless and without friends, he accosted him in a tone of real kindness, which had become strange to Robin's ears.

"Well, my good lad, who are you sitting here?" inquired he. "Can I be of service to you in any way?" [633]

"I am afraid not, sir," replied Robin, despondingly; "yet I shall take it kindly, if you'll answer me a single question. I've been searching, half the night, for one Major Molineux; now, sir, is there really such a person in these parts, or am I dreaming?"

"Major Molineux! The name is not altogether strange to me," said the gentleman, smiling. "Have you any objection to telling me the nature of your business with him?"

Then Robin briefly related that his father was a clergyman, settled on a small salary, at a long distance back in the country, and that he and Major Molineux were brothers' children. The Major, having inherited riches, and acquired civil and military rank, had visited his cousin, in great pomp, a year or two before; had manifested much interest in Robin and an elder brother, and, being childless himself, had thrown out hints respecting the future establishment of one of them in life. The elder brother was destined to succeed to the farm which his father cultivated in the interval of sacred duties; it was therefore determined that Robin should profit by his kinsman's generous intentions, especially as he seemed to be rather the favorite, and was thought to possess other necessary endowments.

"For I have the name of being a shrewd youth," observed Robin, in this part of his story.

"I doubt not you deserve it," replied his new friend, good-naturedly; "but pray proceed."

"Well, sir, being nearly eighteen years old, and well grown, as you see," continued Robin, drawing himself up to his full height, "I thought it high time to begin the world. So my mother and sister put me [634] in handsome trim, and my father gave me half the remnant of his last year's salary, and five days ago I started for this place, to pay the Major a visit. But, would you believe it, sir! I crossed the ferry a little after dark, and have yet found nobody that would show me the way to his dwelling; only, an hour or two since, I was told to wait here, and Major Molineux would pass by."

"Can you describe the man who told you this?" inquired the gentleman.

"Oh, he was a very ill-favored fellow, sir," replied Robin, "with two great bumps on his forehead, a hook nose, fiery eyes; and, what struck me as the strangest, his face was of two different colors. Do you happen to know such a man, sir?"

"Not intimately," answered the stranger, "but I chanced to meet him a little time previous to your stopping me. I believe you may trust his word, and that the Major will very shortly pass through this street. In the mean time, as I have a singular curiosity to witness your meeting, I will sit down here upon the steps and bear you company."

He seated himself accordingly, and soon engaged his companion in animated discourse. It was but of brief continuance, however, for a noise of shouting, which had long been remotely audible, drew so much nearer that Robin inquired its cause.

"What may be the meaning of this uproar?" asked he. "Truly, if your town be always as noisy, I shall find little sleep while I am an inhabitant."

"Why, indeed, friend Robin, there do appear to be three or four riotous fellows abroad to-night," replied the gentleman. "You must not expect all the stillness of your native woods here in our streets. But [635] the watch will shortly be at the heels of these lads and"—

"Ay, and set them in the stocks by peep of day," interrupted Robin, recollecting his own encounter with the drowsy lantern-bearer. "But, dear sir, if I may trust my ears, an army of watchmen would never make head against such a multitude of rioters. There were at least a thousand voices went up to make that one shout."

"May not a man have several voices, Robin, as well as two complexions?" said his friend.

"Perhaps a man may; but Heaven forbid that a woman should!" responded the shrewd youth, thinking of the seductive tones of the Major's housekeeper.

The sounds of a trumpet in some neighboring street now became so evident and continual, that Robin's curiosity was strongly excited. In addition to the shouts, he heard frequent bursts from many instruments of discord, and a wild and confused laughter filled up the intervals. Robin rose from the steps, and looked wistfully towards a point whither people seemed to be hastening.

"Surely some prodigious merry-making is going on," exclaimed he. "I have laughed very little since I left home, sir, and should be sorry to lose an opportunity. Shall we step round the corner by that darkish house, and take our share of the fun?"

"Sit down again, sit down, good Robin," replied the gentleman, laying his hand on the skirt of the gray coat. "You forget that we must wait here for your kinsman; and there is reason to believe that he will pass by, in the course of a very few moments."

The near approach of the uproar had now disturbed the neighborhood; windows flew open on all sides; [636] and many heads, in the attire of the pillow, and confused by sleep suddenly broken, were protruded to the gaze of whoever had leisure to observe them. Eager voices hailed each other from house to house, all demanding the explanation, which not a soul could give. Half-dressed men hurried towards the unknown commotion, stumbling as they went over the stone steps that thrust themselves into the narrow foot-walk. The shouts, the laughter, and the tuneless bray, the antipodes of music, came onwards with increasing din, till scattered individuals, and then denser bodies, began to appear round a corner at the distance of a hundred yards.

"Will you recognize your kinsman, if he passes in this crowd?" inquired the gentleman.

"Indeed, I can't warrant it, sir; but I'll take my stand here, and keep a bright lookout," answered Robin, descending to the outer edge of the pavement.

A mighty stream of people now emptied into the street, and came rolling slowly towards the church. A single horseman wheeled the corner in the midst of them, and close behind him came a band of fearful wind-instruments, sending forth a fresher discord now that no intervening buildings kept it from the ear. Then a redder light disturbed the moon-beams, and a dense multitude of torches shone along the street, concealing, by their glare, whatever object they illuminated. The single horseman, clad in a military dress, and bearing a drawn sword, rode onward as the leader, and, by his fierce and variegated countenance, appeared like war personified; the red of one cheek was an emblem of fire and sword; the blackness of the other betokened the mourning that attends them. In his train were wild figures in the Indian dress, and [637] many fantastic shapes without a model, giving the whole march a visionary air, as if a dream had broken forth from some feverish brain, and were sweeping visibly through the midnight streets. A mass of people, inactive, except as applauding spectators, hemmed the procession in; and several women ran along the sidewalk, piercing the confusion of heavier sounds with their shrill voices of mirth or terror.

"The double-faced fellow has his eye upon me," muttered Robin, with an indefinite but an uncomfortable idea that he was himself to bear a part in the pageantry.

The leader turned himself in the saddle, and fixed his glance full upon the country youth, as the steed went slowly by. When Robin had freed his eyes from those fiery ones, the musicians were passing before him, and the torches were close at hand; but the unsteady brightness of the latter formed a veil which he could not penetrate. The rattling of wheels over the stones sometimes found its way to his ear, and confused traces of a human form appeared at intervals, and then melted into the vivid light. A moment more, and the leader thundered a command to halt: the trumpets vomited a horrid breath, and then held their peace; the shouts and laughter of the people died away, and there remained only a universal hum, allied to silence. Right before Robin's eyes was an uncovered cart. There the torches blazed the brightest, there the moon shone out like day, and there, in tar-and-feathery dignity, sat his kinsman, Major Molineux!

He was an elderly man, of large and majestic person, and strong, square features, betokening a steady soul; but steady as it was, his enemies had found [638] means to shake it. His face was pale as death, and far more

ghastly; the broad forehead was contracted in his agony, so that his eyebrows formed one grizzled line; his eyes were red and wild, and the foam
hung white upon his quivering lip. His whole frame was agitated by a
quick and continual tremor, which his pride strove to quell, even in those
circumstances of overwhelming humiliation. But perhaps the bitterest
pang of all was when his eyes met those of Robin; for he evidently knew
him on the instant, as the youth stood witnessing the foul disgrace of a
head grown gray in honor. They stared at each other in silence, and
Robin's knees shook, and his hair bristled, with a mixture of pity and
terror. Soon, however, a bewildering excitement began to seize upon his
mind; the preceding adventures of the night, the unexpected appearance
of the crowd, the torches, the confused din and the hush that followed,
the spectre of his kinsman reviled by that great multitude,—all this, and,
more than all, a perception of tremendous ridicule in the whole scene,
affected him with a sort of mental inebriety. At that moment a voice of
sluggish merriment saluted Robin's ears; he turned instinctively, and
just behind the corner of the church stood the lantern-bearer, rubbing his
eyes, and drowsily enjoying the lad's amazement. Then he heard a peal
of laughter like the ringing of silvery bells; a woman twitched his arm,
a saucy eye met his, and he saw the lady of the scarlet petticoat. A sharp,
dry cachinnation appealed to his memory, and, standing on tiptoe in the
crowd, with his white apron over his head, he beheld the courteous little
innkeeper. And lastly, there sailed over the heads of the multitude a great,
broad laugh, broken in the midst by two sepulchral hems; thus,[639]
"Haw, haw, haw,—hem, hem,—haw, haw, haw, haw!"

The sound proceeded from the balcony of the opposite edifice, and
thither Robin turned his eyes. In front of the Gothic window stood the
old citizen wrapped in a wide gown, his gray periwig exchanged for a
nightcap, which was thrust back from his forehead, and his silk stockings
hanging about his legs. He supported himself on his polished cane in a
fit of convulsive merriment, which manifested itself on his solemn old
features like a funny inscription on a tombstone. Then Robin seemed to
hear the voices of the barbers, of the guests of the inn, and of all who had
made sport of him that night. The contagion was spreading among the
multitude, when all at once, it seized upon Robin, and he sent forth a
shout of laughter that echoed through the street,—every man shook his
sides, every man emptied his lungs, but Robin's shout was the loudest
there. The cloud-spirits peeped from their silvery islands, as the con-
gregated mirth went roaring up the sky! The Man in the Moon heard
the far bellow. "Oho," quoth he, "the old earth is frolicsome to-night!"

When there was a momentary calm in that tempestuous sea of sound, the leader gave the sign, the procession resumed its march. On they went, like fiends that throng in mockery around some dead potentate, mighty no more, but majestic still in his agony. On they went, in counterfeited pomp, in senseless uproar, in frenzied merriment, trampling all on an old man's heart. On swept the tumult, and left a silent street behind.

"Well, Robin, are you dreaming?" inquired the gentleman, laying his hand on the youth's shoulder.[640]

Robin started, and withdrew his arm from the stone post to which he had instinctively clung, as the living stream rolled by him. His cheek was somewhat pale, and his eye not quite as lively as in the earlier part of the evening.

"Will you be kind enough to show me the way to the ferry?" said he, after a moment's pause.

"You have, then, adopted a new subject of inquiry?" observed his companion, with a smile.

"Why, yes, sir," replied Robin, rather dryly. "Thanks to you, and to my other friends, I have at last met my kinsman, and he will scarce desire to see my face again. I begin to grow weary of a town life, sir. Will you show me the way to the ferry?"

"No, my good friend Robin,—not to-night, at least," said the gentleman. "Some few days hence, if you wish it, I will speed you on your journey. Or, if you prefer to remain with us, perhaps, as you are a shrewd youth, you may rise in the world without the help of your kinsman, Major Molineux." [641]

Hawthorne's "My Kinsman, Major Molineux": History as Moral Adventure*

It is one of the peculiarities of the study of American literature that, despite the abundance of critical effort expended on Hawthorne's fiction, what is perhaps his most powerful short story, "My Kinsman, Major

* Seymour Gross, "Hawthorne's 'My Kinsman, Major Molineux': History as Moral Adventure," *Nineteenth-Century Fiction*, XII (September, 1957), 97–109. Copyright © September, 1957, by The Regents of the University of California. Reprinted by permission of The Regents.

Molineux," has been until only recently all but completely ignored.[1]
To my knowledge, the tale has never been anthologized in a volume of
short stories or selected for inclusion [97] in an anthology of American
literature, although it is, in my estimation, as perceptive a treatment of
the theme of initiation as are, for example, "The Killers" or "I Want to
Know Why," and is from almost any point of view vastly superior to
the oft-selected "Ethan Brand." Moreover, virtually no critical attention
was given the tale until 1955. Earlier, Quentin Anderson mentioned the
tale tangentially in his larger treatment of Henry James; [2] Mark Van
Doren devoted to it one page of his *Nathaniel Hawthorne* (and three to
"Roger Malvin's Burial"); and neither F. O. Matthiessen (*American
Renaissance*) nor Richard H. Fogle (*Hawthorne's Fiction: The Light
and the Dark*) even so much as mentioned the title. Unfortunately, the
first critic to discuss the tale at some length, Mrs. Q. D. Leavis, misread
it, or, at the very least, chose to overlook the moral superstructure which
rises out of the historical situation.

In what must be viewed as a commendable attempt to counteract the
opinion that Hawthorne was merely "a private allegorist" who con-
sistently lacked any sense of society or historical tradition, Mrs. Leavis
reads "My Kinsman, Major Molineux" as "the prophetic forecast of the
rejection of England that was to occur in fact much later." Seeing the tale

[1] Since this paper was accepted for publication three studies of "Molineux"
have appeared. It has been gratifying to note that two of the studies are in
essential agreement with my over-all reading of the story, although both studies,
because they concentrate on different aspects of the story, omit many points
which I consider essential to a complete comprehension of the tale. Professor
Franklin B. Newman (" 'My Kinsman, Major Molineux': an Interpretation,"
University of Kansas City Review, XXI [March, 1955], 203–212) concentrates
primarily on what he calls the story's "allegorical-dream level." Although he
sees the story as concerning initiation, Professor Newman emphasizes Hawthorne's remarkable "hypnagogic" technique, which agrees with a number of
the steps Freud described in the process of dream formulation. Professor
H. H. Waggoner (*Hawthorne: A Critical Study* [Cambridge, Mass., 1955], pp.
46–53), in addition to giving a very perceptive analysis of the story's "subtle
and complex" texture and a résumé of the levels of meaning on which the story
can be read, shows how the story relates to the rest of Hawthorne's fiction. Mr.
Simon O. Lesser ("The Image of the Father: A Reading of 'My Kinsman, Major
Molineux' and 'I Want to Know Why,' " *Partisan Review*, XXII [Summer,
1955], 372–390) reads the story in terms of "depth psychology," replete with
father images and the search for sexual adventure and other such phenomena
of the unconscious mind. The analysis seems to have very little to do with Hawthorne's story.
[2] "Henry James and the New Jerusalem," *KR*, VIII (Autumn, 1946), 565.
Although his discussion is very brief, Mr. Anderson correctly sees "Molineux" as
a metaphysical, not historical, account.

from this point of view, she interprets Robin, the son of a typical farmer-clergyman, as the symbol of Young America, and his humiliated uncle, Major Molineux, as the "representative in New England of the British civil and military rule." [3]

Mrs. Leavis' interpretation is not wholly without relevance; it *is* possible to read "Molineux" as an historical allegory (just as one can read "The Maypole of Merry Mount" in the same [98] way), but only, I believe, at the risk of missing the deeper implications in the tale, and, as a matter of fact, of misconstruing Hawthorne's attitude toward history. Whereas, for example, Scott viewed the past as a continuous object lesson for the present and future, and Cooper looked upon it as a Golden Age to be emulated, Hawthorne found in it both a discipline for, and a prod to, his creative imagination. As the source studies of Hawthorne's historical tales abundantly illustrate, *history as history* had but very little meaning for Hawthorne artistically; and in his careful revision of "The Gentle Boy" we have what is possibly the clearest instance of how Hawthorne deliberately attempted to transmute an historical phenomenon into an elemental condition of existence.[4] Hawthorne's most revealing comment on the relationship between history and the creative imagination can be found in his review of William Gilmore Simms' *Views and Reviews*. Hawthorne criticizes Simms for being that "lesser" kind of writer who merely uses "varnish" to bring out "the lights and shades that lie upon the surface of our history," and who in doing so misses the essence of the historical matter. Such a writer's themes, Hawthorne goes on to say, can never cause "new moral shapes to spring up to the reader's mind. . . ." [5] It is precisely these "new moral shapes" that Mrs. Leavis' interpretation overlooks.[6]

---

[3] Mrs. Leavis' interpretation of "Molineux" is part of her long article on Hawthorne's fiction in general ("Hawthorne as Poet," *SR*, LIX [Spring, 1951], 179–205; [Summer, 1951], 426–458). More recently, Professor Roy Harvey Pearce has used "Molineux" as a starting point for an interesting analysis of Hawthorne's sense of the past ("Hawthorne and the Sense of the Past, or the Immortality of Major Molineux," *ELH*, XXI [Dec., 1954], 327–349).

[4] See Seymour L. Gross, "Hawthorne's Revision of 'The Gentle Boy,'" *AL*, XXVI (May, 1954), 196–208.

[5] Randall Stewart, "Hawthorne's Contributions to *The Salem Advertiser*," *AL*, V (Jan., 1934), 381–382.

[6] That Hawthorne was unwilling to have his story interpreted as an historical narrative can also be seen in his shutting off of the brief historical preface with the following statement: "The reader, in order to avoid a long and dry detail of colonial affairs, is requested to dispense with an account of the train of circumstances that had caused much temporary inflammation of the popular mind."

The story opens with the light of a ferryman's lantern revealing to us the handsome features of Robin, as Hawthorne significantly calls him, who has come to the city to make his way under the patronage of his influential kinsman, Major Molineux. Although country-bred, and now "upon his first visit to town," [99] the youth is cheerfully self-confident, undaunted by the fact that "he knew not whither to direct his steps" (p. 618).[7] In his steady hand he carries a heavy cudgel, with which weapon, he assures himself, this strange city can be successfully tried. The oaken cudgel, as becomes increasingly apparent, is both the emblem of the life Robin has left behind him in the quietly uncomplicated rustic town in which he has been reared, and of the inadequacy of such a life as preparation for an assault on the city of night. As is sensed almost immediately, this is no mere New England metropolis, at least not to those who have never been initiated to its "crooked and narrow streets." The city, like the forest in "Young Goodman Brown," is a dark and terrifying moral labyrinth, through whose tortuous passageways stalk hatred, revenge, sin, and retribution. But for the Robin who still so preposterously relies upon his foolish piece of wood to conquer the world, such moral immensities can have no reality. It is only a thousand moral years later that Robin recognizes the inexorable nature of these windmills, and casts down his weapon. But for now he is only an eager and self-assured stranger in the city.

Lost but unperturbed, Robin optimistically pursues the object of his search, only to meet with successive rebukes. An old man of whom Robin patronizingly inquires the way to his kinsman's house angrily rebuffs the youth and threatens to have him put in the stocks. Robin is startled—but only momentarily. His first reaction is to strike the old man, who has something of death about him: his "two sepulchral hems" break into his reprimand of the boy "like a thought of the cold grave obtruding among wrathful passions" (p. 619). But "being a shrewd youth," Robin (ironically) decides that the old fellow is some country bumpkin who is unacquainted with the fabulous Molineux, and jauntily continues on his search, only to become more and more entangled in a succession of dark streets. In the tavern which he finally comes [100] upon, Robin interprets the innkeeper's professional civility as the obsequiousness due a kinsman of the great Molineux ("The man sees a family likeness!"), and leaning confidently on his cudgel, condescend-

---

[7] All the page references are to the Riverside edition of *The Works of Nathaniel Hawthorne* (Boston, 1883), III.

ingly inquires the way to his kinsman's house. But instead of being assisted he is suddenly, inexplicably, accused of being a fugitive servant and is forcibly thrown out into the street. This is Robin's first taste of blind, unreasoning hatred, although he is not able to identify it for what it is until it later, literally, smashes his moral innocence. For the present, Robin, "with his usual shrewdness," convinces himself that his confession of an empty purse has outweighed the grandeur of his family connections, and consoles himself with thinking, "Oh, if I had one of those grinning rascals in the woods, where I and my oak sapling grew up together, I would teach him that my arm is heavy though my purse be light" (p. 623). But Robin is not safely tucked away in the bucolic innocence of the woods which nourished tree and boy, and he is forced to return again to the dark unfamiliarity of the city's streets.

As his patience begins to wear thin, and hunger and fatigue lend a nightmarish quality to his futile search, he falls back upon the only response he is yet capable of—violence: "Robin began to balance the propriety of demanding, violently, and with lifted cudgel, the necessary guidance from the first solitary stranger whom he should meet" (p. 625). As this resolution is gaining in strength, he wanders into a disreputable neighborhood and is almost enticed into a harlot's house. The dainty figure in the scarlet petticoat assures the boy that he has, indeed, at last found his destination and begins drawing "his half-willing footsteps" across the threshold. The sudden appearance of the night watchman, however, frightens the woman off. This dull-faced "guardian of the midnight order" also unfairly threatens the boy with the stocks, and turns a deaf ear to his inevitable question. When the watchman leaves, the prostitute beckons from the window, but the moral inhibition of his New England clergyman's upbringing, which [101] in the desperation of his frustration had been momentarily suspended, returns to him, and he flees into the night.

To this point in the narrative, Robin's moral obtuseness has been impenetrable: he has been able to rationalize the city away. But now as he returns to wander aimlessly through "strange and desolate streets," occasionally passing small parties of men who utter incomprehensible words to him (a password), and who curse him when he is unable to answer,[8] Robin's hitherto invulnerable carapace of innocence (or ignorance) cracks slightly enough to allow some self-doubt, the harbinger of

[8] My friend, Dr. Milton Stern, has pointed out to me that this situation is an ironic inversion of Robin's own position: he too "curses" those who do not respond to his own particular "password."

self-knowledge, to seep through: "He now roamed desperately, and at random, through the town, almost ready to believe that a spell was on him . . ." (p. 628). But the self-doubt here is merely the substitution of one species of illusion for another; accordingly, when Robin meets another stranger he reverts to the pathetically primitive reaction of force in order to overcome what he conceives to be "the fatality that had hitherto thwarted him." When Robin threateningly waves his cudgel before the man's hidden face and demands to know the whereabouts of his kinsman's abode, the stranger steps back into the moonlight and unveils a hideously parti-colored face, half in red and half in black, "as if two individual devils, a fiend of fire and a fiend of darkness, had united themselves to form this infernal visage" (p. 629). The apparition grins horribly and disappears after telling the youth that Molineux will pass by in an hour. Confronted with this astonishing phenomenon, so utterly alien to what he could possibly know or imagine, Robin, with the characteristic oversimplification of experience which is his shield against reality, "settled the point shrewdly, rationally, and satisfactorily" in a few moments, and calmly sits down on the steps of a church to await his uncle.

For sheer dramatically realized psychological insight, the portion of the tale which follows is difficult to match in the whole [102] range of Hawthorne's fiction. In an attempt to allay the vague uneasiness which is somehow beginning to oppress him, Robin climbs a window to peer into the church, hoping to recapture something of the comforting solidity of his previous life. But this is no church of warming daylight in which his father reads the Scriptures by "the golden light that fell from western clouds": this is the church of the city of night. The utter desolation of the interior, accentuated by trembling moonbeams that hover eerily above the deserted pews, and the "awful radiance" that engulfs the Bible on the pulpit, make "Robin's heart shiver with a sensation of loneliness stronger than he had ever felt in the remotest depths of his native woods" (p. 631). Hawthorne, symbolically, has cut another prop from beneath the boy. The moral suspension is not without effect, however, for Robin becomes dimly aware of his isolation: "Oh that any breathing thing were here with me," he laments into the darkness. But more important, there is also the first blurred perception of the possibility of forces beyond the control of man, forces which will not succumb to the power of a thrashing club. For the first time in his life Robin faces the actuality of death: "What," Robin wonders with horror, "if the object of his search . . . were all the time mouldering in his shroud" (p. 631)? But the fact, as yet, is still too terrible to bear, and Robin forces his thoughts from this "uncomfortable track," away from this "evening of ambiguity," and back to the safe simplicity of his Eden in the country. Robin's nostalgic reconstruction of the idyllic life he has left behind him, however, proves unsubstantial in the face of his new, and as yet but dimly apprehended, commitment: "Then he saw them [his family] go in at the door; and when Robin would have entered also, the latch tinkled into its place, and he was excluded from his home" (p. 632). Thrust from the consolation of past innocence, but not yet being able to come to terms with this new involvement, Robin is confronted by an agonizing doubt of the very nature of his existence: "Am I here or there?" he cries out. In a futile attempt [103] to recapture the solid simplicity of his now jeopardized typical response to experience, Robin desperately fixes his attention on the sturdy edifice before him. But there is no transfer, for "still his mind kept vibrating between fancy and reality; by turns, the pillars of the balcony lengthened into the tall, bare stems of pines, dwindled down to human figures, settled again into their true shape and size, and then commenced a new succession of changes" (p. 633).

This symbolic depiction of the boy's slowly germinating doubt of the terms upon which he has approached experience (the unequivocal pines are no longer unequivocal) is not without salutary effect. It is a markedly altered Robin who calls to the next passer-by. In a voice pathetic rather than proud, and with no thought to force (the cudgel is never again mentioned), Robin pleadingly asks how long he must wait for his kinsman. This stranger is kind. It is no accident that Robin must wait until this moment in his spiritual journey to find a compassionate human being who will talk to him, for the childish façade of physical self-reliance with which he had previously faced the moral universe had to be discarded before adult communication could take place. Aware of what has already befallen the Major, and curious to see how Robin is "to begin the world," although in a sense far different from Robin's pragmatic concept, the stranger decides to wait with the boy. "I have a singular curiosity to witness your meeting," he tells the youth—the sympathetic curiosity of the adult who has already had to come to terms with the inexorable nature of a menacing reality.

The brief bit of dialogue between the man and boy which precedes the impending climax is a symbolic prologue to the actual drama which stands ready to burst upon Robin. When Robin complains of the noise in the street, his friend replies that "you must not expect all the stillness of your native woods here in our streets" (p. 635). And when Robin exclaims that the uproar must be caused by at least a thousand persons, the older man enigmatically asks, "May not a man have several voices . . . as well as [104] two complexions" (p. 636)? But it is only later when he must face the utter degradation of his uncle that Robin perceives that violence in man's soul wholly unknown to its moments of bucolic innocence; it is only then that he discovers that the soul of man has, indeed, two voices, two complexions.

A nightmarish procession suddenly streams down the street. The leader—the ghoulish figure whose face is marked in red and black—fixes his eye full upon the boy, as if the entire proceedings have been arranged solely for his benefit—as indeed in a sense they have. Even Robin himself senses something of his own involvement: "'The double-faced fellow has his eye upon me,'" Robin mutters "with an indefinite but uncomfortable idea that he himself was to bear a part in the pageantry" (p. 638). At first Robin is unable to penetrate "the unsteady brightness" of the torches, but as his eyes adjust to the light, there before his horrified gaze sits his kinsman, Major Molineux, tarred and feathered! The humiliated man and thunderstruck boy stare at each other in mutually painful recognition. But even as Robin's soul is wrung by the tragic "mixture of pity and terror" for the wretched shape of his uncle, he is poignantly aware of the figures of the night—the watchman, the harlot, the deathlike old man,[9] the innkeeper, the habitués of the tavern—all laughing, laughing at him. Suddenly, Robin himself "sent forth a shout of laughter that echoed through the street"—the loudest laugh of all. Almost as if his laugh has dissolved the vision, the procession disappears, leaving "a silent street behind."

The kindly stranger lays his hand sympathetically on the boy's shoulder to bring him out of his stupor. Clinging desperately to a stone post, his "cheek . . . somewhat pale, and his eye not quite as lively as in the earlier part of the evening," Robin wants only to be shown the way home. But his friend dissuades him, assuring him that "you may rise in the world without the help of your kinsman, Major Molineux" (p. 641).[105]

The theme of this remarkable tale is in the direct line of one of Hawthorne's metaphysical preoccupations: the painful but paradoxically curative power of an apprehension of the nature of moral reality. The

___

[9] Hawthorne again describes the old man in terms of death: "convulsive merriment . . . manifested itself on his solemn old features like a funny inscription on a tombstone" (p. 640).

awareness on the part of a simple, naïvely happy young man that the terms upon which he has been accepting life are experientially false is the meaning which informs this tale. If the sole explanation of the action is made in terms of the historical incident, as in Mrs. Leavis' analysis, then the great bulk of the tale, Robin's quest, remains sheer Gothic mystification. When one sees the story from the point of view I am suggesting, however, then even the most seemingly casual elements take on a startling relevance.

One of the most telling elements in the tale is Hawthorne's masterly manipulation of lights and darks. Although Hawthorne used color contrast to good effect throughout his fiction,[10] nowhere is it used so effectively as in "Molineux." The light-dark device is more significant in this story because, where in other stories it is used as a kind of thematic signpost, here the motif is the theme itself: the journey from dark innocence to painfully illuminated knowledge. No reader can fail to notice how Robin's dark wanderings through shadowed streets are periodically lit up by flashes of light which he refuses to understand,[11] until where "the torches blazed the brightest" and "the moon shone out like day," there was a reality too bright to be misunderstood.

With an artistic control which Hawthorne only infrequently managed to achieve, all the various elements in "Molineux" are made to bear in upon the theme. Each of the figures that Robin encounters symbolizes (but not with the irritating obviousness of the later allegorical sticks) some manifestation of the negative [106] principle of life that Robin has hitherto been blind to, while still retaining credibility on the literal level. And the most remarkable of these figures, the parti-colored leader, is not only the nemesis that tracks Robin down ("the double-faced fellow has his eye on me"), but is, as well, the externalization of Robin's experience, for his face, marked in red and black, is the geography of Robin's voyage —the voyage from the blind innocence of a primal paradise to the scorching fire of satanic knowledge. Moreover, even the descriptions function organically; descriptive details, like those of the desolate church,

---

[10] See Walter Blair, "Color, Light, and Shadows in Hawthorne's Fiction," *NEQ*, XV (March, 1942), 74–92.

[11] Robin accosts the first man as "the light from the open door and windows of the barber's shop fell upon both their figures" (p. 618). Robin's next rebuff takes place within the brightly illuminated tavern. The harlot's temptation is effected by the light that passes through the slightly ajar door. The watchman threatens the youth by the light of his lantern. The grotesque leader "stepped back into the moonlight" before unveiling his parti-colored face. Finally, the climax takes place where "the torches blazed the brightest," and "the moon shone out like day" (p. 638).

or the darkly meandering streets, or the seemingly metamorphic edifice, are used as symbolic projections of Robin's psychological (and ultimately moral) states of being. Those final few pages which bring the nightmarish tone to an apex of horror are not only a masterpiece of tonal accompaniment, but are the definition and objectification of Robin's spiritual delirium as well.

Most important, Hawthorne never allows his scrutiny of Robin to waver from the requirements of thematic discovery. Robin moves from a region of primal innocence, where experience is unambiguous because untested, to the city night; from the womb-like security of ingenuous self-reliance to the dark night of the soul. With a strong stick in his hand, and a belief in his own invulnerability that is much his most dangerous attribute, Robin naïvely assumes (as the Goodman Brown who first enters the forest assumes) that he controls the terms of his destiny. At first, although lost in the dark maze of his ignorance, his eyes refuse the light. Each situation that arises to blast the scales from his eyes is easily and satisfactorily rationalized, for Robin has chosen out of the immensity of his moral immaturity the comfort of illusion—the peculiarly ironic illusion of "shrewdness." But steadily, unrelentingly, the city begins to pierce the protective covering in which Robin blindly attempts to butt his way through the darkness. He is unjustly accused of being a thief, unreasonably threatened, almost enticed into sin, hooted after, laughed at, insulted, and cursed—all simply because he does not know. Small [107] wonder that he should attempt to withdraw to the Robin he was ("he saw them [his family] go in at the door . . . and would have entered also"); that he should doubt his sanity ("almost ready to believe that a spell was on him"); that he should question the reality of his kinsman ("Is there really such a person in these parts or am I dreaming?"). But what comfort there may have been in these illusions is brutally dispelled when he is forced to face the shocking reality of his uncle's "overwhelming humiliation." Conscious of the sneering faces, forced to participate in the gratuitously "foul disgrace" of his uncle, but powerless to alleviate the "majestic suffering" of this cruelly broken old man, Robin's laugh is the acme of inarticulate self-condemnation—a wretchedly painful comment on his own moral complacency. Like Nick in "The Killers," Robin wants only to escape the scene of his shattered image, to flee the "fiends" who have destroyed his world. But the friend who has watched with so much sympathetic attention suggests, rather insists, that he remain. The final paragraph of the story implies that Robin's experience is not the end, but rather the beginning, of life.

Mark Van Doren's comment that at the conclusion of the tale Robin is "much as he has been," that he is merely "a young man over whose handsome head a storm has passed," [12] misses the essence of the tale. Robin has learned a great deal, or will have when apprehension becomes knowledge. He has come to sense that man is constantly being assaulted by the powers of darkness, and that "self-reliance" in the face of this negative principle of life is no more substantial or efficacious than the supposedly magical phrase, "my kinsman, Major Molineux." If Robin could not himself so clearly define the nature of his experience, the reader knows (because he himself can) that Robin, no longer the jaunty fledgling, can never go home again. A light has gone out of the world for Robin, but this for Hawthorne was the beginning of wisdom.[108]

One final aspect of the tale ought to be remarked. I believe it is implicit in all I have already said that the over-all excellence of "Molineux" is due to the manner in which Hawthorne approached his material. Whereas in many of his later tales the moral implications are couched in relatively well-defined equivalents of action and idea, therefore necessitating what Coleridge called a "disjunction of faculties" for comprehension, in this tale there is no such hiatus between the literal and symbolic levels because the literal drama *is* the symbolic drama. That Hawthorne was aware of the "un-realism" of allegory can be assumed from his deliberate use of ambiguity, which, as in "Young Goodman Brown" or "Rappaccini's Daughter," is an attempt to bridge the gap caused by the approach.[13] But for all its effective use of deliberate ambiguity, the allegorical "Young Goodman Brown" still requires a

---

[12] Mark Van Doren, *Nathaniel Hawthorne* (New York, 1949), pp. 75–76.

[13] "Young Goodman Brown" is an excellent example. The frequent ambiguous references to illusion and reality in that tale enable Hawthorne to solve the dilemma of having to make assertions too allegorical for the literal flow of action. By stating a fact, and then casting doubt upon it, Hawthorne achieves a kind of dream logic in which rationally impossible occurrences can be simultaneously accepted and rejected. If Hawthorne had insisted upon the experience in the forest literally, then we should be justified in questioning the relationship between a natural situation and resolution (Brown and his wife before and after the forest scene) and a supernatural complication (the forest scene). If, on the other hand, Hawthorne had insisted upon our accepting the experience in the forest as a dream, then we should be justified in questioning a spiritual collapse that stemmed solely from a sleeping man's fantasy. As it is, we can accept the reality of Brown's experience without having to define on precisely what level the reality exists.

"disjunction of faculties" which the symbolic "Molineux" does not. That Hawthorne moved away from the symbolic tale was an economic, not artistic, choice. Writing for magazines and annuals unfortunately kept him poor, and he was forced to cater to the taste for what he called stories of "evident design" in which "the moral [is] plain and manifest," and which kind of tale, he once told his wife, the public much preferred.[14] But before he had to compromise, Hawthorne wrote "My Kinsman, Major Molineux," a story which "escapes," as Yeats asserted was true only of the symbolic work, "from the barrenness and shallowness of a too conscious arrangement, into the abundance and depth of nature." [15] [109]

Yankee Bumpkin and

Scapegoat King *

O N E

'In youth, men are apt to write more wisely than they really know or feel; and the remainder of life may be not idly spent in realizing and convincing themselves of the wisdom which they uttered long ago.' This reflection occurred to Hawthorne as he gathered his fugitive writings of two decades for *The Snow-Image, and Other Twice-Told Tales.* The very last of these, whether so placed as a capstone or an afterthought, proves to be his earliest full success and one of the most durable and contemporary fictions of his entire career. 'My Kinsman, Major Molineux' is unusual among Hawthorne's writings in its overt treatment of the most important political and cultural problem of the American republic: self-determination and its consequences. The tale is striking, too, in its bold and direct appropriation from folk traditions and popular culture of the representative traits of the New England character. Hawthorne would use these humorously in 'Mr. Higginbotham's Catastrophe,' ironically in portraying Holgrave in *The House of the Seven Gables,*

---

[14] Julian Hawthorne, *Nathaniel Hawthorne and His Wife* (Boston, 1884), I, 354.

[15] William Butler Yeats, *Ideas of Good and Evil* (London, 1914), p. 90.

* Daniel G. Hoffman, *Form and Fable in American Fiction,* © 1961 by Daniel G. Hoffman and reprinted by permission of Oxford University Press, Inc.

and descriptively in his war-time account of President Lincoln. But now, in 1832, he anticipates by a quarter-century Melville's use of similar materials and themes in 'Benito Cereno' and *The Confidence-Man* to attack the popular doctrines of optimism and self-reliance which those traditions themselves exemplify. In 'My Kinsman, Major Molineux' these folk themes are placed in dramatic [113] opposition to an eighteenth-century Colonial reenactment of the ancient ritual of the deposition of the Scapegoat King. This ritual occurs in the story as the fulfillment of the hero's quest for his influential kinsman; its function, in terms of his own development, is to provide a ceremony of initiation. What is revealed to him is self-knowledge far deeper than his callow folk-character had hitherto anticipated.

In Hawthorne's tale, a youth named Robin, now eighteen and thinking it 'high time to begin the world,' sets out from his father's farm on his 'first visit to town.' There, with the help of Major Molineux, his father's cousin, he expects to make his fortune. Thus Robin is on the threshold of metamorphosis, like young Ben Franklin walking up Market Street with a loaf of bread under his arm. Committed to upward mobility, he is as yet dependent upon benevolent, paternalistic authority. As he becomes 'entangled in a succession of crooked and narrow streets' his quest for his kinsman brings him only bafflement and mocking laughter from every quarter: from a ridiculously solemn old man, from a barber, an innkeeper, a demoniac fiery-eyed patron at the inn, a trollop in a scarlet petticoat, a watchman. Parties of men approach, speak to him in gibberish, and when he cannot answer curse him in plain English. In desperation Robin accosts a muffled burly stranger with his cudgel and demands to be directed to his kinsman. Instead of forcing his passage the man says, 'Watch here an hour, and Major Molineux will pass by.' With a start Robin recognizes the demoniac of the inn. 'One side of the face blazed an intense red, while the other was black as midnight . . . as if two individual devils, a fiend of fire and a fiend of darkness, had united themselves to form this infernal visage.' Now, waiting by moonlight on the church steps, Robin thinks of the home he has left. In a reverie he sees his father giving the family blessings: 'Then he saw them go in at the door; and when Robin would have entered also, the latch tinkled into place, and he was excluded from his home.' He dreams —or wakes—to see his kinsman's face regarding him from a [114] nearby window. Waking in truth, he asks a passing stranger whether he must wait all night for Major Molineux. The stranger, a mature, prepossessing man, 'perceiving a country youth, apparently homeless and without friends . . . accosted him in a tone of real kindness.' When Robin tells his mission the gentleman replies, 'I have a singular curiosity to witness your meeting,' and sits beside him. Soon sounds of a Saturnalia approach, then a wild procession headed by the double-faced man, who watches Robin the while, swirls past by torch-light, drawing a cart. 'There, in tar-and-feathery dignity, sat his kinsman, Major Molineux!'

He was an elderly man, of large and majestic person, and strong, square features, betokening a steady soul; but steady as it was, his enemies had found means to shake it. . . . But perhaps the bitterest pang of all was when his eyes met those of Robin; for he evidently knew him on the instant, as the youth stood witnessing the foul disgrace of head grown gray in honor. They stared at each other in silence, and Robin's knees shook, and his hair bristled, with a mixture of pity and terror.

Then, one by one, the laughing mockers of his night-long adventure add their derisive voices to the din. 'The contagion . . . all at once seized upon Robin . . . Robin's shout was the loudest there.' At the leader's signal, 'On they went, like fiends that throng in mockery around some dead potentate, mighty no more, but majestic still in his agony . . . and left a silent street behind.' Robin's companion lays a hand on his shoulder. 'Well, Robin, are you dreaming?' Robin, 'his eye not quite as lively as in the earlier part of the evening,' replies by asking to be shown the way to the ferry. 'I grow weary of town life, sir.' But this friendly stranger declines to oblige him, suggesting that 'If you prefer to remain with us, perhaps, as you are a shrewd youth, you may rise in the world without the help of your kinsman, Major Molineux.'

From even this crude précis of the plot it is hard to take seriously Parrington's strictures against Hawthorne as a mere romancer [115] of the murky past who avoided dealing with the problems and issues of Jacksonian democracy. One of the two chief interpretations of 'My Kinsman, Major Molineux,' that of Q. D. Leavis,[1] suggests how deeply involved Hawthorne was with the basic problems of American self-realization. She sees this tale as 'a symbolic action which . . . takes the form of something between a pageant and a ritual drama, disguised in the emotional logic of a dream.' She suggests that the tale be subtitled 'America Comes of Age,' and reads it as an historic parable in which Robin 'represents the young America' who has come to town, 'that is, the contemporary scene where the historic future will be decided.' The

---

[1] 'Hawthorne as Poet' [Part I], *Sewanee Review*, LIX (Spring, 1951), 198–205.

opening paragraphs of the tale establish that popular insurrections and violent deaths of the governors were characteristic of the history of the colonies.

A quite different reading is suggested by Hyatt H. Waggoner and elaborated by Roy R. Male.[2] Waggoner emphasizes the dreamlike manipulation of incident, sound, and color in the tale, and reads its primary meaning as a revelation of an Oedipal conflict. The tale reveals 'man's image of himself as the destroyer of the father—because he has wished the destruction—a destroyer bathed in guilt yet somehow justified. . . . Passing through the stages of initial identification with the father image, rejection, and shame, Robin at last emerges with the help of the stranger into maturity.' Male's elaboration of this Freudian reading suggests 'that visions of the father figure may commonly be split into two or more images.' The pompous old man and the watchman then 'are shapes of what Robin is attempting to leave behind.' Other figures are 'various forms of the cultured kinsman he is seeking.'

Thus as he verges upon maturity the young man's yearnings for freedom from authority and for a worldly patrimony take on exaggerated [116] proportions. The dual aspect of this psychic conflict can be seen in the 'infernal visage' of the 'double-faced fellow,' whose complexions are split. . . . The grotesque fusion of the two forms is a distorted father image in which youthful misrepresentation of both the real father and the real uncle are combined.

Robin's real father appears in his dream of home, and again as the kindly stranger who stays by his side during the imaged destruction of Major Molineux. The kinsman, of course, is the most potent father-image in the story.

T W O

The truth of the tale includes both these theories and more. Hawthorne's most successful fictions may be described by a phrase from one of his least effective stories: 'I can never separate the idea from the symbol in which it manifests itself.'[3] In his best tales, simple arrangements of objects, persons, or actions are the symbols, but these are so economically chosen as to represent complex constellations of ideas. Certainly the pattern of action in 'My Kinsman, Major Molineux' is at the same time a journey, a search, an initiation. Robin is indeed a representative Amer-

[2] Waggoner, *Hawthorne, A Critical Study* (Cambridge, 1955), pp. 47–53; Male, *Hawthorne's Tragic Vision* (Austin, Tex., 1957), pp. 48–53.
[3] 'The Antique Ring,' *Works*, XII, 67.

ican, first as witness, then as participant, in a cultural-political experience of archetypal significance to our national identity. He is also a representative young man who must come to terms with his feelings about his father, about the past, about authority, in order to pass from adolescence into maturity.

In psychological terms, Male is probably right that all the men in the story are displacements or substitutions for the father, in his several aspects: as authority (to be feared, courted, or ridiculed), and as paternity (to be loved, escaped from, and depended upon). But there are other implications necessary to a full involvement with the tale. Major Molineux is not only the Father as Authority, he is also the Past which must be rejected. Specifically, he represents British rule —in political terms he is [117] the representative of the Crown. If psychologically the Major displaces Robin's father, politically and culturally he actually displaces the King. As authority figure, whether patristic or regal, he represents Order, Tradition, Stability. But as the Father-King in a cart whose 'tar-and-feathery dignity' inspire the tragic emotions of pity and terror, Major Molineux takes on yet further dimensions. He is the Sacrificed King, the Royal Scapegoat, the 'dead potentate . . . majestic still in his agony' around whom the townsfolk 'throng in mockery.' Frazer analyzes the Scapegoat King as a ritual role invested with two functions, the expulsion of evil and the sacrificial death of the divine ruler whose declining potency is renewed in his young successor. One can hardly suggest that this modern anthropological theory was available to Hawthorne in 1832, but from his tale we can infer his intuitive understanding of the primitive ritual which he used metaphorically in describing the downfall of Major Molineux. The rebellion in the tale, although dated vaguely around 1730, is clearly a 'type' of the American Revolution. This was indeed the supercession of an old order by a new, from which ensued a revitalization of the energies of American society. Hawthorne remarks that the colonists had frequently attacked the person of their royal governors, however suppliant to their demands the governors, as individuals, had been. In this there is the inference that in tarring and feathering Major Molineux the conspirators are symbolically ridding the colony of a symbol of the chief evil that prepossessed their consciousness as a culture. Further warrant for inferring Major Molineux to represent a Scapegoat King is suggested by one of the identities of his antagonist, the man with the double visage.

This character may be, as Male proposes, a double father-image combining 'youthful misrepresentation of both the real father and the real uncle.' Yet we must also take him more literally than this; or, if we take him in metaphors, let the metaphors be Hawthorne's own. He is described as both 'a fiend of fire and a fiend of darkness,' and, when he rides on horseback [118] at the head of the ceremonial procession, 'his fierce and variegated countenance appeared like war personified; the red of one cheek was an emblem of fire and sword; the blackness of the other betokened the mourning that attends them.' He is War, Death, and Destruction, and again he is the Devil, with 'his train [of] wild figures in Indian dress,' his 'infernal visage,' and his eyes that glowed 'like fire in a cave.' He is well chosen to play the part of Riot, of Disorder, of the Lord of Misrule, in the pageant it is Robin's destiny to behold. He is in charge of the procession of 'fiends' and of their lurid rites, the 'counterfeited pomp,' the 'senseless uproar' in which the tumultuous multitude lead Major Molineux to his humiliation.

And Robin joins this yelling mob! His mocking laughter is the loudest there! Not even the shame, the agony of his kinsman, not even his own emotions of pity and terror, can hold him from making their 'frenzied merriment' his own. There are buffetings of passion, there are possibilities of evil and of guilt, which Robin's callow rationalism cannot fathom. Setting out merely to make his way in the world, he has wandered unknowingly toward an appointed rendezvous, a ceremony which seems to have been prepared specifically for his benefit. It is his initiation.

But an initiation into what? The sensitive suggestions of Mrs. Leavis, Waggoner, and Male may be supplemented by a closer scrutiny of Robin himself. When we have seen who he is and what he represents up to the moment of his initiation, we can better understand the significance of that ritual for him.

Seven times in this tale Robin is characterized as 'a shrewd youth.' Like his antecedent bumpkins in popular tradition—Brother Jonathan, the peddlers of folk anecdote, Jack Downing, Sam Slick—he is nothing if not shrewd. But Robin is shrewd only by his own report. 'I'm not the fool you take me for,' he warns the double-faced demon, yet that is exactly what he is. Although mystified at every turn, denied the common civilities by those he meets, taunted and mocked by strangers at the mention of his [119] kinsman's name, he never once loses confidence in his own shrewdness. Rebuffed by the pompous old man and the innkeeper, fleeing the temptations of the prostitute, his response to their jeering laughter is thrice again to account himself 'a shrewd youth.' Even in his last encounter with the stranger who proves to be kindly, Robin is still depending on his motherwit to carry him through all situations. 'For I have the name of being a shrewd youth,' Robin tells his older friend. 'I doubt not that you deserve it,' the friend replies. Yet at the beginning of his night of misadventure Robin had stepped jauntily off the ferry without realizing that he had no idea where he was going. 'It would have been wise to inquire my way of the ferryman,' he muses, 'But the next man I meet will do as well.' This, however, is not at all the case. Everyone he meets is, unknown to him, involved in the conspiracy to overthrow his kinsman the royal governor. When Robin cannot give their password, parties of conspirators curse him in plain language. When he obstinately inquires for the Major the people in the inn and the barbershop hoot at him. When he tries the door of the pretty little prostitute she tells him that she knows his kinsman well. 'But Robin, being of the household of a New England clergyman, was a good youth, as well as a shrewd one; so he resisted temptation, and fled away.' He cannot yet face the knowledge that Major Molineux, his kinsman (and father), has had carnal knowledge of a woman, just as Young Goodman Brown will be dismayed to learn that his father had followed the Devil to the witches' carnal Sabbath before him.

It is characteristic of Robin that he always accepts the most simplistic rationalizations of the most baffling and ominous experiences. One would think him affrighted by the demoniac double-faced man he accosts before the church. We recognize this portentous apparition as ringleader of the uprising, but Robin merely muses, 'Strange things we travellers see!' and sits down to await the Major. 'A few moments were consumed in philosophical speculations upon the species of man who had [120] just left him; but having settled this point shrewdly, rationally, and satisfactorily, he was compelled to look elsewhere for his amusement'! Now the moonlight plays over the commonplace scene 'like the imaginative power,' and Robin cannot define the forms of distant objects which turn ghostly and indistinct 'just as his eye appeared to grasp them.' His dream of home is more real than the actual things he is now among, and when he wakes 'his mind kept vibrating between fancy and reality' as shapes lengthen and dwindle before him. Despite all these physical sensations of confusion and the constant evidence of his noncomprehension of what is happening, Robin trusts to his 'name of being a shrewd youth.' This is Yankee self-reliance with a vengeance! His 'bright, cheerful eyes were nature's gifts,' and he would seem to think he needs no others. Robin, the shrewd youth from the backwoods, proves to be the Great American Boob, the naïf whose odyssey leads him, all uncomprehending, into the dark center of experience.

When the tale opens, Robin has just made a crossing of the water and entered the city. He has left behind him the security as well as the simplicity of his rural birthplace—in his reverie before the church his country home seemed an Arcadian bower of 'venerable shade' and 'golden light.' But in his dream of returning home the door closes before him. Like Wakefield, Robin has left his home and cannot return. It is true that, as opposed to Wakefield's perverse impulse, he had good reasons (Robin is a younger son and won't inherit the farm), but nonetheless by leaving his appointed place and station to participate in the fluidity of egalitarian city life he too has made himself an exile. Just how egalitarian that city life will prove Robin must learn with dismay. The change to which he has committed himself is not only one of place and status but involves also the breaking of human ties, as every act of independence does to some degree. Much as Robin resembles the folk characters of Yankee yarn and jokelore, the difference—and it is tremendous—is that such characters had no human ties to break.[121]

Robin's journey toward independence is magnified a thousandfold by the throes of the town itself on the evening of his arrival. In their quest for self-determination the urban conspirators of the town are far in advance of the country-bred youth whom they mock. Until the very end of the tale Robin still counts on his kinsman's preferment; the independence he seeks is therefore qualified, not absolute. The townsfolk no longer accept the limited independence granted by royal governors, even those who 'in softening their instructions from beyond the sea . . . incurred the reprehension' of the Crown. They have cast their die for total disseverance of their bonds. Hawthorne's imagery puts them in league with the Devil to do so.

Thus an ironic tension underlies all of Robin's misadventures. Those who deride him are really his mentors, and he, invoking the patronage of their enemy his kinsman, is actually their ally, since both they and he are seeking independence. After his dismay at beholding his kinsman's degradation, Robin's sudden shout of laughter may seem to the reader inexplicable. So it is, from a point of view as rational and 'shrewd' as his own. But the emotional logic that produced his outburst is inescapable. It is an emotional not a rational logic, for in that instant, with neither premeditation nor understanding, Robin has cast off the remaining dependence of his immaturity.

Then, at the Devil's behest, the frenzied procession moves on, leaving Robin behind in the silent street. What has he learned from his initiation? His lessons must be inferred from the tale, for when it ends Robin is still in a state of shock. 'I begin to grow weary of town life,' he says. He wants to go home. But, as his dream has already told him, he has no home now. He must stay. What he might muse on is his new knowledge of the demonic depths from which the impulse of self-determination leaped up in the torchlight. He might give 'a few moments' in 'philosophical speculations' upon the Saturnalian passions which shook him as he, like the populace, dethroned Order and rejected Tradition while [122] under the aegis of the Lord of Misrule. In their act of revolt they have all thrown down the old king of Stability and crowned the new prince of War and Destruction.

To judge from the effect upon Robin of his experiences hitherto, there is little chance of his learning much from these reflections. Although devoted to the dogma of Yankee self-reliance, he had learned nothing from anything that had touched him. We are, however, told that his faith in himself is rather shaken, for 'nature's gift,' his 'bright, cheerful eyes,' are now 'not quite as lively as in the earlier part of the evening.'

One source of hope for Robin is the continued interest of the gentleman who had befriended him. This nameless figure, as we have seen, represents the viable influence of his father upon his soul: the manly guidance of a non-possessive, non-inhibiting paternal love. The tale ends with the steadying voice of this personage, whose interested detachment from the pillorying of Major Molineux hints that he has seen all this before. In his experience he knows that this ritual, like all *rites de passage,* is ever again repeated for the benefit of each initiate. Even his irony at the end is indulgent without being patronizing, for he suggests that Robin will have to make up his own mind, 'as you are a shrewd youth,' whether to stay in town and 'perhaps . . . rise in the world without the help of your kinsman, Major Molineux,' even though he surely knows that Robin cannot return to his pastoral home. This means that Robin now is free of the past, and has the power of self-determination. But this power comes to him inextricable from the terrifying and tragic emotions that have involved him.

And what of the Colony? Is it truly free, or has it exchanged the rule of a benevolent governor for the tyranny of riot and chaos? On the political level Hawthorne's fable is less reassuring than on the personal. There is no double of Major Molineux who represents in the realm of power what Robin's friend stands for as an aspect of the parent. Yet so closely has Hawthorne intertwined the cultural with the psychological implications in this [123] tale that we cannot help taking Robin's friend as representing also the viable aspects of Major Molineux. What his patient and tolerant advice to Robin suggests, then, is that this ordeal has been performed before by society as well as by the self. The implication is that the forces of Order and Stability do in the end prove stronger than those of Destruction and Misrule which dethrone them. Harrowing though these disruptive forces be, in Hawthorne's vision of American history they do serve the end of re-establishing a stable order based on institutions more just than those overthrown. (This was in fact the case, as the fire-brained Committees of Correspondence were superseded, after the reign of War and Death, by the framers of the Constitution and the *Federalist Papers*.[4]) Still another indication that the reign of Riot will be but brief lies in the carnival atmosphere which suggests that Major Molineux's successor, the two-faced man, is the Lord of Misrule. His reign is but a mock reign, a temporary season of emotional debauch necessary to the purification and rebirth of society. At its conclusion Order is imposed again upon the rampaging passions of the Saturnalia. On this succession the continuity of culture itself depends. In 'My Kinsman,' then, there is a qualified, half-skeptical hope that when the town wakes up from its collective nightmare, tradition will be re-established in accordance with the new dispensation of absolute liberty which the Devil's league had won in the darkness.

But as in the case of Robin's personal fate, the consequences of these public actions are not affirmed, not even proposed. All consequences are but inferences from this fable. Our inferences must be guided by the probabilities which the characterization of Robin in terms of the traditional figure of the Yankee naïf suggests.[124] There is no clearer statement in our literature than 'My Kinsman, Major Molineux' of the psychological and cultural burdens of personal freedom and of national independence. Hawthorne's Robin allows us no undue confidence in the degree of understanding with which the American character will bear them.[125]

---

[4] If the spirit of revolt is in this tale a Devil, he appears elsewhere in Hawthorne as 'The Gray Champion,' the regicide Goffe who signed King Charles's death warrant. 'His hour is one of darkness, and adversity, and peril. But should domestic tyranny oppress us . . . still may the Gray Champion come, for he is the type of New England's hereditary spirit.' There, as in 'Legends of the Province House' and 'Endicott and the Red Cross,' rebellion is the divine right of an oppressed people.

Roger Malvin's Burial *

One of the few incidents of Indian warfare naturally susceptible of the moonlight of romance was that expedition undertaken for the defence of the frontiers in the year 1725, which resulted in the well-remembered "Lovell's Fight." Imagination, by casting certain circumstances judicially into the shade, may see much to admire in the heroism of a little band who gave battle to twice their number in the heart of the enemy's country. The open bravery displayed by both parties was in accordance with civilized ideas of valor; and chivalry itself might not blush to record the deeds of one or two individuals. The battle, though so fatal to those who fought, was not unfortunate in its consequences to the country; for it broke the strength of a tribe and conduced to the peace which subsisted during several ensuing years. History and tradition are unusually minute in their memorials of this affair; and the captain of a scouting party of frontier men has acquired as actual a military renown as many a victorious leader of thousands. Some of the incidents contained in the following pages will be recognized, notwithstanding the substitution of fictitious names, by such as have heard, from old men's lips, the fate of the few combatants who were in a condition to retreat after "Lovell's Fight."

The early sunbeams hovered cheerfully upon the tree-tops, beneath which two weary and wounded men [381] had stretched their limbs the night before. Their bed of withered oak leaves was strewn upon the small level space, at the foot of a rock, situated near the summit of one of the gentle swells by which the face of the country is there diversified. The mass of granite, rearing its smooth, flat surface fifteen or twenty feet above their heads, was not unlike a gigantic gravestone, upon which the veins seemed to form an inscription in forgotten characters. On a tract of several acres around this rock, oaks and other hard-wood trees had supplied the place of the pines, which were the usual growth of the

* This story appeared in *The Token* in 1832 and in *Mosses from an Old Manse* in 1846.

land; and a young and vigorous sapling stood close beside the travellers. The severe wound of the elder man had probably deprived him of sleep; for, so soon as the first ray of sunshine rested on the top of the highest tree, he reared himself painfully from his recumbent posture and sat erect. The deep lines of his countenance and the scattered gray of his hair marked him as past the middle age; but his muscular frame would, but for the effects of his wound, have been as capable of sustaining fatigue as in the early vigor of life. Languor and exhaustion now sat upon his haggard features; and the despairing glance which he sent forward through the depths of the forest proved his own conviction that his pilgrimage was at an end. He next turned his eyes to the companion who reclined by his side. The youth—for he had scarcely attained the years of manhood—lay, with his head upon his arm, in the embrace of an unquiet sleep, which a thrill of pain from his wounds seemed each moment on the point of breaking. His right hand grasped a musket; and, to judge from the violent action of his features, his slumbers were bringing back a vision of the conflict of which he was one [382] of the few survivors. A shout—deep and loud in his dreaming fancy—found its way in an imperfect murmur to his lips; and, starting even at the slight sound of his own voice, he suddenly awoke. The first act of reviving recollection was to make anxious inquiries respecting the condition of his wounded fellow-traveller. The latter shook his head.

"Reuben, my boy," said he, "this rock beneath which we sit will serve for an old hunter's gravestone. There is many and many a long mile of howling wilderness before us yet; nor would it avail me anything if the smoke of my own chimney were but on the other side of that swell of land. The Indian bullet was deadlier than I thought."

"You are weary with our three days' travel," replied the youth, "and a little longer rest will recruit you. Sit you here while I search the woods for the herbs and roots that must be our sustenance; and, having eaten, you shall lean on me, and we will turn our faces homeward. I doubt not that, with my help, you can attain to some one of the frontier garrisons."

"There is not two days' life in me, Reuben," said the other, calmly, "and I will no longer burden you with my useless body, when you can scarcely support your own. Your wounds are deep and your strength is failing fast; yet, if you hasten onward alone, you may be preserved. For me there is no hope, and I will await death here."

"If it must be so, I will remain and watch by you," said Reuben, resolutely.

"No, my son, no," rejoined his companion. "Let the wish of a dying man have weight with you; give me one grasp of your hand, and get you hence. Think you that my last moments will be eased by the [383] thought that I leave you to die a more lingering death? I have loved you like a father, Reuben; and at a time like this I should have something of a father's authority. I charge you to be gone that I may die in peace."

"And because you have been a father to me, should I therefore leave you to perish and to lie unburied in the wilderness?" exclaimed the youth. "No; if your end be in truth approaching, I will watch by you and receive your parting words. I will dig a grave here by the rock, in which, if my weakness overcome me, we will rest together; or, if Heaven gives me strength, I will seek my way home."

"In the cities and wherever men dwell," replied the other, "they bury their dead in the earth; they hide them from the sight of the living; but here, where no step may pass perhaps for a hundred years, wherefore should I not rest beneath the open sky, covered only by the oak leaves when the autumn winds shall strew them? And for a monument, here is this gray rock, on which my dying hand shall carve the name of Roger Malvin; and the traveller in days to come will know that here sleeps a hunter and a warrior. Tarry not, then, for a folly like this, but hasten away, if not for your own sake, for hers who will else be desolate."

Malvin spoke the last few words in a faltering voice, and their effect upon his companion was strongly visible. They reminded him that there were other and less questionable duties than that of sharing the fate of a man whom his death could not benefit. Nor can it be affirmed that no selfish feeling strove to enter Reuben's heart, though the consciousness made him more earnestly resist his companion's entreaties.

"How terrible to wait the slow approach of death in this solitude!" exclaimed he. "A brave man does not [384] shrink in the battle; and, when friends stand round the bed, even women may die composedly; but here"—

"I shall not shrink even here, Reuben Bourne," interrupted Malvin. "I am a man of no weak heart, and, if I were, there is a surer support than that of earthly friends. You are young, and life is dear to you. Your last moments will need comfort far more than mine; and when you have laid me in the earth, and are alone, and night is settling on the forest, you will feel all the bitterness of the death that may now be escaped. But I will urge no selfish motive to your generous nature. Leave me for my sake, that, having said a prayer for your safety, I may have space to settle my account undisturbed by worldly sorrows."

"And your daughter,—how shall I dare to meet her eye?" exclaimed

Reuben. "She will ask the fate of her father, whose life I vowed to defend with my own. Must I tell her that he travelled three days' march with me from the field of battle and that then I left him to perish in the wilderness? Were it not better to lie down and die by your side than to return safe and say this to Dorcas?"

"Tell my daughter," said Roger Malvin, "that, though yourself sore wounded, and weak, and weary, you led my tottering footsteps many a mile, and left me only at my earnest entreaty, because I would not have your blood upon my soul. Tell her that through pain and danger you were faithful, and that, if your lifeblood could have saved me, it would have flowed to its last drop; and tell her that you will be something dearer than a father, and that my blessing is with you both, and that my dying eyes can see a long and pleasant path in which you will journey together." [385]

As Malvin spoke he almost raised himself from the ground, and the energy of his concluding words seemed to fill the wild and lonely forest with a vision of happiness; but, when he sank exhausted upon his bed of oak leaves, the light which had kindled in Reuben's eye was quenched. He felt as if it were both sin and folly to think of happiness at such a moment. His companion watched his changing countenance, and sought with generous art to wile him to his own good.

"Perhaps I deceived myself in regard to the time I have to live," he resumed. "It may be that, with speedy assistance, I might recover of my wound. The foremost fugitives must, ere this, have carried tidings of our fatal battle to the frontiers, and parties will be out to succor those in like condition with ourselves. Should you meet one of these and guide them hither, who can tell but that I may sit by my own fireside again?"

A mournful smile strayed across the features of the dying man as he insinuated that unfounded hope,—which, however, was not without its effect on Reuben. No merely selfish motive, nor even the desolate condition of Dorcas, could have induced him to desert his companion at such a moment—but his wishes seized on the thought that Malvin's life might be preserved, and his sanguine nature heightened almost to certainty the remote possibility of procuring human aid.

"Surely there is reason, weighty reason, to hope that friends are not far distant," he said, half aloud. "There fled one coward, unwounded, in the beginning of the fight, and most probably he made good speed. Every true man on the frontier would shoulder his musket at the news; and, though no party may range so far into the woods as this, I shall perhaps encounter [386] them in one day's march. Counsel me faithfully," he added, turning to Malvin, in distrust of his own motives. "Were your situation mine, would you desert me while life remained?"

"It is now twenty years," replied Roger Malvin,—sighing, however, as he secretly acknowledged the wide dissimilarity between the two cases, —"it is now twenty years since I escaped with one dear friend from Indian captivity near Montreal. We journeyed many days through the woods, till at length overcome with hunger and weariness, my friend lay down and besought me to leave him; for he knew that, if I remained, we both must perish; and, with but little hope of obtaining succor, I heaped a pillow of dry leaves beneath his head and hastened on."

"And did you return in time to save him?" asked Reuben, hanging on Malvin's words as if they were to be prophetic of his own success.

"I did," answered the other. "I came upon the camp of a hunting party before sunset of the same day. I guided them to the spot where my comrade was expecting death; and he is now a hale and hearty man upon his own farm, far within the frontiers, while I lie wounded here in the depths of the wilderness."

This example, powerful in affecting Reuben's decision, was aided, unconsciously to himself, by the hidden strength of many another motive. Roger Malvin perceived that the victory was nearly won.

"Now, go, my son, and Heaven prosper you!" he said. "Turn not back with your friends when you meet them, lest your wounds and weariness overcome you; but send hitherward two or three, that may be spared, to search for me; and believe me, Reuben, my heart will be lighter with every step you take towards [387] home." Yet there was, perhaps, a change both in his countenance and voice as he spoke thus; for, after all, it was a ghastly fate to be left expiring in the wilderness.

Reuben Bourne, but half convinced that he was acting rightly, at length raised himself from the ground and prepared himself for his departure. And first, though contrary to Malvin's wishes, he collected a stock of roots and herbs, which had been their only food during the last two days. This useless supply he placed within reach of the dying man, for whom, also, he swept together a bed of dry oak leaves. Then climbing to the summit of the rock, which on one side was rough and broken, he bent the oak sapling downward, and bound his handkerchief to the topmost branch. This precaution was not unnecessary to direct any who might come in search of Malvin; for every part of the rock, except its broad, smooth front, was concealed at a little distance by the dense undergrowth of the forest. The handkerchief had been the bandage of a wound upon Reuben's arm; and, as he bound it to the tree, he vowed by the blood that stained it that he would return, either to save his companion's life or to lay his body in the grave. He then descended, and stood, with downcast eyes, to receive Roger Malvin's parting words.

The experience of the latter suggested much and minute advice respecting the youth's journey through the trackless forest. Upon this subject he spoke with calm earnestness, as if he were sending Reuben to the battle or the chase while he himself remained secure at home, and not as if the human countenance that was about to leave him were the last he would ever behold. But his firmness was shaken before he concluded.[388]

"Carry my blessing to Dorcas, and say that my last prayer shall be for her and you. Bid her to have no hard thoughts because you left me here," —Reuben's heart smote him,—"for that your life would not have weighed with you if its sacrifice could have done me good. She will marry you after she has mourned a little while for her father; and Heaven grant you long and happy days, and may your children's children stand round your death bed! And, Reuben," added he, as the weakness of mortality made its way at last, "return, when your wounds are healed and your weariness refreshed,—return to this wild rock, and lay my bones in the grave, and say a prayer over them."

An almost superstitious regard, arising perhaps from the customs of the Indians, whose war was with the dead as well as the living, was paid by the frontier inhabitants to the rites of sepulture; and there are many instances of the sacrifice of life in the attempt to bury those who had fallen by the "sword of the wilderness." Reuben, therefore, felt the full importance of the promise which he most solemnly made to return and perform Roger Malvin's obsequies. It was remarkable that the latter, speaking his whole heart in his parting words, no longer endeavored to persuade the youth that even the speediest succor might avail to the preservation of his life. Reuben was internally convinced that he should see Malvin's living face no more. His generous nature would fain have delayed him, at whatever risk, till the dying scene were past; but the desire of existence and the hope of happiness had strengthened in his heart, and he was unable to resist them.

"It is enough," said Roger Malvin, having listened to Reuben's promise. "Go, and God speed you!"

The youth pressed his hand in silence, turned, and [389] was departing. His slow and faltering steps, however, had borne him but a little way before Malvin's voice recalled him.

"Reuben, Reuben," said he, faintly; and Reuben returned and knelt down by the dying man.

"Raise me, and let me lean against the rock," was his last request. "My face will be turned towards home, and I shall see you a moment longer as you pass among the trees."

Reuben, having made the desired alteration in his companion's posture, again began his solitary pilgrimage. He walked more hastily at first than was consistent with his strength; for a sort of guilty feeling, which sometimes torments men in their most justifiable acts, caused him to seek concealment from Malvin's eyes; but after he had trodden far upon the rustling forest leaves he crept back, impelled by a wild and painful curiosity, and, sheltered by the earthy roots of an uptorn tree, gazed earnestly at the desolate man. The morning sun was unclouded, and the trees and shrubs imbibed the sweet air of the month of May; yet there seemed a gloom on Nature's face, as if she sympathized with mortal pain and sorrow. Roger Malvin's hands were uplifted in a fervent prayer, some of the words of which stole through the stillness of the woods and entered Reuben's heart, torturing it with an unutterable pang. They were the broken accents of a petition for his own happiness and that of Dorcas; and, as the youth listened, conscience, or something in its similitude, pleaded strongly with him to return and lie down again by the rock. He felt how hard was the doom of the kind and generous being whom he had deserted in his extremity. Death would come like the slow approach of a corpse, stealing gradually towards [390] him through the forest, and showing its ghastly and motionless features from behind a nearer and yet a nearer tree. But such must have been Reuben's own fate had he tarried another sunset; and who shall impute blame to him if he shrink from so useless a sacrifice? As he gave a parting look, a breeze waved the little banner upon the sapling oak and reminded Reuben of his vow.

Many circumstances combined to retard the wounded traveller in his way to the frontiers. On the second day the clouds, gathering densely over the sky, precluded the possibility of regulating his course by the position of the sun; and he knew not but that every effort of his almost exhausted strength was removing him farther from the home he sought. His scanty sustenance was supplied by the berries and other spontaneous products of the forest. Herds of deer, it is true, sometimes bounded past him, and partridges frequently whirred up before his footsteps; but his ammunition had been expended in the fight, and he had no means of slaying them. His wounds, irritated by the constant exertion in which lay the only hope of life, wore away his strength and at intervals confused his reason. But, even in the wanderings of intellect, Reuben's young heart clung strongly to existence; and it was only through absolute incapacity of motion that he at last sank down beneath a tree, compelled there to await death.

In this situation he was discovered by a party who, upon the first intelligence of the fight, had been despatched to the relief of the survivors. They conveyed him to the nearest settlement, which chanced to be that of his own residence.

Dorcas, in the simplicity of the olden time, watched by [391] the bedside of her wounded lover, and administered all those comforts that are in the sole gift of woman's heart and hand. During several days Reuben's recollection strayed drowsily among the perils and hardships through which he had passed, and he was incapable of returning definite answers to the inquiries with which many were eager to harass him. No authentic particulars of the battle had yet been circulated; nor could mothers, wives, and children tell whether their loved ones were detained by captivity or by the stronger chain of death. Dorcas nourished her apprehensions in silence till one afternoon when Reuben awoke from an unquiet sleep, and seemed to recognize her more perfectly than at any previous time. She saw that his intellect had become composed, and she could no longer restrain her filial anxiety.

"My father, Reuben?" she began; but the change in her lover's countenance made her pause.

The youth shrank as if with a bitter pain, and the blood gushed vividly into his wan and hollow cheeks. His first impulse was to cover his face; but, apparently with a desperate effort, he half raised himself and spoke vehemently, defending himself against an imaginary accusation.

"Your father was sore wounded in the battle, Dorcas; and he bade me not burden myself with him, but only to lead him to the lakeside, that he might quench his thirst and die. But I would not desert the old man in his extremity, and, though bleeding myself, I supported him; I gave him half my strength, and led him away with me. For three days we journeyed on together, and your father was sustained beyond my hopes, but, awaking at sunrise on the fourth day, I found him faint and exhausted; he was unable to proceed; his life had ebbed away fast; and"—[392]

"He died!" exclaimed Dorcas, faintly.

Reuben felt it impossible to acknowledge that his selfish love of life had hurried him away before her father's fate was decided. He spoke not; he only bowed his head; and, between shame and exhaustion, sank back and hid his face in the pillow. Dorcas wept when her fears were thus confirmed; but the shock, as it had been long anticipated, was on that account the less violent.

"You dug a grave for my poor father in the wilderness, Reuben?" was the question by which her filial piety manifested itself.

"My hands were weak; but I did what I could," replied the youth in a smothered tone. "There stands a noble tombstone above his head; and I would to Heaven I slept as soundly as he!"

Dorcas, perceiving the wildness of his latter words, inquired no further at the time; but her heart found ease in the thought that Roger Malvin had not lacked such funeral rites as it was possible to bestow. The tale of Reuben's courage and fidelity lost nothing when she communicated it to her friends; and the poor youth, tottering from his sick chamber to breathe the sunny air, experienced from every tongue the miserable and humiliating torture of unmerited praise. All acknowledged that he might worthily demand the hand of the fair maiden to whose father he had been "faithful unto death;" and, as my tale is not of love, it shall suffice to say that in the space of a few months Reuben became the husband of Dorcas Malvin. During the marriage ceremony the bride was covered with blushes, but the bridegroom's face was pale.

There was now in the breast of Reuben Bourne an incommunicable thought—something which he was to [393] conceal most heedfully from her whom he most loved and trusted. He regretted, deeply and bitterly, the moral cowardice that had restrained his words when he was about to disclose the truth to Dorcas; but pride, the fear of losing her affection, the dread of universal scorn, forbade him to rectify this falsehood. He felt that for leaving Roger Malvin he deserved no censure. His presence, the gratuitous sacrifice of his own life, would have added only another and a needless agony to the last moments of the dying man; but concealment had imparted to a justifiable act much of the secret effect of guilt; and Reuben, while reason told him that he had done right, experienced in no small degree the mental horrors which punish the perpetrator of undiscovered crime. By a certain association of ideas, he at times almost imagined himself a murderer. For years, also, a thought would occasionally recur, which, though he perceived all its folly and extravagance, he had not power to banish from his mind. It was a haunting and torturing fancy that his father-in-law was yet sitting at the foot of the rock, on the withered forest leaves, alive, and awaiting his pledged assistance. These mental deceptions, however, came and went, nor did he ever mistake them for realities; but in the calmest and clearest moods of his mind he was conscious that he had a deep vow unredeemed, and that an unburied corpse was calling to him out of the wilderness. Yet such was the consequence of his prevarication that he could not obey the call. It was now too late to require the assistance of Roger Malvin's friends in performing his long-deferred sepulture; and superstitious fears, of which none were more susceptible than the people of the outward settlements, forbade Reuben to go [394] alone. Neither did he know where in the pathless and illimitable forest to seek that smooth and lettered rock at the base of which the body lay: his remembrance of every portion of his travel thence was indistinct, and the latter part had left no impression upon his mind. There was, however, a continual impulse, a voice audible only to himself, commanding him to go forth and redeem his vow; and he had a strange impression that, were he to make the trial, he would be led straight to Malvin's bones. But year after year that summons, unheard but felt, was disobeyed. His one secret thought became like a chain binding down his spirit and like a serpent gnawing into his heart; and he was transformed into a sad and downcast yet irritable man.

In the course of a few years after their marriage changes began to be visible in the external prosperity of Reuben and Dorcas. The only riches of the former had been his stout heart and strong arm; but the latter, her father's sole heiress, had made her husband master of a farm, under older cultivation, larger, and better stocked than most of the frontier establishments. Reuben Bourne, however, was a neglectful husbandman; and, while the lands of the other settlers became annually more fruitful, his deteriorated in the same proportion. The discouragements to agriculture were greatly lessened by the cessation of Indian war, during which men held the plough in one hand and the musket in the other, and were fortunate if the products of their dangerous labor were not destroyed, either in the field or in the barn, by the savage enemy. But Reuben did not profit by the altered condition of the country; nor can it be denied that his intervals of industrious attention to his affairs were but scantily [395] rewarded with success. The irritability by which he had recently become distinguished was another cause of his declining prosperity, as it occasioned frequent quarrels in his unavoidable intercourse with the neighboring settlers. The results of these were innumerable lawsuits; for the people of New England, in the earliest stages and wildest circumstances of the country, adopted, whenever attainable, the legal mode of deciding their differences. To be brief, the world did not go well with Reuben Bourne; and, though not till many years after his marriage, he was finally a ruined man, with but one remaining expedient against the evil fate that had pursued him. He was to throw sunlight into some deep recess of the forest, and seek subsistence from the virgin bosom of the wilderness. The only child of Reuben and Dorcas was a son, now arrived at the age of fifteen years, beautiful in youth, and giving promise of a glorious manhood. He was peculiarly qualified for, and already began to excel in, the wild accomplishments of frontier life. His foot was fleet, his aim true, his apprehension quick, his heart glad and high; and all who anticipated the return of Indian war spoke of Cyrus Bourne as a future leader in the land. The boy was loved by his father with a deep and silent strength, as if whatever was good and happy in his own nature had been transferred to his child, carrying his affections with it. Even Dorcas, though loving and beloved, was far less dear to him; for Reuben's secret thoughts and insulated emotions had gradually made him a selfish man, and he could no longer love deeply except where he saw or imagined some reflection or likeness of his own mind. In Cyrus he recognized what he had himself been in other days; and at intervals he seemed to partake of [396] the boy's spirit, and to be revived with a fresh and happy life. Reuben was accompanied by his son in the expedition, for the purpose of selecting a tract of land and felling and burning the timber, which necessarily preceded the removal of the household gods. Two months of autumn were thus occupied, after which Reuben Bourne and his young hunter returned to spend their last winter in the settlements.

It was early in the month of May that the little family snapped asunder whatever tendrils of affections had clung to inanimate objects, and bade farewell to the few who, in the blight of fortune, called themselves their friends. The sadness of the parting moment had, to each of the pilgrims, its peculiar alleviations. Reuben, a moody man, and misanthropic because unhappy, strode onward with his usual stern brow and downcast eye, feeling few regrets and disdaining to acknowledge any. Dorcas, while she wept abundantly over the broken ties by which her simple and affectionate nature had bound itself to everything, felt that the inhabitants of her inmost heart moved on with her, and that all else would be supplied wherever she might go. And the boy dashed one tear-drop from his eye, and thought of the adventurous pleasures of the untrodden forest.

Oh, who, in the enthusiasm of a daydream, has not wished that he were a wanderer in a world of summer wilderness, with one fair and gentle being hanging lightly on his arm? In youth his free and exulting step would know no barrier but the rolling ocean or the snow-topped mountains; calmer manhood would choose a home where Nature had strewn a double wealth in the vale of some transparent stream; and when hoary age,[397] after long, long years of that pure life, stole on and found him there, it would find him the father of a race, the patriarch of a people, the founder of a mighty nation yet to be. When death, like the sweet sleep which we welcome after a day of happiness, came over him, his far descendants would mourn over the venerated dust. Enveloped by tradition in mysterious attributes, the men of future generations would call him godlike; and remote posterity would see him standing, dimly glorious, far up the valley of a hundred centuries.

The tangled and gloomy forest through which the personages of my tale were wandering differed widely from the dreamer's land of fantasy; yet there was something in their way of life that Nature asserted as her own, and the gnawing cares which went with them from the world were all that now obstructed their happiness. One stout and shaggy steed, the bearer of all their wealth, did not shrink from the added weight of Dorcas; although her hardy breeding sustained her, during the latter part of each day's journey, by her husband's side. Reuben and his son, their muskets on their shoulders and their axes slung behind them, kept an unwearied pace, each watching with a hunter's eye for the game that supplied their food. When hunger bade, they halted and prepared their meal on the bank of some unpolluted forest brook, which, as they knelt down with thirsty lips to drink, murmured a sweet unwillingness, like a maiden at love's first kiss. They slept beneath a hut of branches, and awoke at peep of light refreshed for the toils of another day. Dorcas and the boy went on joyously, and even Reuben's spirit shone at intervals with an outward gladness; but inwardly there was a cold, cold sorrow, which he compared to the snowdrifts lying deep in the glens and hollows [398] of the rivulets while the leaves were brightly green above.

Cyrus Bourne was sufficiently skilled in the travel of the woods to observe that his father did not adhere to the course they had pursued in their expedition of the preceding autumn. They were now keeping farther to the north, striking out more directly from the settlements, and into a region of which savage beasts and savage men were as yet the sole possessors. The boy sometimes hinted his opinions upon the subject, and Reuben listened attentively, and once or twice altered the direction of their march in accordance with his son's counsel; but, having so done, he seemed ill at ease. His quick and wandering glances were sent forward, apparently in search of enemies lurking behind the tree trunks; and, seeing nothing there, he would cast his eyes backwards as if in fear of some pursuer. Cyrus, perceiving that his father gradually resumed the old direction, forbore to interfere; nor, though something began to weigh upon his heart, did his adventurous nature permit him to regret the increased length and the mystery of their way.

On the afternoon of the fifth day they halted, and made their simple encampment nearly an hour before sunset. The face of the country, for the last few miles, had been diversified by swells of land resembling huge waves of a petrified sea; and in one of the corresponding hollows, a wild and romantic spot, had the family reared their hut and kindled their fire. There is something chilling, and yet heart-warming, in the thought of these three, united by strong bands of love and insulated from all that breathe beside. The dark and gloomy pines looked down upon them, and, as the wind swept through their tops, a pitying sound was heard in [399] the forest; or did those old trees groan in fear that men were come to lay the axe to their roots at last? Reuben and his son, while Dorcas made ready their meal, proposed to wander out in search of game, of which that day's march had afforded no supply. The boy, promising not to quit the vicinity of the encampment, bounded off with a step as light and elastic as that of the deer he hoped to slay; while his father, feeling a transient happiness as he gazed after him, was about to pursue an opposite direction. Dorcas, in the meanwhile, had seated herself near their fire of fallen branches, upon the mossgrown and mouldering trunk of a tree uprooted years before. Her employment, diversified by an occasional glance at the pot, now beginning to simmer over the blaze, was the perusal of the current year's Massachusetts Almanac, which, with the exception of an old black-letter Bible, comprised all the literary wealth of the family. None pay a greater regard to arbitrary divisions of time than those who are excluded from society; and Dorcas mentioned, as if the information were of importance, that it was now the twelfth of May. Her husband started.

"The twelfth of May! I should remember it well," muttered he, while many thoughts occasioned a momentary confusion in his mind. "Where am I? Whither am I wandering? Where did I leave him?"

Dorcas, too well accustomed to her husband's wayward moods to note any peculiarity of demeanor, now laid aside the almanac and addressed him in that mournful tone which the tender hearted appropriate to griefs long cold and dead.

"It was near this time of the month, eighteen years ago, that my poor father left this world for a better. He had a kind arm to hold his head and a kind voice [400] to cheer him, Reuben, in his last moments; and the thought of the faithful care you took of him has comforted me many a time since. Oh, death would have been awful to a solitary man in a wild place like this!"

"Pray Heaven, Dorcas," said Reuben, in a broken voice,—"pray Heaven that neither of us three dies solitary and lies unburied in this howling wilderness!" And he hastened away, leaving her to watch the fire beneath the gloomy pines.

Reuben Bourne's rapid pace gradually slackened as the pang, unintentionally inflicted by the words of Dorcas, became less acute. Many strange reflections, however, thronged upon him; and, straying onward rather like a sleep walker than a hunter, it was attributable to no care of his own that his devious course kept him in the vicinity of the encampment. His steps were imperceptibly led almost in a circle; nor did he observe that he was on the verge of a tract of land heavily timbered, but not with pine-trees. The place of the latter was here supplied by oaks and other of the harder woods; and around their roots clustered a dense and bushy under-growth, leaving, however, barren spaces between the trees, thick strewn with withered leaves. Whenever the rustling of the branches or the creaking of the trunks made a sound, as if the forest were waking from slumber, Reuben instinctively raised the musket that rested on his arm, and cast a quick, sharp glance on every side; but, convinced by a partial observation that no animal was near, he would again give himself up to his thoughts. He was musing on the strange influence that had led him away from his premeditated course, and so far into the depths of the wilderness. Unable [401] to penetrate to the secret place of his soul where his motives lay hidden, he believed that a supernatural voice had called him onward, and that a supernatural power had obstructed his retreat. He trusted that it was Heaven's intent to afford him an opportunity of expiating his sin; he hoped that he might find the bones so long unburied; and that, having laid the earth over them, peace would throw its sunlight into the sepulchre of his heart. From these thoughts he was aroused by a rustling in the forest at some distance from the spot to which he had wandered. Perceiving the motion of some object behind a thick veil of undergrowth, he fired, with the instinct of a hunter and the aim of a practised marksman. A low moan, which told his success, and by which even animals can express their dying agony, was unheeded by Reuben Bourne. What were the recollections now breaking upon him?

The thicket into which Reuben had fired was near the summit of a swell of land, and was clustered around the base of a rock, which, in the shape and smoothness of one of its surfaces, was not unlike a gigantic gravestone. As if reflected in a mirror, its likeness was in Reuben's memory. He even recognized the veins which seemed to form an inscription in forgotten characters: everything remained the same, except that a thick covert of bushes shrouded the lower part of the rock, and would have hidden Roger Malvin had he still been sitting there. Yet in the next moment Reuben's eye was caught by another change that time had effected since he last stood where he was now standing again behind the earthy roots of the uptorn tree. The sapling to which he had bound the bloodstained symbol of his vow had [402] increased and strengthened into an oak, far indeed from its maturity, but with no mean spread of shadowy branches. There was one singularity observable in this tree which made Reuben tremble. The middle and lower branches were in luxuriant life, and an excess of vegetation had fringed the trunk almost to the ground; but a blight had apparently stricken the upper part of the oak, and the very topmost bough was withered, sapless, and utterly dead. Reuben remembered how the little banner had fluttered on that topmost bough, when it was green and lovely, eighteen years before. Whose guilt had blasted it?

Dorcas, after the departure of the two hunters, continued her preparations for their evening repast. Her sylvan table was the moss-covered trunk of a large fallen tree, on the broadest part of which she had spread a snow-white cloth and arranged what were left of the bright pewter vessels that had been her pride in the settlements. It had a strange aspect, that one little spot of homely comfort in the desolate heart of Nature. The sunshine yet lingered upon the higher branches of the trees that grew on rising ground; but the shadows of evening had deepened into the hollow where the encampment was made, and the firelight began to redden as it gleamed up the tall trunks of the pines or hovered on the dense and obscure mass of foliage that circled round the spot. The heart of Dorcas was not sad; for she felt that it was better to journey in the wilderness with two whom she loved than to be a lonely woman in a crowd that cared not for her. As she busied herself in arranging seats of mouldering wood, covered with leaves, for Reuben and her son, her voice danced through [403] the gloomy forest in the measure of a song that she had learned in youth. The rude melody, the production of a bard who won no name, was descriptive of a winter evening in a frontier cottage, when, secured from savage inroad by the high-piled snow-drifts, the family rejoiced by their own fireside. The whole song possessed the nameless charm peculiar to unborrowed thought, but four continually-recurring lines shone out from the rest like the blaze of the hearth whose joys they celebrated. Into them, working magic with a few simple words, the poet had instilled the very essence of domestic love and household happiness, and they were poetry and picture joined in one. As Dorcas sang, the walls of her forsaken home seemed to encircle her; she no longer saw the gloomy pines, nor heard the wind which still, as she began each verse, sent a heavy breath through the branches, and died away in a hollow moan from the burden of the song. She was aroused by the report of a gun in the vicinity of the encampment; and either the sudden sound, or her loneliness by the glowing fire, caused her to tremble violently. The next moment she laughed in the pride of a mother's heart. "My beautiful young hunter! My boy has slain a deer!" she exclaimed, recollecting that in the direction whence the shot proceeded Cyrus had gone to the chase.

She waited a reasonable time to hear her son's light step bounding over the rustling leaves to tell of his success. But he did not immediately appear; and she sent her cheerful voice among the trees in search of him. "Cyrus! Cyrus!"

His coming was still delayed; and she determined,[404] as the report had apparently been very near, to seek for him in person. Her assistance, also, might be necessary in bringing home the venison which she flattered herself he had obtained. She therefore set forward, directing her steps by the long-past sound, and singing as she went, in order that the boy might be aware of her approach and run to meet her. From behind the trunk of every tree, and from every hiding-place in the thick foliage of the undergrowth, she hoped to discover the countenance of her son, laughing with the sportive mischief that is born of affection. The sun was now beneath the horizon, and the light that came down among the leaves was sufficiently dim to create many illusions in her expecting fancy. Several times she seemed indistinctly to see his face gazing out from among the leaves; and once she imagined that he stood beckoning to her at the base of a craggy rock. Keeping her eyes on this object, however, it proved to be no more than the trunk of an oak fringed to the very ground with little branches, one of which, thrust out farther than the rest, was shaken by the breeze. Making her way round the foot of the rock, she suddenly found herself close to her husband, who had approached in another direction. Leaning upon the butt of his gun, the muzzle of which rested upon the withered leaves, he was apparently absorbed in the contemplation of some object at his feet.

"How is this, Reuben? Have you slain the deer and fallen asleep over

him?" exclaimed Dorcas, laughing cheerfully, on her first slight observation of his posture and appearance.

He stirred not, neither did he turn his eyes towards her; and a cold,
shuddering fear, indefinite in its source and object, began to creep into
her blood. She [405] now perceived that her husband's face was ghastly
pale, and his features were rigid, as if incapable of assuming any other
expression than the strong despair which had hardened upon them. He
gave not the slightest evidence that he was aware of her approach.

"For the love of Heaven, Reuben, speak to me!" cried Dorcas; and
the strange sound of her own voice affrighted her even more than the
dead silence.

Her husband started, stared into her face, drew her to the front of
the rock, and pointed with his finger.

Oh, there lay the boy, asleep, but dreamless, upon the fallen forest
leaves! His cheek rested upon his arm—his curled locks were thrown
back from his brow—his limbs were slightly relaxed. Had a sudden
weariness overcome the youthful hunter? Would his mother's voice
arouse him? She knew that it was death.

"This broad rock is the gravestone of your near kindred, Dorcas,"
said her husband. "Your tears will fall at once over your father and
your son."

She heard him not. With one wild shriek, that seemed to force its
way from the sufferer's inmost soul, she sank insensible by the side of
her dead boy. At that moment the withered topmost bough of the oak
loosened itself in the stilly air, and fell in soft, light fragments upon the
rock, upon the leaves, upon Reuben, upon his wife and child, and upon
Roger Malvin's bones. Then Reuben's heart was stricken, and the tears
gushed out like water from a rock. The vow that the wounded youth
had made the blighted man had come to redeem. His sin was expiated,—
the curse was gone from him; and in the hour when he had shed blood
dearer to him than his own, a prayer, the first for years, went up to
Heaven from the lips of Reuben Bourne.[406]

Lovewell's Fight and Hawthorne's "Roger Malvin's Burial" *

The historical source of Nathaniel Hawthorne's "Roger Malvin's Burial" (according to its introductory paragraph) was admittedly Lovewell's Fight. Hawthorne wrote that "History and tradition are unusually minute in their memorials of the affair." [1] In his extensive reading about New England he must have come upon numerous accounts of the fatal battle between the colonial farmers of Massachusetts under Captain John Lovewell of Dunstable and the Indians of Pigwacket. [2] [527]

In retaliation against Indian depredations on the frontier villages of Massachusetts and New Hampshire, Lovewell led a small company of colonists toward Pigwacket, near what is now Fryeburg, Maine, in April, 1725. After manning a temporary fortification at Ossipee with a small group of reserves, including a surgeon, Lovewell proceeded with thirty-four men against the Indians. On the eighth of May he and his company were ambushed by approximately eighty savages under Paugus, their chief. One of the colonists fled at the first encounter, and finding his way back to the fort, he related there such a bloody tale of defeat that the reserve hastily retreated to the settlements. Lovewell and eight others were killed at the outset of the skirmish; the remaining men fought until late in the evening when the Indians retired, their number greatly diminished. About midnight, twenty of the white survivors began the long march homeward leaving the dead upon the field. This group ar-

[1] The *Works of Nathaniel Hawthorne* (Boston, 1882–1896), II, 381. Elizabeth L. Chandler has determined that "Roger Malvin's Burial" was written about 1829. It was first published by S. G. Goodrich in *The Token* in 1832. "A Study of the Sources of the Tales and Romances Written by Nathaniel Hawthorne Before 1853," *Smith College Studies in Modern Languages*, VII (July, 1926), 55.

[2] In addition to the sources cited in the text it is reasonable to assume that Hawthorne was familiar with the following histories which mention Lovewell's Fight: Samuel Penhallow, *The History of the Wars of New England, With the Eastern Indians*, Thomas Hutchinson, *The History of the Province of Massachusetts-Bay*, Jeremy Belknap, *The History of New Hampshire* and James Sullivan, *The History of the District of Maine*.

* David S. Lovejoy, "Lovewell's Fight and Hawthorne's 'Roger Malvin's Burial,'" *New England Quarterly*, XXVII (December, 1954), 527–31. Reprinted by permission.

rived in Dunstable in a body, with the exception of four of the wounded who were barely able to walk. These were left in the forest not far from the scene of the battle, expecting in vain to obtain relief from the men who remained at the fort. Two of them survived the slow march through the wilderness, but the remaining two were left to perish.

In 1938 an investigation by G. Harrison Orians [3] revealed that Hawthorne derived much of the historical material for his tale from a contemporary account written in 1725 by the Reverend Thomas Symmes of Bradford, Massachusetts.[4] Symmes's memoir, which was the most authentic and complete extant, was printed in the first volume of *Collections, Topographical, Historical and Biographical,* published in Concord, New Hampshire, by John Farmer and Jacob B. Moore in 1822. Mr. Orians has shown that Hawthorne borrowed a number of Symmes's facts and incorporated them into his tale. Moreover, there is no doubt that Hawthorne had access to this work since his aunt, Mary Manning, who at this time was living with the Hawthornes, owned a share in the Salem Athenæum and was charged with the three volumes of Farmer and Moore's *Collections* in December, 1827. Hawthorne [528] took over his aunt's share in May, 1828, and on April 24 of the next year he was charged with the third volume.[5]

The initial theme of this early tale is that of one man leaving another alone to die in the forest. Reuben Bourne, a critically wounded survivor of Lovewell's Fight, reluctantly departed from the dying Roger Malvin only because both were convinced that there was no chance for either to live if he remained. In Symmes's narrative, Mr. Orians has shown that there are three instances of wounded men left unattended in the forest by the band of returning frontiersmen. These, he asserts, could easily have suggested the subject to Hawthorne. Mr. Orians has further pointed out that a second source of the tale was "Lovewell's Fight, a Ballad," published in Farmer and Moore's *Collections* for 1824.[6] The few stanzas

[3] "The Source of Hawthorne's 'Roger Malvin's Burial,' " *American Literature*, X, 315, 1938–1939.

[4] For a discussion of the authenticity of Thomas Symmes's memoir, see Fannie Hardy Eckstorm, "Pigwacket and Parson Symmes," *New England Quarterly*, IX, 378–402 (September, 1936).

[5] Marion L. Kesselring, *Hawthorne's Reading, 1828–1850, A Transcription and Identification of Titles Recorded in the Charge-Books of the Salem Athenæum* (New York, 1949), 21, 25, 50.

[6] III, 94. George Lyman Kittredge has attributed this ballad to Thomas C. Upham, *Bibliographical Essays, a Tribute to Wilberforce Eames* (Cambridge, 1924), 107. Upham was a New Hampshire clergyman who became a professor at Bowdoin College in 1825, three months before Hawthorne was graduated.

he has quoted depict with unabashed sentiment the heart-rending departure of Lieutenant Farwell from young Chaplain Frye. This departure, Mr. Orians believes, probably served as a model for Reuben Bourne's leave-taking of Roger Malvin.

Symmes's memoir of Lovewell's Fight and the ballad mentioned above were not the only sources from which Hawthorne borrowed facts for "Roger Malvin's Burial." In the October issue of Farmer and Moore's *Collections* for 1823 there was printed an article entitled "Indian Troubles at Dunstable" by a writer who left only his initials, "J. B. H.", at the end of his short introduction.[7] These anecdotes, as he has called them, refer to the Indian attacks upon Dunstable, Massachusetts (now New Hampshire), and the surrounding villages from 1722 to 1725.

There is one paragraph in "J. B. H." 's account which describes the parting of Farwell and still another combatant, Davis, so similar to that between Reuben Bourne and Roger Malvin, that it was [529] unquestionably used by Hawthorne as a source for the tale. This paragraph is reproduced here in full because from it Hawthorne acquired a number of details. Having related some of Farwell's exploits before 1725, "J. B. H." writes:

Farwell was afterwards engaged as Lieutenant in Lovewell's fight, and in the commencement of the action was shot through the belly. He survived the contest two or three days, and with one Eleazer Davis, from Concord, attempted to reach home. They were destitute of provisions, and finding some cranberries, greedily devoured them. Those eaten by Farwell came out at his wound. Though his case was hopeless, Davis continued with and assisted him till he became so weak as to be unable to stand, and then, at Farwell's earnest entreaties that he would provide for his own safety, left him to his fate. Previous to this he had taken Farwell's handkerchief and tied it to the top of a bush that it might afford a mark by which his remains could the more easily be found. After going from him a short distance, Farwell called him back and requested to be turned upon the other side. This was done, and was the last that was known of him. Davis reached Concord in safety.[8]

The first part of "Roger Malvin's Burial" is obviously an elaboration of this paragraph. Although Symmes's narrative suggested, in three in-

---

[7] II, 303. "J. B. H." was doubtless the Reverend Joseph Bancroft Hill of Mason and Colebrook, New Hampshire, to whom John Farmer, co-editor of the *Collections*, wrote in September, 1823, about the original ballad of Lovewell's Fight written in 1725. See part of this letter in George Lyman Kittredge, *Bibliographical Essays . . .* , 117n.

[8] *Collections*, II, 306.

stances, the leaving of dying men in the forest, the idea is more graph-
ically presented in the above paragraph. Farwell traveled homeward
with Davis for "two or three days"; Roger and Reuben had walked for
three days, and the story commences early on the morning of the fourth
day. Farwell and Davis, like their counterparts in the tale, were without
food. Davis continued with Farwell until the latter's condition was hopeless, and then abandoned him at Farwell's "earnest entreaties." " 'Tell my
daughter,' said Roger Malvin, 'that, though yourself sore wounded, and
weak, and weary, you led my tottering footsteps many a mile, and left
me only at my earnest entreaty . . .' " [9]

In order to mark more easily Farwell's position in the forest, Davis,
before leaving his friend, tied Farwell's handkerchief to an adjacent
bush. Hawthorne, more imaginatively, has Reuben bind his own handkerchief to the topmost branch of a young oak tree where it becomes a
cogent symbol. Hawthorne explains, "The handkerchief had been the
bandage of a wound upon Reuben's [530] arm; and, as he bound it to
the tree, he vowed by the blood that stained it that he would return,
either to save his companion's life or to lay his body in the grave." [10]

The paragraph by "J. B. H." continues: "After going from him a short
distance, Farwell called him back and requested to be turned upon the
other side. This was done, and was the last that was known of him."
Similarly, Malvin recalled Reuben and requested that he be lifted and
braced against the rock so that he might see Reuben as he retreated
through the forest. Farwell's body was never found. To Hawthorne this
was an important detail for it suggested a psychological treatment of
the conscience-stricken Reuben who failed to return, as he had vowed,
to bury the body of Roger Malvin, the father of the woman he soon
married.

Hawthorne has deliberately divided "Roger Malvin's Burial" into two
distinct parts. For the first, which describes the parting of Reuben Bourne
from Roger Malvin and the former's struggle homeward, he relied
heavily on two sources: Symmes's memoir and the short account by
"J. B. H." From the historical facts of Lovewell's Fight he has constructed
the first half of one of his finest tales. The second half, however, is free
of historical material; it is the product of Hawthorne's imagination, a
psychological study of a young man burdened by the torment of his
secret guilt. [531]

[9] *Works*, II, 385.　　　　　　　　　[10] *Works*, II, 388.

The Tales: The Discovery of Meaning *

If "The Canterbury Pilgrims" suggests a scale up and down which the meaning moves like a melody stated and elaborated with classic artistry, "Roger Malvin's Burial" is more likely to suggest to most readers a dream, with more than the usual dream's depths visible beneath the limpid surface. The immense difference between these two tales suggests the range of Hawthorne's artistry, but the two are alike in one respect: in both, the burden of meaning carried by structure is relatively greater than it is in some of the better-known later tales such as "Rappaccini's Daughter."

Like "My Kinsman, Major Molineux," "Roger Malvin's Burial" opens with a paragraph of historical background, not properly a part of the tale itself but a preparation for it. "The fate of the few combatants who were in a condition to retreat after 'Lovell's Fight' " in the border wars of 1725 will provide the subject for a tale which will play "the moonlight of romance" over a page of Colonial history. The tale that follows provides further evidence of what Hawthorne meant by "romance" and of the use to which he put history, but what chiefly concerns us now is the way in which the structure of the tale expresses the meaning.

In summary, the situation is this. Two of Lovell's men, one old and the other young, have escaped the destruction of their force and are making their way back to the settlements. The older of the two, however, has been severely wounded in the fight, and as the story opens he is resting beneath a rock in a forest glade, unable to go farther. He urges the young man to go on and save himself if possible, pointing out that staying with him will mean that two lives will be [78] lost instead of one. Finally the younger man decides to do so, comforting himself with the thought that he may thus be able to send back help for the older. Later as he is about to die of his own severe wounds he is found near the edge of the settle-

* Reprinted by permission of the publishers from Hyatt H. Waggoner, *Hawthorne: A Critical Study*, Cambridge, Mass.: The Belknap Press of Harvard University Press, Copyright, 1955, by The President and Fellows of Harvard College.

ment and nursed back to health by the girl whom he later marries, the daughter of the friend he left to die in the forest. Although he intends to tell of the circumstances of the older man's death, he never actually does so. He marries the daughter of his friend, keeps his secret to himself, and rears a son who grows to adolescence. But a feeling of guilt increases within him until he can bear it no longer, and he sets out with his family for new land to the west. Journeying through the forest, he finds himself drawn continually away from the planned course and in the direction of the place where years before he had left his friend to die alone. Arrived at the spot without the man's recognizing it at first, the family makes camp, and father and son go into the woods separately. Hearing a sound near him, the father fires blindly, killing his son, who has been his only comfort in the unhappy isolation that has grown on him through the years.

Even a bare summary of this sort suffices to suggest some of the overtones of the tale. Here, most clearly, is the usual preoccupation with secret guilt, with the resulting isolation, and with a sense of compulsion. The young man who grows old in bitterness is another Goodman Brown, introduced to the evil in the world by his own participation in it. He is Robin of "My Kinsman, Major Molineux," in later years compelled to return to the spot where he had joined in laughter at his kinsman's expense. He is Abraham sacrificing Isaac: compelled as it seemed to him by a "supernatural power," he kills his son. The plot of the tale is as elemental and suggestive as any that Hawthorne ever wrote.

The deepening and strengthening of the suggestions implicit in the basic situation is accomplished with great economy, without the profusion of imagery common in the later [79] tales. The rock against which the dying old man leaned and beneath which the child is later killed is explicitly a gravestone and implicitly an altar like those in the Old Testament on which sacrifice was offered. The two key scenes of the story take place deep in the *heart* of the dark forest, in a glade which Reuben is unable to forget as he is unable to cast out the secret that lies in "the sepulchre of his heart." The branch around which he had tied his handkerchief upon leaving his older friend so that he might find the spot again has been withered by time ("Whose guilt had blasted it?") and falls in "soft light fragments upon the rock, upon the leaves, upon Reuben, upon his wife and child, and upon Roger Malvin's bones" after the son has been sacrificed. These few are the outstanding symbolic devices in this tale rich in its depths and deceptively plain on its surface.

For the rest, the implications are developed in the contours of the situations. Did Reuben do wrong in leaving the dying man? He himself was gravely wounded, and staying, though it could be conceived as a religious duty, could certainly have no practical benefits. Where would the right lie in a situation like this? Surely one's duty to others should not require self-sacrifice when the sacrifice would almost certainly be useless to the other person. It is not at all certain that Reuben did any wrong in leaving the dying man.

Why then was he consumed by a sense of guilt thereafter until he had killed what was most dear to him? Hawthorne suggests that, in the first place, it was not so much the overt act of desertion as the conditions under which it took place that justified the feeling of guilt. When Roger Malvin urges his "son" to leave him, he plays shrewdly upon the capacity of man to rationalize his interests. He points out that if Reuben leaves he will be able to look after the daughter he is to marry, he may get help to come, and that at any rate it is his duty to obey the one who has loved him like a father and who "should have something of a father's authority." [80] Thus in the conflict between the claims of opposed duties it is possible for Reuben to follow self-interest without admitting to himself that he has done so. Malvin's words

reminded him that there were other and less questionable duties than that of sharing the fate of a man whom his death could not benefit. Nor can it be affirmed that no selfish feeling strove to enter Reuben's heart, though the consciousness made him more earnestly resist his companion's entreaties. . . . No merely selfish motive, nor even the desolate condition of Dorcas, could have induced him to desert his companion at such a moment—but his wishes seized on the thought that Malvin's life might be preserved, and his sanguine nature heightened almost to certainty the remote possibility of procuring human aid.

The moral complexity of the original situation, in short, amounts to almost complete ambiguity. In a situation so opaque with conflicting rights, no clear judgment can be brought against Reuben for his action. But the state of mind and heart which permitted and prompted the action is another matter. Reuben was not honest with himself about his motives. Here if anywhere lay a clear reason for the feeling of guilt that came to torment him.

And this original failure of honesty was compounded by another act of rationalization that was likewise almost, if not entirely, justifiable: he did not tell Dorcas and the others that he had left her father to die alone. Circumstances conspired to make it easy for him to keep this to himself. He was near death when he was discovered near the settlement. He found that everyone assumed that he had heroically remained with the dying man, to do what he could for him at the end and to bury his body. When, once, he tried to tell the truth he found that his words were interpreted according to the preconceptions of his hearers. The thought occurred to him that to tell the truth would inflict upon his wife useless suffering which he would like to spare her. So he allowed the untruth to be believed. Again, whose motives are so [81] perfect that he can safely, as Hawthorne puts it, "impute blame"?

But the actions which thus far had seemed so natural, so justifiable, involved a consequence which Reuben could not escape or justify to himself. When he had left Roger Malvin to die, he had promised that he would return to give the bones of his friend Christian burial. Now he was unable to keep that vow without revealing that he had permitted a lie to be believed. Here at last was a great and perfectly clear wrong: a promise to a dying man, and especially to a "father," must surely be kept. But what would once have been easy was now impossible without an intolerable sacrifice. Thus Reuben Bourne was guilty without ever having committed any clear overt wrong. His "sin," indeed, lay not so much in anything he had done as in what he had failed to do. But the end of ambiguity was not there, for the only unambiguous wrong of which he was guilty—failing to keep his promise—was itself the necessary result not of a clear-cut present choice but of previous choices made in ambiguous situations without full knowledge of the consequences.

The story then is concerned not with the obvious guilt of recognized sinners but with the complex and obscure guilt in which one who "means well" and is as good as the next man gets involved. Like Original Sin, Reuben's guilt is at once, and paradoxically, the result of a chain of previous wrong choices and the consequence of a "fatal necessity." Like Original Sin too, it required a dramatic and extraordinary sacrifice for the undoing of its consequences.

Nothing in the tale clarifies the "simple" and "obvious" question of how much if any wrong Reuben did in leaving the dying man. Indeed the answer to the abstract ethical question of the degree of self-sacrifice demanded by Christian ethics is deliberately obscured. In terms of purely rational ethics the only implication of the surface level of the story would be the same as the explicit moral of *The Scarlet* [82] *Letter*, "Be true! Be true! Show freely to the world, if not your worst, yet some trait whereby the worst may be inferred." Reuben was not true. From one point of view not sin but refusal to acknowledge sin drove him to his doom.

Although this theme of the effects of concealment—so common in Hawthorne that there is a temptation to call it *the* meaning once we have discovered it—is surely developed, the central meaning of the story is not to be found here either, but equally, and alternatively, on the levels of myth and of the unconscious. In our day, when readings of stories in these terms are being overdone with the enthusiasm of fresh discovery, it may be natural to suspect that at this point we are overreading, seeing too much in a simple tale. But Hawthorne himself has answered this objection: he has made it impossible to disregard the mythical and the unconscious in reading the story.

In the first place, his emphasis on Reuben's motives in his two "guilty" acts prepares us for what is to follow. Hawthorne understood consciously and thoroughly the process we now call rationalization, and he described the process as it took place in Reuben's mind. To discern the motives of thinking is to penetrate some little way below the level of what is normally in the consciousness. But more significantly, he makes Reuben's return to the place of his first "guilt" compulsive. From the route which had been consciously selected to take them to their new home Reuben continually strays, though he is an excellent woodsman, and his straying takes always the same direction. Corrected by his son, who notices the strange "mistake," Reuben agrees and changes his direction, only to turn again and again in the way he was obscurely compelled to take. "Cyrus, perceiving that his father gradually resumed the old direction, forbore to interfere; nor, though something began to weigh upon his heart, did his adventurous nature permit him to regret the increased length and mystery of their way." [83]

And it was indeed a mysterious journey which they were undertaking. After they have arrived near the place of Roger Malvin's death, Reuben leaves Dorcas at the fire to follow Cyrus into the woods in search of game. I have said that Hawthorne underscores the "mystery" here, but the precise emphasis he gives to the mystery deserves to be noted. Reuben, wholly preoccupied with the "strange reflections" arising from his feeling of guilt, which has lately come so much to the foreground as to destroy the man Dorcas had loved and married, "strays" through the woods "rather like a sleepwalker than a hunter," circling the camp and approaching without realizing it the nearby great rock in the glade.

He was musing on the strange influence that had led him away from his premeditated course, and so far into the depths of the wilderness. Unable to penetrate the secret place of his soul where his motives lay hidden, he believed that a supernatural voice had called him onward, and that a supernatural power had obstructed his retreat. He trusted that it was Heaven's intent to afford him an opportunity of expiating his sin; he hoped that he might find the bones so long unburied; and that, having laid the earth over them, peace would throw its sunlight into the sepulchre of his heart. From these thoughts he was aroused by a rustling in the forest at some distance from the spot to which he had wandered. Perceiving the motion of some object behind a thick veil of undergrowth, he fired, with the instinct of a hunter and the aim of a practised marksman. A low moan, which told of his success, and by which even animals can express their dying agony, was unheeded by Reuben Bourne. What were the recollections now breaking upon him?

I suppose Hawthorne could not have made the element of unconscious compulsion in the return to the spot and the shooting of the son more explicit than he has without dropping entirely the surface level of the story. But there is another aspect of the situation that Hawthorne merely hints. As he has been ridden by his feeling of guilt through the years, Reuben has grown away from Dorcas until there is a [84] wall of separation between them. But he does not lose his love for his son. "The boy was loved by his father with a deep and silent strength, as if whatever was good and happy in his own nature had been transferred to his child, carrying his affections with it." When he kills the child, then, he is killing what he most loved, but he is doing more than that: he is killing the symbolic extension of himself. A feeling of guilt arising out of one's relation to the father may lead, the psychologist might say, to the need to destroy or mutilate the guilty self. What the psychologist would know and document systematically, Hawthorne knew in his creative mind in this story and wrought into a structure of relationships that involve archetypal patterns.

The relation between this tale and the stories of Leonard Doane, who suffered from the fantasy that he had killed his father, and Robin, who laughed cruelly at the man he hoped would be like a father to him, should by now be clear enough. But there are other aspects of the story that deserve mention. In all of Hawthorne's tales there is perhaps no subtler presentation of certain aspects of the nature of secret guilt—its springs, its nature, and its effects. Reuben Bourne is guilty, in so far as his guilt can be related to the objective moral world and is not merely "psychological," of what Hawthorne calls "moral cowardice": he cannot bring himself first to face the truth about himself and then to share it with others, even those he loves. "Unable to penetrate to the secret place of his soul where his motives lay hidden," he is prevented from knowing himself, and so from changing himself constructively. A psychologist might say that he lacked "insight." A theologian would say that his blindness and cowardice spring, like Dimmesdale's, from a very subtle, quite unconscious, pride. He is unable to humble himself to the extent that would be required by a recognition of his true motives and nature and by subsequent confession of sin. He suffers but, like Dimmesdale again, does not really repent [85] until he is driven by his suffering to the self-sacrificial act which brings his release. Then "His sin was expiated,—the curse was gone from him; and in the hour when he had shed blood dearer to him than his own, a prayer, the first for years, went up to Heaven from the lips of Reuben Bourne."

These closing words of the story, like the Biblical allusions throughout, make it clear that a reading of the tale in terms of both primitive religious myth and the historical and theological aspects of creedal Christianity are as clearly justified as the psychological reading is. Oedipus and the sacrificial savior loom in the background of this tale whose foreground is fashioned out of Colonial history and the nature and effects of concealed guilt. Original Sin and the Atonement are as clearly involved in Reuben Bourne's story as are the psychology of guilt and the demands of the unconscious.

And all these meanings are embodied in structure—in situation and character and action, in motive to action and result of action. The tale is not as rich in texture as the greatest of Hawthorne's later stories; not so much of the meaning is carried by image and symbol. But it is one of Hawthorne's greatest tales nevertheless, for there is no part of its structure which is not instinct with meaning, and no meaning in the tale which is not embodied in its structure. In it we see exemplified the structure of meaning as Hawthorne created it.[86]

. . . . .

Hawthorne's besetting danger of over-intellectualization was only the misuse of his greatest strength. "Roger Malvin's Burial" is certainly one of his best tales, but it . . . has very [87] little action and its characters are only sufficiently sketched in to make them credible. Its illusion of reality is slight by comparison with contemporary practice, and its burden of meaning great by any standard. Any reader wholly insensitive to its meanings as they develop would surely find it something less than compelling. It does not invite us so much to share Reuben Bourne's

experience as to contemplate it. The experience it affords is highly intellectual, but it is experience conceived and structured in aesthetic, not in
philosophic, terms.

Like "Wakefield," "The Canterbury Pilgrims," and "Roger Malvin's
Burial," most of Hawthorne's tales contain very little overt action, but
what action there is, is symbolic. In the greater tales this economy helps
to produce the effect of concentrated brilliance. In the weaker ones, it
contributes to our impression that the tales are not fiction at all, but
sketches. Lack of action is characteristic of both the weaker sketchlike
tales and the very best among both the tales and the novels. It has often
been noted that *The Scarlet Letter* begins after the actions that would
provide the plot of most novels; and the subsequent "actions" it does
treat take place almost entirely within the minds and hearts of the
characters. *The Marble Faun*, in contrast, which has a great deal more
overt action, is clearly an inferior novel. "Young Goodman Brown,"
one of the very finest of the tales, contains so little and such simple
overt action that a summary concerned with its plot alone could be
adequately given in an uncrowded sentence. "Mr. Higginbotham's
Catastrophe," on the other hand, has a rather full and complicated plot,
but it is surely not one of Hawthorne's best works.

The action is not only relatively little in proportion to the length of
the tales but is usually of the simplest character. One form that plot
commonly takes is the journey. "My Kinsman, Major Molineux" is
built around Robin's trip to and through, and implied later departure
from, Boston. We [88] see him arrive and wander through the streets,
receiving the revelations that lead to his departure. The physical action
in "Roger Malvin's Burial" is limited to Reuben's preparing to leave his
friend and his later return to the same spot, the events of the intervening
years being chiefly summarized rather than presented as they happen.
In "The Canterbury Pilgrims" travelers going in opposite directions
meet, talk, and depart on their different ways; that is all the action there
is. Wakefield leaves his home and later returns. The searchers for the
great carbuncle, once they have been introduced in their camp, set out
on their quest; what they discover on the way is the essence of the story.
The man of adamant journeys to his cave and there receives a visitor
from across the sea; since he does not depart with her, he is lost. Ethan
Brand searches far and wide for the Unpardonable Sin, returns to his
lime kiln, and throws himself into the flames because he has at last found,
in an unexpected place, that for which he has sought. Goodman Brown
journeys into and returns from the forest, bringing back with him the

revelations he has gained there. This journey-plot is so frequent in Hawthorne that sketches like "The Procession of Life" and "Main Street"
differ from the tales not so much in "lacking plot" as in failing to develop
character: the casual reflections of the narrator, clearly in these pieces
Hawthorne himself, are not an adequate substitute for the creation of a
Goodman Brown, or even of a Reverend Mr. Hooper with his veil.

From these very simple patterns of action Hawthorne developed
designs of great complexity. Once he had seen the general meanings
implicit in his basic situation, he saw reflections and qualifications of
them everywhere. The *Gestalt* once perceived came to dominate everything, even the style. Everything fell into place in the pattern. Actions,
characters, and scenes fell naturally into pairs, or into groups of three or
four. Sometimes of course he overdid it, especially when [89] "imagination" failed and "fancy" took over. He liked to bring balance out of
apparently random arrangements, or to experiment with unbalance when
balance was too strongly expected. Leland Schubert has commented
on many of these features of Hawthorne's tales adequately so far as the
mere existence of rhythmically balanced "artistic" patterns is concerned.
What he does not adequately explore is the functional aspect of the
devices he notes. The subject contains material for a monograph; I shall
give only two examples of the sort of thing that should be looked for
in the tales.

"The Canterbury Pilgrims" is wrought in terms of duality. Everything comes in pairs. The incoming travelers balance the outgoing pair
—in circumstances as well as in the direction and intent of their journey.
The community on the hill balances the world in the valley—in its
nature as well as in its location. The incoming group of six travelers may
be divided into two groups of two and four persons, with the four
divisible into two and two: the poet and the merchant who speak first
and are united by the "likeness" Josiah sees between them; the farmer
and his wife, whose tales follow and complement each other, and their
two sleeping children. At the end of the story, when the two contrasting
groups prepare to continue each in its own direction, even the style is
affected by the strength of the controlling pattern. "The Shaker youth
and maiden," Hawthorne writes,

looked mournfully into each other's eyes. They had stepped across the
threshold of their homes, when lo! the dark array of cares and sorrows
that rose up to warn them back. The varied narratives of the strangers
had arranged themselves into a parable; they seemed not merely instances of woeful fate that had befallen others, but shadowy omens of

disappointed hope and unavailing toil, domestic grief and estranged affection, that would cloud the onward path of these poor fugitives. But after one instant's hesitation, they opened their arms, and sealed their resolve with as pure and fond an embrace as ever youthful love had hallowed.[90]

Everything here—and on through the next two paragraphs to the final sentence of the tale—is in twos: *youth* and *maiden; had but stepped* when *cares and sorrows rose;* not merely *instances* but *shadowy omens; disappointed hope* and *unavailing toil; domestic grief* and *estranged affection;* they *opened their arms* and *sealed their resolve; pure* and *fond.* Even the rhythm is a reminder of the basic dualisms in the tale. Lightly suggested in the passage I have quoted, it comes out more strongly as we move toward the final sentence: "The lovers drank at the Shaker spring, and then, with chastened hopes, but more confiding affections, went on to mingle in an untried life." At the risk of seeming to some overobvious and to others arbitrary, I shall arrange this sentence to emphasize the sound patterns as they appear to me:

The lovers drank	at the Shaker spring,
(and then)	
with chastened hopes,	but more confiding affections,
went on to mingle	in an untried life.

This sort of thing is much too common in Hawthorne to require extended comment or emphasis.* What needs to be said, and what may be said briefly since it must be obvious, is that the passage I have analyzed for its rhythm is evidence that even the sound of this tale is expressive. Rhythm, sentence structure, image and symbol, structure in its larger aspects as patterns of action and character and situation—all are subdued to the demands of the "subject," with its contrasts of the world and the spirit, pride and love, the life of full experience and the life of renunciation, pessimism [91] and optimism, despair and hope, past and future, death and life. (It is equally true, of course, to say that we do not know what this "subject" comprises until we see its various aspects grow out of the structures which embody and express them.)

If the number two permeates "The Canterbury Pilgrims," three is no

---

* Compare, for example, the ending of "Young Goodman Brown," where rhythm and euphony, including alliteration and assonance, combine to add their emotional intensities to the tale: "And when he had lived long, and was borne to his grave a hoary corpse, followed by Faith, an aged woman, and children and grandchildren, a goodly procession, besides neighbors not a few, they carved no hopeful verse upon his tombstone, for his dying hour was gloom."

less prominent in "Roger Malvin's Burial." The action, as we have seen, falls into three parts: Reuben's leaving Roger Malvin, living with the secret guilt, and returning to expiate the sin. (This may of course also be thought of as journeys in opposite directions over the same route, from and then to the place of guilt, with a pause in between, during which the effects of the wrongful departure accumulate to require the expiating return.) The characters, too, are a part of the pattern. For though there are four chief characters in all, they do not exist at the same time, so that effectively there are first one set of three, then another set of three: father-in-law to be, son-in-law to be, and wife to be; then father, wife, and son.

The persons making up the pattern change, but the pattern remains. Roger dies and Reuben becomes a father, thus taking his place in the pattern, while Cyrus moves into the place formerly occupied by Reuben. Only Dorcas does not move or develop, either in terms of this pattern or in terms of her status as a fictional character, as a person with recognizable traits. She is static because, like Rosina in "Egotism," she embodies a truth which does not change. Reuben "kills" his father-in-law, then is driven by his guilt to kill his symbolic self, his son. He develops through the stages of blindness, guilt, and redemption. But Dorcas is first and last perfect love, which knows no change.

With this triadic design dominant throughout the tale, as it is, we should not be surprised to find that the last sentence catches up all these suggestions and expresses them in one final pattern in which sound, grammar, and rational content all work together to express what is at once and [92] alternatively the "matter" and the "manner," the subject and the vehicle, the theme and the expression, of one of the great tales in the language:

His sin was expiated,—the curse was gone from him; and in the hour when he had shed blood dearer to him than his own, a prayer, the first for years, went up to Heaven from the lips of Reuben Bourne.[93]

Wakefield *

In some old magazine or newspaper I recollect a story, told as truth, of a man—let us call him Wakefield—who absented himself for a long time from his wife. The fact, thus abstractedly stated, is not very uncommon, nor—without a proper distinction of circumstances—to be condemned either as naughty or nonsensical. Howbeit, this, though far from the most aggravated, is perhaps the strangest, instance on record, of marital delinquency; and, moreover, as remarkable a freak as may be found in the whole list of human oddities. The wedded couple lived in London. The man, under pretence of going a journey, took lodgings in the next street to his own house, and there, unheard of by his wife or friends, and without the shadow of a reason for such self-banishment, dwelt upwards of twenty years. During that period, he beheld his home every day, and frequently the forlorn Mrs. Wakefield. And after so great a gap in his matrimonial felicity—when his death was reckoned certain, his estate settled, his name dismissed from memory, and his wife, long, long ago, resigned to her autumnal widowhood—he entered the door one evening, quietly, as from a day's absence, and became a loving spouse till death.

This outline is all that I remember. But the incident, though of the purest originality, unexampled, and probably never to be repeated, is one, I think, which appeals to the generous sympathies of mankind.[153] We know, each for himself, that none of us would perpetrate such a folly, yet feel as if some other might. To my own contemplations, at least, it has often recurred, always exciting wonder, but with a sense that the story must be true, and a conception of its hero's character. Whenever any subject so forcibly affects the mind, time is well spent in thinking of it. If the reader choose, let him do his own meditation; or if he prefer to ramble with me through the twenty years of Wakefield's vagary, I bid him welcome; trusting that there will be a pervading spirit and a moral, even should we fail to find them, done up neatly, and

* This story was printed in *The New England Magazine* in May, 1835. It appeared in *Twice-Told Tales* in 1837.

condensed into the final sentence. Thought has always its efficacy, and every striking incident its moral.

What sort of a man was Wakefield? We are free to shape out our own idea, and call it by his name. He was now in the meridian of life; his matrimonial affections, never violent, were sobered into a calm, habitual sentiment; of all husbands, he was likely to be the most constant, because a certain sluggishness would keep his heart at rest, wherever it might be placed. He was intellectual, but not actively so; his mind occupied itself in long and lazy musings, that ended to no purpose, or had not vigor to attain it; his thoughts were seldom so energetic as to seize hold of words. Imagination, in the proper meaning of the term, made no part of Wakefield's gifts. With a cold but not depraved nor wandering heart, and a mind never feverish with riotous thoughts, nor perplexed with originality, who could have anticipated that our friend would entitle himself to a foremost place among the doers of eccentric deeds? Had his acquaintances been asked, who was the man in London the surest to perform nothing to-day which should [154] be remembered on the morrow, they would have thought of Wakefield. Only the wife of his bosom might have hesitated. She, without having analyzed his character, was partly aware of a quiet selfishness, that had rusted into his inactive mind; of a peculiar sort of vanity, the most uneasy attribute about him; of a disposition to craft, which had seldom produced more positive effects than the keeping of petty secrets, hardly worth revealing; and, lastly, of what she called a little strangeness, sometimes, in the good man. This latter quality is indefinable, and perhaps non-existent.

Let us now imagine Wakefield bidding adieu to his wife. It is the dusk of an October evening. His equipment is a drab great-coat, a hat covered with an oilcloth, top-boots, an umbrella in one hand and a small portmanteau in the other. He has informed Mrs. Wakefield that he is to take the night coach into the country. She would fain inquire the length of his journey, its object, and the probable time of his return; but, indulgent to his harmless love of mystery, interrogates him only by a look. He tells her not to expect him positively by the return coach, nor to be alarmed should he tarry three or four days; but, at all events, to look for him at supper on Friday evening. Wakefield himself, be it considered, has no suspicion of what is before him. He holds out his hand, she gives her own, and meets his parting kiss in the matter-of-course way of a ten years' matrimony; and forth goes the middle-aged Mr. Wakefield, almost resolved to perplex his good lady by a whole week's absence. After the door has closed behind him, she perceives it thrust partly open, and a vision of her husband's face, through the aperture, smiling on her,[155] and gone in a moment. For the time, this little incident is dismissed without a thought. But, long afterwards, when she has been more years a widow than a wife, that smile recurs, and flickers across all her reminiscences of Wakefield's visage. In her many musings, she surrounds the original smile with a multitude of fantasies, which make it strange and awful: as, for instance, if she imagines him in a coffin, that parting look is frozen on his pale features; or, if she dreams of him in heaven, still his blessed spirit wears a quiet and crafty smile. Yet, for its sake, when all others have given him up for dead, she sometimes doubts whether she is a widow.

But our business is with the husband. We must hurry after him along the street, ere he lose his individuality, and melt into the great mass of London life. It would be vain searching for him there. Let us follow close at his heels, therefore, until, after several superfluous turns and doublings, we find him comfortably established by the fireside of a small apartment, previously bespoken. He is in the next street to his own, and at his journey's end. He can scarcely trust his good fortune, in having got thither unperceived—recollecting that, at one time, he was delayed by the throng, in the very focus of a lighted lantern; and, again, there were footsteps that seemed to tread behind his own, distinct from the multitudinous tramp around him; and, anon, he heard a voice shouting afar, and fancied that it called his name. Doubtless, a dozen busybodies had been watching him, and told his wife the whole affair. Poor Wakefield! Little knowest thou thine own insignificance in this great world! No mortal eye but mine has traced thee. Go quietly to thy bed, foolish man; and, on the morrow,[156] if thou wilt be wise, get thee home to good Mrs. Wakefield, and tell her the truth. Remove not thyself, even for a little week, from thy place in her chaste bosom. Were she, for a single moment, to deem thee dead, or lost, or lastingly divided from her, thou wouldst be wofully conscious of a change in thy true wife forever after. It is perilous to make a chasm in human affections; not that they gape so long and wide—but so quickly close again!

Almost repenting of his frolic, or whatever it may be termed, Wakefield lies down betimes, and starting from his first nap, spreads forth his arms into the wide and solitary waste of the unaccustomed bed. "No," —thinks he, gathering the bedclothes about him,—"I will not sleep alone another night."

In the morning he rises earlier than usual, and sets himself to consider what he really means to do. Such are his loose and rambling modes of thought that he has taken this very singular step with the consciousness of a purpose, indeed, but without being able to define it sufficiently for his own contemplation. The vagueness of the project, and the convulsive effort with which he plunges into the execution of it, are equally characteristic of a feeble-minded man. Wakefield sifts his ideas, however, as minutely as he may, and finds himself curious to know the progress of matters at home—how his exemplary wife will endure her widowhood of a week; and, briefly, how the little sphere of creatures and circumstances, in which he was a central object, will be affected by his removal. A morbid vanity, therefore, lies nearest the bottom of the affair. But, how is he to attain his ends? Not, certainly, by keeping close in this comfortable lodging, where, though he slept and awoke in the next street to his [157] home, he is as effectually abroad as if the stage-coach had been whirling him away all night. Yet, should he reappear, the whole project is knocked in the head. His poor brains being hopelessly puzzled with this dilemma, he at length ventures out, partly resolving to cross the head of the street, and send one hasty glance towards his forsaken domicile. Habit—for he is a man of habits—takes him by the hand, and guides him, wholly unaware, to his own door, where, just at the critical moment, he is aroused by the scraping of his foot upon the step. Wakefield! whither are you going?

At that instant his fate was turning on the pivot. Little dreaming of the doom to which his first backward step devotes him, he hurries away, breathless with agitation hitherto unfelt, and hardly dares turn his head at the distant corner. Can it be that nobody caught sight of him? Will not the whole household—the decent Mrs. Wakefield, the smart maid servant, and the dirty little footboy—raise a hue and cry, through London streets, in pursuit of their fugitive lord and master? Wonderful escape! He gathers courage to pause and look homeward, but is perplexed with a sense of change about the familiar edifice, such as affects us all, when, after a separation of months or years, we again see some hill or lake, or work of art, with which we were friends of old. In ordinary cases, this indescribable impression is caused by the comparison and contrast between our imperfect reminiscences and the reality. In Wakefield, the magic of a single night has wrought a similar transformation, because, in that brief period, a great moral change has been effected. But this is a secret from himself. Before leaving the spot, he catches a far and momentary [158] glimpse of his wife, passing athwart the front window, with her face turned towards the head of the street. The crafty nincompoop takes to his heels, scared with the idea that, among a thousand such atoms of mortality, her eye must have detected him. Right glad is his heart, though his brain be somewhat dizzy, when he finds himself by the coal fire of his lodgings.

So much for the commencement of this long whim-wham. After the initial conception, and the stirring up of the man's sluggish temperament to put it in practice, the whole matter evolves itself in a natural train. We may suppose him, as the result of deep deliberation, buying a new wig, of reddish hair, and selecting sundry garments, in a fashion unlike his customary suit of brown, from a Jew's old-clothes bag. It is accomplished. Wakefield is another man. The new system being now established, a retrograde movement to the old would be almost as difficult as the step that placed him in his unparalleled position. Furthermore, he is rendered obstinate by a sulkiness occasionally incident to his temper, and brought on at present by the inadequate sensation which he conceives to have been produced in the bosom of Mrs. Wakefield. He will not go back until she be frightened half to death. Well; twice or thrice has she passed before his sight, each time with a heavier step, a paler cheek, and more anxious brow; and in the third week of his non-appearance he detects a portent of evil entering the house, in the guise of an apothecary. Next day the knocker is muffled. Towards nightfall comes the chariot of a physician, and deposits its big-wigged and solemn burden at Wakefield's door, whence, after a quarter of an hour's visit, he emerges, perchance the herald of a funeral. Dear woman! Will she die? [159] By this time, Wakefield is excited to something like energy of feeling, but still lingers away from his wife's bedside, pleading with his conscience that she must not be disturbed at such a juncture. If aught else restrains him, he does not know it. In the course of a few weeks she gradually recovers; the crisis is over; her heart is sad, perhaps, but quiet; and, let him return soon or late, it will never be feverish for him again. Such ideas glimmer through the mist of Wakefield's mind, and render him indistinctly conscious that an almost impassable gulf divides his hired apartment from his former home. "It is but in the next street!" he sometimes says. Fool! it is in another world. Hitherto, he has put off his return from one particular day to another; henceforward, he leaves the precise time undetermined. Not to-morrow—probably next week—pretty soon. Poor man! The dead have nearly as much chance of revisiting their earthly homes as the self-banished Wakefield.

Would that I had a folio to write, instead of an article of a dozen pages! Then might I exemplify how an influence beyond our control lays its strong hand on every deed which we do, and weaves its consequences into an iron tissue of necessity. Wakefield is spell-bound. We must leave him, for ten years or so, to haunt around his house, without once crossing the threshold, and to be faithful to his wife, with all the affection of which his heart is capable, while he is slowly fading out of hers. Long since, it must be remarked, he had lost the perception of singularity in his conduct.

Now for a scene! Amid the throng of a London street we distinguish a man, now waxing elderly, with few characteristics to attract careless observers, yet [160] bearing, in his whole aspect, the handwriting of no common fate, for such as have the skill to read it. He is meagre; his low and narrow forehead is deeply wrinkled; his eyes, small and lustreless, sometimes wander apprehensively about him, but oftener seem to look inward. He bends his head, and moves with an indescribable obliquity of gait, as if unwilling to display his full front to the world. Watch him long enough to see what we have described, and you will allow that circumstances—which often produce remarkable men from nature's ordinary handiwork—have produced one such here. Next, leaving him to sidle along the footwalk, cast your eyes in the opposite direction, where a portly female, considerably in the wane of life, with a prayer-book in her hand, is proceeding to yonder church. She has the placid mien of settled widowhood. Her regrets have either died away, or have become so essential to her heart, that they would be poorly exchanged for joy. Just as the lean man and well-conditioned woman are passing, a slight obstruction occurs, and brings these two figures directly in contact. Their hands touch; the pressure of the crowd forces her bosom against his shoulder; they stand, face to face, staring into each other's eyes. After a ten years' separation, thus Wakefield meets his wife!

The throng eddies away, and carries them asunder. The sober widow, resuming her former pace, proceeds to church, but pauses in the portal, and throws a perplexed glance along the street. She passes in, however, opening her prayer-book as she goes. And the man! with so wild a face that busy and selfish London stands to gaze after him, he hurries to his lodgings, bolts the door, and throws himself upon the bed. The [161] latent feelings of years break out; his feeble mind acquires a brief energy from their strength; all the miserable strangeness of his life is revealed to him at a glance: and he cries out, passionately, "Wakefield! Wakefield! You are mad!"

Perhaps he was so. The singularity of his situation must have so moulded him to himself, that, considered in regard to his fellow-creatures and the business of life, he could not be said to possess his right mind.

He had contrived, or rather he had happened, to dissever himself from the world—to vanish—to give up his place and privileges with living men, without being admitted among the dead. The life of a hermit is nowise parallel to his. He was in the bustle of the city, as of old; but the crowd swept by and saw him not; he was, we may figuratively say, always beside his wife and at his hearth, yet must never feel the warmth of the one nor the affection of the other. It was Wakefield's unprecedented fate to retain his original share of human sympathies, and to be still involved in human interests, while he had lost his reciprocal influence on them. It would be a most curious speculation to trace out the effect of such circumstances on his heart and intellect, separately, and in unison. Yet, changed as he was, he would seldom be conscious of it, but deem himself the same man as ever; glimpses of the truth, indeed, would come, but only for the moment; and still he would keep saying, "I shall soon go back!"—nor reflect that he had been saying so for twenty years.

I conceive, also, that these twenty years would appear, in the retrospect, scarcely longer than the week to which Wakefield had at first limited his absence. He would look on the affair as no more than an interlude [162] in the main business of his life. When, after a little while more, he should deem it time to reënter his parlor, his wife would clap her hands for joy, on beholding the middle-aged Mr. Wakefield. Alas, what a mistake! Would Time but await the close of our favorite follies, we should be young men, all of us, and till Doomsday.

One evening, in the twentieth year since he vanished, Wakefield is taking his customary walk towards the dwelling which he still calls his own. It is a gusty night of autumn, with frequent showers that patter down upon the pavement, and are gone before a man can put up his umbrella. Pausing near the house, Wakefield discerns, through the parlor windows of the second floor, the red glow and the glimmer and fitful flash of a comfortable fire. On the ceiling appears a grotesque shadow of good Mrs. Wakefield. The cap, the nose and chin, and the broad waist, form an admirable caricature, which dances, moreover, with the up-flickering and down-sinking blaze, almost too merrily for the shade of an elderly widow. At this instant a shower chances to fall, and is driven, by the unmannerly gust, full into Wakefield's face and bosom. He is quite penetrated with its autumnal chill. Shall he stand, wet and shivering here, when his own hearth has a good fire to warm him, and his own wife will run to fetch the gray coat and small-clothes, which, doubtless, she has kept carefully in the closet of the bed chamber? No!

Wakefield is no such fool. He ascends the steps—heavily!—for twenty years have stiffened his legs since he came down—but he knows it not. Stay, Wakefield! Would you go to the sole home that is left you? Then step into your grave! The door opens. As he passes in, we have a parting [163] glimpse of his visage, and recognize the crafty smile, which was the precursor of the little joke that he has ever since been playing off at his wife's expense. How unmercifully has he quizzed the poor woman! Well, a good night's rest to Wakefield!

This happy event—supposing it to be such—could only have occurred at an unpremeditated moment. We will not follow our friend across the threshold. He has left us much food for thought, a portion of which shall lend its wisdom to a moral, and be shaped into a figure. Amid the seeming confusion of our mysterious world, individuals are so nicely adjusted to a system, and systems to one another and to a whole, that, by stepping aside for a moment, a man exposes himself to a fearful risk of losing his place forever. Like Wakefield, he may become, as it were, the Outcast of the Universe.[164]

The Moment and the Endless Voyage: A Study of Hawthorne's "Wakefield" *

The "modernity" of Hawthorne resides in the fact that he is so very old-fashioned. The opening out of the moment and the exploration of its meaning as moral adventure (which is the modernity of Henry James and James Joyce), the metaphysical translation of moral dialectic into dramatic activity (which is the modernity of Kafka) are Hawthorne's basic fictional propositions. About them agglutinate more local and extricable devices, such as symbol, similitude and emblem. It is small wonder that we have had to learn to read Joyce, James and Kafka before we could read Hawthorne. The history of his esteem has been one of consistent popularity and underestimation, which is an illustration of a literary truth, that we must be able to run before we can walk. Just as in the plastic arts we needed sophisticated imitators to teach us to feel African sculpture, so we have been a long time coming to under-

* Andrew Schiller, "The Moment and the Endless Voyage: A Study of Hawthorne's 'Wakefield,' " *Diameter*, I (March, 1951), 7–12. Reprinted by permission.

stand that in Hawthorne's work we have an ur-form of modern fiction, and in him an original.

Among the short stories, *Wakefield* is a case in point (and *My Kinsman, Major Molineux* another). That is, it is more readily intelligible to the modern reader if he reads it "as if it were Kafka." On the other hand, *Wakefield* is a type of story common to Hawthorne: a queer event expanded into a moral allegory. Hawthorne invites the reader to "do his own meditation," should he fail to find the moral "done up neatly, and condensed into the final sentence." He concludes, "Thought has always its efficacy, and every striking incident its moral."

Thematically, *Wakefield* is in the mainstream of Hawthorne's thought. It is a variation upon two familiar motifs: the isolation of man from the world, and the heartless attempt of a person to spy upon and influence the life of another. But the character of Wakefield is [7] unusual in Hawthorne. He has his relations, of varying degrees of remoteness, but that is for later discussion.

Wakefield is described as a middle-aged, sluggish man with an inactive intellect; "his mind occupied itself in long and lazy musings." He was purposeless and unimaginative, and his mind was "cold but not depraved." His wife, who knew him best, "was partly aware of a quiet selfishness, that had rusted into his inactive mind; of a peculiar sort of vanity, the most uneasy attribute about him; of a disposition to craft, which had seldom produced more positive effects than the keeping of petty secrets, hardly worth revealing; and, lastly, of what she called a little strangeness, sometimes, in the good man."

One day Wakefield bids his wife adieu, not even suspecting himself what he is about to do. As he leaves, she notices the door partially re-opened, and her husband's face smiling back through the aperture. The "quiet and crafty smile" she sees then recurs to her many times in the years to come. In that look, though its significance is obviously lost upon Mrs. Wakefield herself, is the decision to play the practical "joke"—only to pretend to leave London, and instead to take an apartment on the next street. The look bore, in short, the nature of his particular sin—his deliberate estrangement from the world.

As he hurries down the street, Hawthorne bids us follow him "ere he lose his individuality." Wakefield imagines that he has been seen and his secret betrayed. But not so. It is the irony of the situation that Wakefield does not realize the insignificance of his action in relation to the total social organism. Hawthorne comments: "It is perilous to make a chasm in human affections; not that they gape so long and wide—but so quickly close again!"

Wakefield's first reaction after going to bed in his secret apartment is an awareness of the inanity of his plan. "No—I will not sleep alone another night." But this is his last protest. The next morning he is intrigued once more by the plan. "The vagueness of the project, and the convulsive effort with which he plunges into the execution of it, are equally characteristic of a feeble-minded man." Wakefield's chief motivation at this point is a desire to observe the effect of his absence upon his wife and friends, "a morbid vanity." But how to do this without being recognized? "His poor brains being hopelessly puzzled with this dilemma," he starts walking home out of habit—"for he is a man of habits." His foot is on the doorstep; he becomes aware of where he is. "At that instant his fate was turning on the pivot. Little dreaming of the doom to which his first backward step devotes him, he hurries away. . . ." Once again, he is amazed that no one has seen him.[8]

But a great moral change has been effected overnight. He had caught a glimpse of his wife, and "the crafty nincompoop takes to his heels." He returns to his apartment and evolves a new exterior for himself, a red wig, unusual clothes. When it is done, "Wakefield is another man." His estrangement from society is now symbolically complete. By the act of assuming a mask, he has destroyed Wakefield. But has he created a new personality to take the old Wakefield's place?

The sensation Wakefield expected upon his disappearance has not materialized, and he becomes more obstinate. "He will not go back until she be frightened half to death." Shortly, however, there are signs of illness at his house; the knocker is muffled, a physician visits. "By this time, Wakefield is excited to something like energy of feeling, but still lingers away from his wife's bedside, pleading with his conscience that she must not be disturbed at such a juncture." Wakefield at this point seems to be manifesting an unconscious desire to kill his wife. He is convinced that she may die, yet he rationalizes his way out of returning.

His wife's recovery makes Wakefield "indistinctly conscious" that an "almost impassable gulf" divides him from his former life. Still, he does not comprehend that the next street has become another world, that "The dead have nearly as much chance of revisiting their earthly homes as the self-banished Wakefield."

Ten years pass, during which Wakefield haunts about his house, ever faithful to his wife, while she, ironically, is forgetting him. Then one day he sees her in a crowd going to church. In another touch of symbolism, he is a "lean man" now, and she a "well-conditioned woman." The crowd jostles them into bodily contact. "They stand, face to face, staring into each other's eyes." But she does not recognize him. They go their separate ways, Wakefield to his room where he throws himself upon his bed and cries out passionately that he is mad!

Hawthorne points out that "He had contrived, or rather he had happened, to discover himself from the world—to vanish—to give up his place and privileges with living men, without being admitted among the dead. . . . It was Wakefield's unprecedented fate to retain his original share of human sympathies, and to be still involved in human interests, while he had lost his reciprocal influence on them."

Then the final scene, twenty years after Wakefield's departure. He takes his customary walk to the house, "which he still calls his own." He is caught in a rainburst, steps for shelter into his own doorway, realizes a moment later where he is. It suddenly occurs to him that it is ridiculous for him to be standing there, wet and shivering, [9] when beyond the door are the comforts of his own home and his wife to minister to him. He enters, and on his face is the same "crafty smile."

Thus the story ends. The ending is "sensational" in a reverse manner. In cutting off the story at the very moment the dramatist would begin his favorite scene, Hawthorne conveys trickery of the-lady-or-the-tiger variety. But it should be pointed out, for the sake of cutting away an obviously unreasonable interpretation, that the ending is not an instance of a fallible sense of dramatic construction. The scene impends too obviously. That Hawthorne himself is aware of his sidestepping of the "inevitable" scene is made sufficiently clear in the last paragraph. "We will not follow our friend across the threshold. He has left us much food for thought, a portion of which shall lend its wisdom to a moral, and be shaped into a figure."

It is sufficiently clear from the story that the last scene would be gratuitous. Wakefield's fate has already been decided. There is no dramatic issue left. The structural (that is, moral) climax is elsewhere. It is the "accident," the meeting of the couple in the crowd, which brings Wakefield back into the real world, like a ghost who doesn't know he died. This is the real moment of climax. At this point it is made dramatically evident that the fortunes of Wakefield have turned irrevocably.

On one level, the story is concerned with an analysis of Wakefield's psychological inability to make a decisive move to return. Each day of absence makes his problem more insuperable. But there is no real dilemma. His return is impossible. He is caught in the "iron tissue of necessity." He has no volition whatsoever. He passes the house like a ghost, unseen—touches his wife and even exchanges a look, in which she does not recognize him. His return to the house, therefore, must of necessity be accidental, like the touch and the look, for in Hawthorne's allegorical sense Wakefield is actually not there.

It is necessary, however, to inquire further into the character of Wakefield if one is to understand this story. It is a fact that among Hawthorne's characters he is unusual, but he is not unique. He fits into none of the seven major types into which Hawthorne's male characters fall, a classification made by Randall Stewart in the Introduction to *The American Note-Books of Nathaniel Hawthorne*. On the other hand, Wakefield shares, with interesting differences, the main characteristics of several types.

The most immediate resemblance is to the character-motif of which Chillingworth is the archetype. Wakefield has committed the sin of detachment, of observing from without the workings of another [10] heart, of attempting to change the course of another life—but without sympathetic participation in it. The chief difference between the two is one of intellect. Wakefield's "feeble mind" is referred to three times. Chillingworth enters into another life maliciously, diabolically, intellectually. Wakefield detaches himself to observe, but in doing so without benefit of Chillingworth's motive power—his intellectual diabolism—he looses the tie that held him to the whirling world, and he is flung centrifugally outward forever. Hence the symbol of Wakefield getting leaner with the passing years and his wife getting stouter. For the tie that held him to the world was his wife, his home, and his small social and business circle —the tenuous everyday things that link us to the world by sheer force of custom. He breaks this centripetal force of custom and is destroyed. The artist can do it, for he has other holds—and so, for that matter, can the fiend—but the common, unintellectual man cannot. He holds to the earth as with his fingernails.

There is a dimmer kinship in the character of Wakefield to that of Kenyon and Holgrave, the archetypal impartial observers. But again, he is unlike them in that he is not, nor cannot be involved in the world in which he nominally exists. Wakefield, neither alive nor dead, is in a state of social limbo. His purgation is to be tormented by the life around him, of which he cannot partake, to be suspended between the states of perception and non-perception. He is physically in the world, but though it affects him he can no longer affect it. Ironically, he learns to apprehend the world emotionally, but only after he can no longer have it.

Looking at it still another way, we might consider Wakefield as a further commentary on the mythic American type of successful man (though this story ingenuously takes place in London). As such, Wakefield

116   HYATT H. WAGGONER

is the end-product of a Culture Hero, the Yankee Peddler become Babbitt. He is, in short, Dominicus Pike come to middle age, now the man of commerce, of the city, settled and established. But the necessary act of eager embrace of the workaday world by which Pike transforms himself into a Wakefield entails also an inevitable price. In *Mr. Higginbotham's Catastrophe* we see the first signs of the deterioration of the shrewd humor of Dominicus Pike—the beginning of the process of payment. Humor, after all, demands perspective, some point of view removed from the object. When the humorist accepts the object to the extent of identifying himself with it he undermines, by that act, his power to see humorously. In Wakefield, Hawthorne gives us a man who has paid the price in full. All that is left of a sense of humor in him has been debased to a sly craftiness.

In this light, Wakefield becomes a kind of *reductio ad absurdum* of [11] the shrewd, hardheaded businessman of the world who, devoid of the ability to enter empathetically into other human lives, plays an insensitive and ultimately cruel practical joke. The sense of humor of Dominicus Pike is a vestigial stump which, the sense of empathy lacking, is in Wakefield the specific instrument of his cruelty.

But the final joke is on Wakefield. While thinking that he had absented himself from the world, the world took its leave of him. The basic volition was not his, but that of his environment. It was his intention to absent himself for a short period, but he did not know that a moment is as much as forever.[12]

"Wakefield": The Story Is the Meaning *

. . . It is truer to say that Hawthorne's stories are fictional thinking—or processes of insight conceived and structured in narrative terms—than it is to say that the narratives *originate* in thoughts, ideas, or insights. The Notebooks have misled many into conceiving of the tales as though

* Reprinted by permission of the publishers from Hyatt H. Waggoner, *Hawthorne: A Critical Study*, Cambridge, Mass.: The Belknap Press of Harvard University Press, Copyright, 1955, by the President and Fellows of Harvard College. The title used here is the present editor's.

they were clothes draped loosely over already created skeletons of abstract thought. But of all the Notebooks jottings that Hawthorne used in existing stories, I know of none that can serve as an even approximately adequate statement of the meaning of the story to which it finally led, or in which it got embodied.

If this were not so, we should be able to measure the conceptual value of Hawthorne's tales by applying a yardstick—subjective, presumably—to the value of his "philosophy," his ideas as he expressed them outside his tales, for example in his Notebooks. But when we do so, we find—by my yardstick, at least, and it is applied sympathetically—that Hawthorne's thinking outside his tales is much less impressive than his thinking in his tales. It is, to be sure, instinct with the realism that made him unable to read Emerson or Emerson him. It is attractive in the quality of absolute honesty that shines through it, and the shrewdness that so often deflated the pompous and redefined the stereotyped. But still I suppose the most sympathetic commentator would not claim for Hawthorne a place among the world's—or even America's—great philosophers or "thinkers." Yet his tales are generally held to be among America's great short stories, and their greatness has been conceived by nearly all critics to be a product of their depth and complexity of meaning.

One way of resolving this seeming paradox is to recall Hawthorne's words, already quoted, on what he had hoped to accomplish in his English romance. In his fiction, he said, he could apprehend "more of various modes of truth" than he could grasp by "direct effort." What we have to recognize [62] is that in some sense the story *is* the meaning, and the meaning the story. Sometimes this is very clear, indeed almost obvious when we stop to think of it, even if we are not used to thinking in terms of the critical concept of embodiment. "Wakefield," for example, which is in some of the most important respects typical of Hawthorne's procedure (though a failure of development, a failure of creative energy, keeps it from being one of the great tales) begins like this:

> In some old magazine or newspaper I recollect a story, told as truth, of a man—let us call him Wakefield—who absented himself for a long time from his wife. The fact, thus abstractly stated, is not very uncommon, nor—without a proper distinction of circumstances—to be condemned either as naughty or nonsensical.

The fact "thus abstractly stated" is not meaningful, though it is the starting point of the story, the stimulus, in contact with Hawthorne's sensibility, to meaning. But the tale that Hawthorne developed from it has all kinds of meanings, including some that Hawthorne tried to state for us. It means, among other things, what Hawthorne said abstractly in his final sentences, though we shall not fully understand these words unless we know their context:

> Amid the seeming confusion of our mysterious world, individuals are so nicely adjusted to a system, and systems to one another and to a whole, that, by stepping aside for a moment, a man exposes himself to a fearful risk of losing his place forever. Like Wakefield, he may become, as it were, the Outcast of the Universe.

It means, then, that we must not break what Hawthorne called in "Ethan Brand" the "magnetic chain" of organic relationships that bind us to society. Or it means that individualistic isolation, complete independence if you will, is possible only at the price of death. Or it means that our lives are only partially under our control, so that we are not the masters of our fate, the captains of our souls. Hawthorne interrupts his tale at one point to express his wish that he might "exemplify how an influence beyond our control lays [63] its strong hand on every deed which we do, and weaves its consequences into an iron tissue of necessity." The tale "means" all these things, and more.

And these meanings which it has are discovered, as Hawthorne makes clear in his introductory paragraphs, in the course and structure of the tale itself—discovered by Hawthorne as well as by the reader. Hawthorne's own words should be quoted at this point:

> This outline is all that I remember. But the incident, though of the purest originality, unexampled, and probably never to be repeated, is one, I think, which appeals to the generous sympathies of mankind. We know, each for himself, that none of us would perpetrate such a folly, yet feel as if some other might. To my own contemplations, at least, it has often recurred, always exciting wonder, but with a sense that the story must be true, and a conception of its hero's character. Whenever any subject so forcibly affects the mind, time is well spent in thinking of it. If the reader choose, let him do his own meditation; or if he prefer to ramble with me through the twenty years of Wakefield's vagary, I bid him welcome; trusting that there will be a pervading spirit and a moral, even should we fail to find them, done up neatly, and condensed into the final sentence. Thought has always its efficacy, and every striking incident its moral.

In "The Canterbury Pilgrims" and "Roger Malvin's Burial" Hawthorne did not even attempt to abstract and condense the moral "neatly" in the final sentences, but they are stories in which everything is dominated by what we may call their "moral meaning." They will serve better than some of the more famous tales—partly because we can approach them with fewer preconceptions—to illustrate the kind of "efficacy" which "thought" has in Hawthorne, and the way in which the "moral" is discovered through the "incident." [64]

. . . . .

Hawthorne's weaker tales make it clear that the danger he constantly faced was that he would over-intellectualize his material. "Wakefield" carries too great a burden of thought for so slight a framework: what stimulated Hawthorne here was the initial situation of a man who willfully isolates himself.[86] Between Wakefield's departure from his wife and his return, Hawthorne merely summarizes the actions of twenty years. The story never expands much beyond anecdote.

"The Canterbury Pilgrims" is stronger, I think—though that has not been the usual opinion, if we may judge by frequency of inclusion in the anthologies. In it we have more immediacy, more life, more concreteness. Even so the characters are rather abstractly conceived: the romantic young couple, the vain little poet, the embittered merchant, the defeated farm couple. These are descendants of the Virtues and the Vices of the medieval morality plays. Josiah is Everyman, young and in love and wondering whether his dreams will be fulfilled. With "The Christmas Banquet," "The Man of Adamant," "The Great Carbuncle," "Lady Eleanor's Mantle," and a half dozen or so others, "The Canterbury Pilgrims" seems almost to justify the description of Hawthorne as an allegorist.

Yet even in these tales there is a significant difference between Hawthorne's practice and allegory as we see it in Spenser and Bunyan. Hawthorne does not start with a wholly preconceived, an abstract and external, set of meanings and then embody them, even in his most allegorical tales. We may say that a system of values and beliefs such as Bunyan knew was not available to him; or at any rate, that he could not accept whatever was available. But whatever explanation we may give of the fact, the fact remains that Hawthorne's "allegories" are more subjective, more complex, and more ambiguous than anything in *Pilgrim's Progress* or *The Faerie Queene*. If these tales are allegory, they are allegory in a new mode, a mode which it might be less misleading to call a highly intellectualized form of symbolism.

. . . . . [87]

The Gentle Boy *

In the course of the year 1656, several of the people called Quakers, led, as they professed, by the inward movement of the spirit, made their appearance in New England. Their reputation, as holders of mystic and pernicious principles, having spread before them, the Puritans early endeavored to banish, and to prevent the further intrusion of the rising sect. But the measures by which it was intended to purge the land of heresy, though more than sufficiently vigorous, were entirely unsuccessful. The Quakers, esteeming persecution as a divine call to the post of danger, laid claim to a holy courage, unknown to the Puritans themselves, who had shunned the cross, by providing for the peaceable exercise of their religion in a distant wilderness. Though it was the singular fact, that every nation of the earth rejected the wandering enthusiasts who practised peace towards all men, the place of greatest uneasiness and peril, and therefore, in their eyes the most eligible, was the province of Massachusetts Bay.

The fines, imprisonments, and stripes, liberally distributed by our pious forefathers; the popular antipathy, so strong that it endured nearly a hundred years after actual persecution had ceased, were attractions as powerful for the Quakers, as peace, honor, and reward, would have been for the worldly minded. Every European vessel brought new cargoes of the sect, eager to testify against the oppression which they hoped to [85] share; and when shipmasters were restrained by heavy fines from affording them passage, they made long and circuitous journeys through the Indian country, and appeared in the province as if conveyed by a supernatural power. Their enthusiasm, heightened almost to madness by the treatment which they received, produced actions contrary to the rules of decency, as well as of rational religion, and presented a singular contrast to the calm and staid deportment of their sectarian successors of the present day. The command of the spirit, inaudible

* This story appeared in *The Token* in 1832. Hawthorne later revised it and printed it in *Twice-Told Tales* in 1837. This *Casebook* follows the revised version.

except to the soul, and not to be controverted on grounds of human wisdom, was made a plea for most indecorous exhibitions, which, abstractedly considered, well deserved the moderate chastisement of the rod. These extravagances, and the persecution which was at once their cause and consequence, continued to increase, till, in the year 1659, the government of Massachusetts Bay indulged two members of the Quaker sect with the crown of martyrdom.

An indelible stain of blood is upon the hands of all who consented to this act, but a large share of the awful responsibility must rest upon the person then at the head of the government. He was a man of narrow mind and imperfect education, and his uncompromising bigotry was made hot and mischievous by violent and hasty passions; he exerted his influence indecorously and unjustifiably to compass the death of the enthusiasts; and his whole conduct, in respect to them, was marked by brutal cruelty. The Quakers, whose revengeful feelings were not less deep because they were inactive, remembered this man and his associates in after times. The historian of the sect affirms that, by the wrath of Heaven, a blight fell upon the land in [86] the vicinity of the "bloody town" of Boston, so that no wheat would grow there; and he takes his stand, as it were, among the graves of the ancient persecutors, and triumphantly recounts the judgments that overtook them, in old age or at the parting hour. He tells us that they died suddenly and violently and in madness; but nothing can exceed the bitter mockery with which he records the loathsome disease, and "death by rottenness," of the fierce and cruel governor.

On the evening of the autumn day that had witnessed the martyrdom of two men of the Quaker persuasion, a Puritan settler was returning from the metropolis to the neighboring country town in which he resided. The air was cool, the sky clear, and the lingering twilight was made brighter by the rays of a young moon, which had now nearly reached the verge of the horizon. The traveller, a man of middle age, wrapped in a gray frieze cloak, quickened his pace when he had reached the outskirts of the town, for a gloomy extent of nearly four miles lay between him and his home. The low, straw-thatched houses were scattered at considerable intervals along the road, and the country having been settled but about thirty years, the tracts of original forest still bore no small proportion to the cultivated ground. The autumn wind wandered among the branches, whirling away the leaves from all except the pine-trees, and moaning as if it lamented the desolation of which it was the instrument. The road had penetrated the mass of woods that lay nearest to the town, and was just emerging into an open space, when the traveller's ears were saluted by a sound more mournful than even [87] that of the wind. It was like the wailing of some one in distress, and it seemed to proceed from beneath a tall and lonely fir-tree, in the centre of a cleared but uninclosed and uncultivated field. The Puritan could not but remember that this was the very spot which had been made accursed a few hours before by the execution of the Quakers, whose bodies had been thrown together into one hasty grave, beneath the tree on which they suffered. He struggled, however, against the superstitious fears which belonged to the age, and compelled himself to pause and listen.

"The voice is most likely mortal, nor have I cause to tremble if it be otherwise," thought he, straining his eyes through the dim moonlight. "Methinks it is like the wailing of a child; some infant, it may be, which has strayed from its mother, and chanced upon this place of death. For the ease of mine own conscience I must search this matter out."

He therefore left the path, and walked somewhat fearfully across the field. Though now so desolate, its soil was pressed down and trampled by the thousand footsteps of those who had witnessed the spectacle of that day, all of whom had now retired, leaving the dead to their loneliness. The traveller at length reached the fir-tree, which from the middle upward was covered with living branches, although a scaffold had been erected beneath, and other preparations made for the work of death. Under this unhappy tree, which in after times was believed to drop poison with its dew, sat the one solitary mourner for innocent blood. It was a slender and light clad little boy, who leaned his face upon a hillock of fresh-turned and half-frozen earth, and wailed bitterly, yet in a suppressed tone, as if his grief might receive the punishment [88] of crime. The Puritan, whose approach had been unperceived, laid his hand upon the child's shoulder, and addressed him compassionately.

"You have chosen a dreary lodging, my poor boy, and no wonder that you weep," said he. "But dry your eyes, and tell me where your mother dwells. I promise you, if the journey be not too far, I will leave you in her arms to-night."

The boy had hushed his wailing at once, and turned his face upward to the stranger. It was a pale, bright-eyed countenance, certainly not more than six years old, but sorrow, fear, and want had destroyed much of its infantile expression. The Puritan seeing the boy's frightened gaze, and feeling that he trembled under his hand, endeavored to reassure him.

"Nay, if I intended to do you harm, little lad, the readiest way were to leave you here. What! you do not fear to sit beneath the gallows on a new-made grave, and yet you tremble at a friend's touch. Take heart, child, and tell me what is your name and where is your home?"

"Friend," replied the little boy, in a sweet though faltering voice, "they call me Ilbrahim, and my home is here."

The pale, spiritual face, the eyes that seemed to mingle with the moonlight, the sweet, airy voice, and the outlandish name, almost made the Puritan believe that the boy was in truth a being which had sprung up out of the grave on which he sat. But perceiving that the apparition stood the test of a short mental prayer, and remembering that the arm which he had touched was lifelike, he adopted a more rational supposition. "The poor child is stricken in his intellect," thought he, "but verily his words are fearful in a [89] place like this." He then spoke soothingly, intending to humor the boy's fantasy.

"Your home will scarce be comfortable, Ilbrahim, this cold autumn night, and I fear you are ill-provided with food. I am hastening to a warm supper and bed, and if you will go with me you shall share them!"

"I thank thee, friend, but though I be hungry, and shivering with cold, thou wilt not give me food nor lodging," replied the boy, in the quiet tone which despair had taught him, even so young. "My father was of the people whom all men hate. They have laid him under this heap of earth, and here is my home."

The Puritan, who had laid hold of little Ilbrahim's hand, relinquished it as if he were touching a loathsome reptile. But he possessed a compassionate heart, which not even religious prejudice could harden into stone.

"God forbid that I should leave this child to perish, though he comes of the accursed sect," said he to himself. "Do we not all spring from an evil root? Are we not all in darkness till the light doth shine upon us? He shall not perish, neither in body, nor, if prayer and instruction may avail for him, in soul." He then spoke aloud and kindly to Ilbrahim, who had again hid his face in the cold earth of the grave. "Was every door in the land shut against you, my child, that you have wandered to this unhallowed spot?"

"They drove me forth from the prison when they took my father thence," said the boy, "and I stood afar off watching the crowd of people, and when they were gone I came hither, and found only his grave. I knew that my father was sleeping here, and I said this shall be my home." [90]

"No, child, no; not while I have a roof over my head, or a morsel to share with you!" exclaimed the Puritan, whose sympathies were now fully excited. "Rise up and come with me, and fear not any harm."

The boy wept afresh, and clung to the heap of earth as if the cold heart beneath it were warmer to him than any in a living breast. The traveller, however, continued to entreat him tenderly, and seeming to acquire some degree of confidence, he at length arose. But his slender limbs tottered with weakness, his little head grew dizzy, and he leaned against the tree of death for support.

"My poor boy, are you so feeble?" said the Puritan. "When did you taste food last?"

"I ate of bread and water with my father in the prison," replied Ilbrahim, "but they brought him none neither yesterday nor to-day, saying that he had eaten enough to bear him to his journey's end. Trouble not thyself for my hunger, kind friend, for I have lacked food many times ere now."

The traveller took the child in his arms and wrapped his cloak about him, while his heart stirred with shame and anger against the gratuitous cruelty of the instruments in this persecution. In the awakened warmth of his feelings he resolved that, at whatever risk, he would not forsake the poor little defenceless being whom Heaven had confided to his care. With this determination he left the accursed field, and resumed the homeward path from which the wailing of the boy had called him. The light and motionless burden scarcely impeded his progress, and he soon beheld the fire rays from the windows of the cottage which he, a native of a distant clime, had built in the western wilderness. It was surrounded by a considerable extent [91] of cultivated ground, and the dwelling was situated in the nook of a wood-covered hill, whither it seemed to have crept for protection.

"Look up, child," said the Puritan to Ilbrahim, whose faint head had sunk upon his shoulder, "there is our home."

At the word "home," a thrill passed through the child's frame, but he continued silent. A few moments brought them to a cottage door, at which the owner knocked; for at that early period, when savages were wandering everywhere among the settlers, bolt and bar were indispensable to the security of a dwelling. The summons was answered by a bond-servant, a coarse-clad and dull-featured piece of humanity, who, after ascertaining that his master was the applicant, undid the door, and held a flaring pine-knot torch to light him in. Farther back in the passage-way, the red blaze discovered a matronly woman, but no little crowd of children came bounding forth to greet their father's return. As the Puritan entered, he thrust aside his cloak, and displayed Ilbrahim's face to the female.

"Dorothy, here is a little outcast, whom Providence hath put into our hands," observed he. "Be kind to him, even as if he were of those dear ones who have departed from us."

"What pale and bright-eyed little boy is this, Tobias?" she inquired. "Is he one whom the wilderness folk have ravished from some Christian mother?"

"No, Dorothy, this poor child is no captive from the wilderness," he replied. "The heathen savage would have given him to eat of his scanty morsel, and to drink of his birchen cup; but Christian men, alas! had cast him out to die." [92]

Then he told her how he had found him beneath the gallows, upon his father's grave; and how his heart had prompted him, like the speaking of an inward voice, to take the little outcast home, and be kind unto him. He acknowledged his resolution to feed and clothe him, as if he were his own child, and to afford him the instruction which should counteract the pernicious errors hitherto instilled into his infant mind. Dorothy was gifted with even a quicker tenderness than her husband, and she approved of all his doings and intentions.

"Have you a mother, dear child?" she inquired.

The tears burst forth from his full heart, as he attempted to reply; but Dorothy at length understood that he had a mother, who, like the rest of her sect, was a persecuted wanderer. She had been taken from the prison a short time before, carried into the uninhabited wilderness, and left to perish there by hunger or wild beasts. This was no uncommon method of disposing of the Quakers, and they were accustomed to boast that the inhabitants of the desert were more hospitable to them than civilized man.

"Fear not, little boy, you shall not need a mother, and a kind one," said Dorothy, when she had gathered this information. "Dry your tears, Ilbrahim, and be my child, as I will be your mother."

The good woman prepared the little bed, from which her own children had successively been borne to another resting-place. Before Ilbrahim would consent to occupy it, he knelt down, and as Dorothy listened to his simple and affecting prayer, she marvelled how the parents that had taught it to him could have been judged worthy of death. When the boy had fallen asleep, she bent over his pale and spiritual countenance,[93] pressed a kiss upon his white brow, drew the bedclothes up about his neck, and went away with a pensive gladness in her heart.

Tobias Pearson was not among the earliest emigrants from the old country. He had remained in England during the first years of the civil war, in which he had borne some share as a cornet of dragoons, under Cromwell. But when the ambitious designs of his leader began to develop themselves, he quitted the army of the Parliament, and sought a refuge from the strife, which was no longer holy, among the people of his persuasion in the colony of Massachusetts. A more worldly consideration had perhaps an influence in drawing him thither; for New England offered advantages to men of unprosperous fortunes, as well as to dissatisfied religionists, and Pearson had hitherto found it difficult to provide for a wife and increasing family. To this supposed impurity of motive the more bigoted Puritans were inclined to impute the removal by death of all the children, for whose earthly good the father had been overthoughtful. They had left their native country blooming like roses, and like roses they had perished in a foreign soil. Those expounders of the ways of Providence, who had thus judged their brother, and attributed his domestic sorrows to his sin, were not more charitable when they saw him and Dorothy endeavoring to fill up the void in their hearts by the adoption of an infant of the accursed sect. Nor did they fail to communicate their disapprobation to Tobias; but the latter, in reply, merely pointed at the little, quiet, lovely boy, whose appearance and deportment were indeed as powerful arguments as could possibly have been adduced in his own favor. Even his beauty, however, and his [94] winning manners, sometimes produced an effect ultimately unfavorable; for the bigots, when the outer surfaces of their iron hearts had been softened and again grew hard, affirmed that no merely natural cause could have so worked upon them.

Their antipathy to the poor infant was also increased by the ill success of divers theological discussions, in which it was attempted to convince him of the errors of his sect. Ilbrahim, it is true, was not a skilful controversialist; but the feeling of his religion was strong as instinct in him, and he could neither be enticed nor driven from the faith which his father had died for. The odium of this stubbornness was shared in a great measure by the child's protectors, insomuch that Tobias and Dorothy very shortly began to experience a most bitter species of persecution, in the cold regards of many a friend whom they had valued. The common people manifested their opinions more openly. Pearson was a man of some consideration, being a representative to the General Court, and an approved lieutenant in the trainbands, yet within a week after his adoption of Ilbrahim he had been both hissed and hooted. Once, also, when walking through a solitary piece of woods, he heard a loud voice from some invisible speaker; and it cried, "What shall be done to the backslider? Lo! the scourge is knotted for him, even the whip of nine cords, and every cord three knots!" These insults irritated Pearson's temper for the moment; they entered also into his heart, and became imperceptible but powerful workers towards an end which his most secret thought had not yet whispered.

On the second Sabbath after Ilbrahim became a [95] member of their family, Pearson and his wife deemed it proper that he should appear with them at public worship. They had anticipated some opposition to this measure from the boy, but he prepared himself in silence, and at the appointed hour was clad in the new mourning suit which Dorothy had wrought for him. As the parish was then, and during many subsequent years, unprovided with a bell, the signal for the commencement of religious exercises was the beat of a drum. At the first sound of that martial call to the place of holy and quiet thoughts, Tobias and Dorothy set forth, each holding a hand of little Ilbrahim, like two parents linked together by the infant of their love. On their path through the leafless woods they were overtaken by many persons of their acquaintance, all of whom avoided them, and passed by on the other side; but a severer trial awaited their constancy when they had descended the hill, and drew near the pine-built and undecorated house of prayer. Around the door, from which the drummer still sent forth his thundering summons, was drawn up a formidable phalanx, including several of the oldest members of the congregation, many of the middle aged, and nearly all the younger males. Pearson found it difficult to sustain their united and disapproving gaze, but Dorothy, whose mind was differently circumstanced, merely drew the boy closer to her, and faltered not in her approach. As they entered the door, they overheard the muttered sentiments of the assemblage, and when the reviling voices of the little children smote Ilbrahim's ear, he wept.

The interior aspect of the meeting-house was rude. The low ceiling, the unplastered walls, the naked wood work, and the undraperied pulpit, offered nothing [96] to excite the devotion, which, without such external aids, often remains latent in the heart. The floor of the building was occupied by rows of long, cushionless benches, supplying the place of pews, and the broad aisle formed a sexual division, impassable except by children beneath a certain age.

Pearson and Dorothy separated at the door of the meeting-house, and

Ilbrahim, being within the years of infancy, was retained under the care of the latter. The wrinkled beldams involved themselves in their rusty cloaks as he passed by; even the mild-featured maidens seemed to dread contamination; and many a stern old man arose, and turned his repulsive and unheavenly countenance upon the gentle boy, as if the sanctuary were polluted by his presence. He was a sweet infant of the skies that had strayed away from his home, and all the inhabitants of this miserable world closed up their impure hearts against him, drew back their earth-soiled garments from his touch, and said, "We are holier than thou."

Ilbrahim, seated by the side of his adopted mother, and retaining fast hold of her hand, assumed a grave and decorous demeanor, such as might befit a person of matured taste and understanding, who should find himself in a temple dedicated to some worship which he did not recognize, but felt himself bound to respect. The excercises had not yet commenced, however, when the boy's attention was arrested by an event, apparently of trifling interest. A woman, having her face muffled in a hood, and a cloak drawn completely about her form, advanced slowly up the broad aisle and took a place upon the foremost bench. Ilbrahim's faint color varied, his nerves fluttered, he was unable to turn his eyes from the muffled female.[97]

When the preliminary prayer and hymn were over, the minister arose, and having turned the hour-glass which stood by the great Bible, commenced his discourse. He was now well stricken in years, a man of pale, thin countenance, and his gray hairs were closely covered by a black velvet skullcap. In his younger days he had practically learned the meaning of persecution from Archbishop Laud, and he was not now disposed to forget the lesson against which he had murmured then. Introducing the often discussed subject of the Quakers, he gave a history of that sect, and a description of their tenets, in which error predominated, and prejudice distorted the aspect of what was true. He adverted to the recent measures in the province, and cautioned his hearers of weaker parts against calling in question the just severity which God-fearing magistrates had at length been compelled to exercise. He spoke of the danger of pity, in some cases a commendable and Christian virtue, but inapplicable to this pernicious sect. He observed that such was their devilish obstinacy in error, that even the little children, the sucking babes, were hardened and desperate heretics. He affirmed that no man, without Heaven's especial warrant, should attempt their conversion, lest while he lent his hand to draw them from the slough, he should himself be precipitated into its lowest depths.

The sands of the second hour were principally in the lower half of the glass when the sermon concluded. An approving murmur followed, and the clergyman, having given out a hymn, took his seat with much self-congratulation, and endeavored to read the effect of his eloquence in the visages of the people. But while voices from all parts of the house were tuning [98] themselves to sing, a scene occurred, which, though not very unusual at that period in the province, happened to be without precedent in this parish.

The muffled female, who had hitherto sat motionless in the front rank of the audience, now arose, and with slow, stately, and unwavering step, ascended the pulpit stairs. The quiverings of incipient harmony were hushed, and the divine sat in speechless and almost terrified astonishment, while she undid the door, and stood up in the sacred desk from which his maledictions had just been thundered. She then divested herself of the cloak and hood, and appeared in a most singular array. A shapeless robe of sackcloth was girded about her waist with a knotted cord; her raven hair fell down upon her shoulders, and its blackness was defiled by pale streaks of ashes, which she had strown upon her head. Her eyebrows, dark and strongly defined, added to the deathly whiteness of a countenance, which, emaciated with want, and wild with enthusiasm and strange sorrows, retained no trace of earlier beauty. This figure stood gazing earnestly on the audience, and there was no sound, nor any movement, except a faint shuddering which every man observed in his neighbor, but was scarcely conscious of in himself. At length, when her fit of inspiration came, she spoke, for the first few moments, in a low voice, and not invariably distinct utterance. Her discourse gave evidence of an imagination hope-lessly entangled with her reason; it was a vague and incomprehensible rhapsody, which, however, seemed to spread its own atmosphere round the hearer's soul, and to move his feelings by some influence uncon-nected with the words. As she proceeded, beautiful but shadowy images would sometimes be seen, like [99] bright things moving in a turbid river; or a strong and singularly-shaped idea leaped forth, and seized at once on the understanding or the heart. But the course of her unearthly eloquence soon led her to the persecutions of her sect, and from thence the step was short to her own peculiar sorrows. She was naturally a woman of mighty passions, and hatred and revenge now wrapped themselves in the garb of piety; the character of her speech was changed, her images became distinct though wild, and her denunciations had an almost hellish bitter-ness.

"The Governor and his mighty men," she said, "have gathered together, taking counsel among themselves and saying, 'What shall we do unto this people—even unto the people that have come into this land to put our iniquity to the blush?' And lo! the devil entereth into the council chamber, like a lame man of low stature and gravely apparelled, with a dark and twisted countenance, and a bright, downcast eye. And he standeth up among the rulers; yea, he goeth to and fro, whispering to each; and every man lends his ear, for his word is 'Slay, slay!' But I say unto ye, Woe to them that slay! Woe to them that shed the blood of saints! Woe to them that have slain the husband, and cast forth the child, the tender infant, to wander homeless and hungry and cold, till he die; and have saved the mother alive, in the cruelty of their tender mercies! Woe to them in their lifetime! cursed are they in the delight and pleasure of their hearts! Woe to them in their death hour, whether it come swiftly with blood and violence, or after long and lingering pain! Woe, in the dark house, in the rottenness of the grave, when the children's children shall revile the ashes of the fathers! Woe, woe, woe, at [100] the judgment, when all the persecuted and all the slain in this bloody land, and the father, the mother, and the child, shall await them in a day that they cannot escape! Seed of the faith, seed of the faith, ye whose hearts are moving with a power that ye know not, arise, wash your hands of this innocent blood! Lift your voices, chosen ones; cry aloud, and call down a woe and a judgment with me!"

Having thus given vent to the flood of malignity which she mistook for inspiration, the speaker was silent. Her voice was succeeded by the hysteric shrieks of several women, but the feelings of the audience generally had not been drawn onward in the current with her own. They remained stupefied, stranded as it were, in the midst of a torrent, which deafened them by its roaring, but might not move them by its violence. The clergyman, who could not hitherto have ejected the usurper of his pulpit otherwise than by bodily force, now addressed her in the tone of just indignation and legitimate authority.

"Get you down, woman, from the holy place which you profane," he said. "Is it to the Lord's house that you come to pour forth the foulness of your heart and the inspiration of the devil? Get you down, and remember that the sentence of death is on you; yea, and shall be executed, were it but for this day's work!"

"I go, friend, I go, for the voice hath had its utterance," replied she, in a depressed and even mild tone. "I have done my mission unto thee and to thy people. Reward me with stripes, imprisonment, or death, as ye shall be permitted."

The weakness of exhausted passion caused her steps to totter as she descended the pulpit stairs. The people,[101] in the mean while, were stirring to and fro on the floor of the house, whispering among themselves, and glancing towards the intruder. Many of them now recognized her as the woman who had assaulted the Governor with frightful language as he passed by the window of her prison; they knew, also, that she was adjudged to suffer death, and had been preserved only by an involuntary banishment into the wilderness. The new outrage, by which she had provoked her fate, seemed to render further lenity impossible; and a gentleman in military dress, with a stout man of inferior rank, drew towards the door of the meeting-house, and awaited her approach.

Scarcely did her feet press the floor, however, when an unexpected scene occurred. In that moment of her peril, when every eye frowned with death, a little timid boy pressed forth, and threw his arms around his mother.

"I am here, mother; it is I, and I will go with thee to prison," he exclaimed.

She gazed at him with a doubtful and almost frightened expression, for she knew that the boy had been cast out to perish, and she had not hoped to see his face again. She feared, perhaps, that it was but one of the happy visions with which her excited fancy had often deceived her, in the solitude of the desert or in prison. But when she felt his hand warm within her own, and heard his little eloquence of childish love, she began to know that she was yet a mother.

"Blessed art thou, my son," she sobbed. "My heart was withered; yea, dead with thee and with thy father; and now it leaps as in the first moment when I pressed thee to my bosom."

She knelt down and embraced him again and again,[102] while the joy that could find no words expressed itself in broken accents, like the bubbles gushing up to vanish at the surface of a deep fountain. The sorrows of past years, and the darker peril that was nigh, cast not a shadow on the brightness of that fleeting moment. Soon, however, the spectators saw a change upon her face, as the consciousness of her sad estate returned, and grief supplied the fount of tears which joy had opened. By the words she uttered, it would seem that the indulgence of natural love had given her mind a momentary sense of its errors, and made her know how far she had strayed from duty in following the dictates of a wild fanaticism.

"In a doleful hour art thou returned to me, poor boy," she said, "for thy mother's path has gone darkening onward, till now the end is death.

Son, son, I have borne thee in my arms when my limbs were tottering, and I have fed thee with the food that I was fainting for; yet I have ill performed a mother's part by thee in life, and now I leave thee no inheritance but woe and shame. Thou wilt go seeking through the world, and find all hearts closed against thee and their sweet affections turned to bitterness for my sake. My child, my child, how many a pang awaits thy gentle spirit, and I the cause of all!"

She hid her face on Ilbrahim's head, and her long, raven hair, discolored with the ashes of her mourning, fell down about him like a veil. A low and interrupted moan was the voice of her heart's anguish, and it did not fail to move the sympathies of many who mistook their involuntary virtue for a sin. Sobs were audible in the female section of the house, and every man who was a father drew his hand across his eyes. Tobias Pearson was agitated and uneasy, but a certain [103] feeling like the consciousness of guilt oppressed him, so that he could not go forth and offer himself as the protector of the child. Dorothy, however, had watched her husband's eye. Her mind was free from the influence that had begun to work on his, and she drew near the Quaker woman, and addressed her in the hearing of all the congregation.

"Stranger, trust this boy to me, and I will be his mother," she said, taking Ilbrahim's hand. "Providence has signally marked out my husband to protect him, and he has fed at our table and lodged under our roof now many days, till our hearts have grown very strongly unto him. Leave the tender child with us, and be at ease concerning his welfare."

The Quaker rose from the ground, but drew the boy closer to her, while she gazed earnestly in Dorothy's face. Her mild but saddened features, and neat matronly attire, harmonized together, and were like a verse of fireside poetry. Her very aspect proved that she was blameless, so far as mortal could be so, in respect to God and man; while the enthusiast, in her robe of sackcloth and girdle of knotted cord, had as evidently violated the duties of the present life and the future, by fixing her attention wholly on the latter. The two females, as they held each a hand of Ilbrahim, formed a practical allegory; it was rational piety and unbridled fanaticism contending for the empire of a young heart.

"Thou art not of our people," said the Quaker, mournfully.

"No, we are not of your people," replied Dorothy, with mildness, "but we are Christians, looking upward to the same heaven with you. Doubt not that your boy shall meet you there, if there be a blessing [104] on our tender and prayerful guidance of him. Thither, I trust, my own children have gone before me, for I also have been a mother; I am no longer so," she added, in a faltering tone, "and your son will have all my care."

"But will ye lead him in the path which his parents have trodden?" demanded the Quaker. "Can ye teach him the enlightened faith which his father has died for, and for which I, even I, am soon to become an unworthy martyr? The boy has been baptized in blood; will ye keep the mark fresh and ruddy upon his forehead?"

"I will not deceive you," answered Dorothy. "If your child become our child, we must breed him up in the instruction which Heaven has imparted to us; we must pray for him the prayers of our own faith; we must do towards him according to the dictates of our own consciences, and not of yours. Were we to act otherwise, we should abuse your trust, even in complying with your wishes."

The mother looked down upon her boy with a troubled countenance, and then turned her eyes upward to heaven. She seemed to pray internally, and the contention of her soul was evident.

"Friend," she said at length to Dorothy, "I doubt not that my son shall receive all earthly tenderness at thy hands. Nay, I will believe that even thy imperfect lights may guide him to a better world, for surely thou art on the path thither. But thou hast spoken of a husband. Doth he stand here among this multitude of people? Let him come forth, for I must know to whom I commit this most precious trust."

She turned her face upon the male auditors, and after a momentary delay, Tobias Pearson came forth [105] from among them. The Quaker saw the dress which marked his military rank, and shook her head; but then she noted the hesitating air, the eyes that struggled with her own, and were vanquished; the color that went and came, and could find no resting-place. As she gazed, an unmirthful smile spread over her features, like sunshine that grows melancholy in some desolate spot. Her lips moved inaudibly, but at length she spake.

"I hear it, I hear it. The voice speaketh within me and saith, 'Leave thy child, Catharine, for his place is here, and go hence, for I have other work for thee. Break the bonds of natural affection, martyr thy love, and know that in all these things eternal wisdom hath its ends.' I go, friends; I go. Take ye my boy, my precious jewel. I go hence, trusting that all shall be well, and that even for his infant hands there is a labor in the vineyard."

She knelt down and whispered to Ilbrahim, who at first struggled and clung to his mother, with sobs and tears, but remained passive when she had kissed his cheek and arisen from the ground. Having held her hands over his head in mental prayer, she was ready to depart.

"Farewell, friends in mine extremity," she said to Pearson and his wife; "the good deed ye have done me is a treasure laid up in heaven, to be returned a thousand-fold hereafter. And farewell ye, mine enemies, to whom it is not permitted to harm so much as a hair of my head, nor to stay my footsteps even for a moment. The day is coming when ye shall call upon me to witness for ye to this one sin uncommitted, and I will rise up and answer."

She turned her steps towards the door, and the men,[106] who had stationed themselves to guard it, withdrew, and suffered her to pass. A general sentiment of pity overcame the virulence of religious hatred. Sanctified by her love and her affliction, she went forth, and all the people gazed after her till she had journeyed up the hill, and was lost behind its brow. She went, the apostle of her own unquiet heart, to renew the wanderings of past years. For her voice had been already heard in many lands of Christendom; and she had pined in the cells of a Catholic Inquisition before she felt the lash and lay in the dungeons of the Puritans. Her mission had extended also to the followers of the Prophet, and from them she had received the courtesy and kindness which all the contending sects of our purer religion united to deny her. Her husband and herself had resided many months in Turkey, where even the Sultan's countenance was gracious to them; in that pagan land, too, was Ilbrahim's birthplace, and his oriental name was a mark of gratitude for the good deeds of an unbeliever.

When Pearson and his wife had thus acquired all the rights over Ilbrahim that could be delegated, their affection for him became like the memory of their native land, or their mild sorrow for the dead, a piece of the immovable furniture of their hearts. The boy, also, after a week or two of mental disquiet, began to gratify his protectors by many inadvertent proofs that he considered them as parents, and their house as home. Before the winter snows were melted, the persecuted infant, the little wanderer from a remote and heathen country, seemed native in the New England cottage, and inseparable from the warmth and security of its hearth. Under the influence of kind treatment,[107] and in the consciousness that he was loved, Ilbrahim's demeanor lost a premature manliness, which had resulted from his earlier situation; he became more childlike, and his natural character displayed itself with freedom. It was in many respects a beautiful one, yet the disordered imaginations of both his father and mother had perhaps propagated a certain unhealthiness in the mind of the boy. In his general state, Ilbrahim would derive enjoyment from the most trifling events, and from every object about him; he seemed to discover rich treasures of happiness, by a faculty analogous to that of the witch hazel, which points to hidden gold where all is barren to the eye. His airy gayety, coming to him from a thousand sources, communicated itself to the family, and Ilbrahim was like a domesticated sunbeam, brightening moody countenances, and chasing away the gloom from the dark corners of the cottage.

On the other hand, as the susceptibility of pleasure is also that of pain, the exuberant cheerfulness of the boy's prevailing temper sometimes yielded to moments of deep depression. His sorrows could not always be followed up to their original source, but most frequently they appeared to flow, though Ilbrahim was young to be sad for such a cause, from wounded love. The flightiness of his mirth rendered him often guilty of offences against the decorum of a Puritan household, and on these occasions he did not invariably escape rebuke. But the slightest word of real bitterness, which he was infallible in distinguishing from pretended anger, seemed to sink into his heart and poison all his enjoyments, till he became sensible that he was entirely forgiven. Of the malice, which generally accompanies a superfluity of sensitiveness, Ilbrahim [108] was altogether destitute: when trodden upon, he would not turn; when wounded, he could but die. His mind was wanting in the stamina for self-support; it was a plant that would twine beautifully round something stronger than itself, but if repulsed, or torn away, it had no choice but to wither on the ground. Dorothy's acuteness taught her that severity would crush the spirit of the child, and she nurtured him with the gentle care of one who handles a butterfly. Her husband manifested an equal affection, although it grew daily less productive of familiar caresses.

The feelings of the neighboring people, in regard to the Quaker infant and his protectors, had not undergone a favorable change, in spite of the momentary triumph which the desolate mother had obtained over their sympathies. The scorn and bitterness, of which he was the object, were very grievous to Ilbrahim, especially when any circumstance made him sensible that the children, his equals in age, partook of the enmity of their parents. His tender and social nature had already overflowed in attachments to everything about him, and still there was a residue of unappropriated love, which he yearned to bestow upon the little ones who were taught to hate him. As the warm days of spring came on, Ilbrahim was accustomed to remain for hours, silent and inactive, within hearing of the children's voices at their play; yet, with his usual delicacy of feeling, he avoided their notice, and would flee and hide himself from the smallest individual among them. Chance, however, at length seemed to open a medium of communication between his heart and theirs; it was by means of a boy about two years older than Ilbrahim, who was injured by a fall from a tree in the vicinity of Pearson's habitation. As the [109] sufferer's own home was at some distance, Dorothy willingly received him under her roof, and became his tender and careful nurse.

Ilbrahim was the unconscious possessor of much skill in physiognomy, and it would have deterred him, in other circumstances, from attempting to make a friend of this boy. The countenance of the latter immediately impressed a beholder disagreeably, but it required some examination to discover that the cause was a very slight distortion of the mouth, and the irregular, broken line, and near approach of the eyebrows. Analogous, perhaps, to these trifling deformities, was an almost imperceptible twist of every joint, and the uneven prominence of the breast; forming a body, regular in its general outline, but faulty in almost all its details. The disposition of the boy was sullen and reserved, and the village schoolmaster stigmatized him as obtuse in intellect; although, at a later period of life, he evinced ambition and very peculiar talents. But whatever might be his personal or moral irregularities, Ilbrahim's heart seized upon, and clung to him, from the moment that he was brought wounded into the cottage; the child of persecution seemed to compare his own fate with that of the sufferer, and to feel that even different modes of misfortune had created a sort of relationship between them. Food, rest, and the fresh air, for which he languished, were neglected; he nestled continually by the bedside of the little stranger, and, with a fond jealousy, endeavored to be the medium of all the cares that were bestowed upon him. As the boy became convalescent, Ilbrahim contrived games suitable to his situation, or amused him by a faculty which he had perhaps breathed in with the air of his barbaric [110] birthplace. It was that of reciting imaginary adventures, on the spur of the moment, and apparently in inexhaustible succession. His tales were of course monstrous, disjointed, and without aim; but they were curious on account of a vein of human tenderness which ran through them all, and was like a sweet, familiar face, encountered in the midst of wild and unearthly scenery. The auditor paid much attention to these romances, and sometimes

interrupted them by brief remarks upon the incidents, displaying shrewdness above his years, mingled with a moral obliquity which grated very
harshly against Ilbrahim's instinctive rectitude. Nothing, however, could
arrest the progress of the latter's affection, and there were many proofs
that it met with a response from the dark and stubborn nature on which it
was lavished. The boy's parents at length removed him, to complete his
cure under their own roof.

Ilbrahim did not visit his new friend after his departure; but he made
anxious and continual inquiries respecting him, and informed himself of
the day when he was to reappear among his playmates. On a pleasant
summer afternoon, the children of the neighborhood had assembled in the
little forest-crowned amphitheatre behind the meeting-house, and the
recovering invalid was there, leaning on a staff. The glee of a score of
untainted bosoms was heard in light and airy voices, which danced among
the trees like sunshine become audible; the grown men of this weary
world, as they journeyed by the spot, marvelled why life, beginning in
such brightness, should proceed in gloom; and their hearts, or their
imaginations, answered them and said, that the bliss of childhood gushes
from its innocence. But it happened that an unexpected addition [111] was
made to the heavenly little band. It was Ilbrahim, who came towards the
children with a look of sweet confidence on his fair and spiritual face, as
if, having manifested his love to one of them, he had no longer to fear
a repulse from their society. A hush came over their mirth the moment
they beheld him, and they stood whispering to each other while he drew
nigh; but, all at once, the devil of their fathers entered into the unbreeched fanatics, and sending up a fierce, shrill cry, they rushed upon the
poor Quaker child. In an instant, he was the centre of a brood of baby-
fiends, who lifted sticks against him, pelted him with stones, and displayed
an instinct of destruction far more loathsome than the bloodthirstiness
of manhood.

The invalid, in the meanwhile, stood apart from the tumult, crying out
with a loud voice, "Fear not, Ilbrahim, come hither and take my hand;"
and his unhappy friend endeavored to obey him. After watching the
victim's struggling approach with a calm smile and unabashed eye, the
foul-hearted little villain lifted his staff and struck Ilbrahim on the
mouth, so forcibly that the blood issued in a stream. The poor child's
arms had been raised to guard his head from the storm of blows; but
now he dropped them at once. His persecutors beat him down, trampled
upon him, dragged him by his long, fair locks, and Ilbrahim was on the
point of becoming as veritable a martyr as ever entered bleeding into

heaven. The uproar, however, attracted the notice of a few neighbors, who put themselves to the trouble of rescuing the little heretic, and of conveying him to Pearson's door.

Ilbrahim's bodily harm was severe, but long and careful nursing accomplished his recovery; the injury [112] done to his sensitive spirit was more serious, though not so visible. Its signs were principally of a negative character, and to be discovered only by those who had previously known him. His gait was thenceforth slow, even, and unvaried by the sudden bursts of sprightlier motion, which had once corresponded to his overflowing gladness; his countenance was heavier, and its former play of expression, the dance of sunshine reflected from moving water, was destroyed by the cloud over his existence; his notice was attracted in a far less degree by passing events, and he appeared to find greater difficulty in comprehending what was new to him than at a happier period. A stranger, founding his judgment upon these circumstances, would have said that the dulness of the child's intellect widely contradicted the promise of his features; but the secret was in the direction of Ilbrahim's thoughts, which were brooding within him when they should naturally have been wandering abroad. An attempt of Dorothy to revive his former sportiveness was the single occasion on which his quiet demeanor yielded to a violent display of grief; he burst into passionate weeping, and ran and hid himself, for his heart had become so miserably sore that even the hand of kindness tortured it like fire. Sometimes, at night and probably in his dreams, he was heard to cry "Mother! Mother!" as if her place, which a stranger had supplied while Ilbrahim was happy, admitted of no substitute in his extreme affliction. Perhaps, among the many life-weary wretches then upon the earth, there was not one who combined innocence and misery like this poor, broken-hearted infant, so soon the victim of his own heavenly nature.

While this melancholy change had taken place in [113] Ilbrahim, one of an earlier origin and of different character had come to its perfection in his adopted father. The incident with which this tale commences found Pearson in a state of religious dulness, yet mentally disquieted, and longing for a more fervid faith than he possessed. The first effect of his kindness to Ilbrahim was to produce a softened feeling, and incipient love for the child's whole sect; but joined to this, and resulting perhaps from self-suspicion, was a proud and ostentatious contempt of all their tenets and practical extravagances. In the course of much thought, however, for the subject struggled irresistibly into his mind, the foolishness of the doctrine began to be less evident, and the points which had particularly offended his reason assumed another aspect, or vanished entirely away. The work within him appeared to go on even while he slept, and that which had been a doubt, when he laid down to rest, would often hold the place of a truth, confirmed by some forgotten demonstration, when he recalled his thoughts in the morning. But while he was thus becoming assimilated to the enthusiasts, his contempt, in nowise decreasing towards them, grew very fierce against himself; he imagined, also, that every face of his acquaintance wore a sneer, and that every word addressed to him was a gibe. Such was his state of mind at the period of Ilbrahim's misfortune; and the emotions consequent upon that event completed the change, of which the child had been the original instrument.

In the mean time, neither the fierceness of the persecutors, nor the infatuation of their victims, had decreased. The dungeons were never empty; the streets of almost every village echoed daily with the lash; the life of a woman, whose mild and Christian spirit no [114] cruelty could embitter, had been sacrificed; and more innocent blood was yet to pollute the hands that were so often raised in prayer. Early after the Restoration, the English Quakers represented to Charles II that a "vein of blood was open in his dominions;" but though the displeasure of the voluptuous king was roused, his interference was not prompt. And now the tale must stride forward over many months, leaving Pearson to encounter ignominy and misfortune; his wife to a firm endurance of a thousand sorrows; poor Ilbrahim to pine and droop like a cankered rosebud; his mother to wander on a mistaken errand, neglectful of the holiest trust which can be committed to a woman.

A winter evening, a night of storm, had darkened over Pearson's habitation, and there were no cheerful faces to drive the gloom from his broad hearth. The fire, it is true, sent forth a glowing heat and a ruddy light, and large logs, dripping with half-melted snow, lay ready to be cast upon the embers. But the apartment was saddened in its aspect by the absence of much of the homely wealth which had once adorned it; for the exaction of repeated fines, and his own neglect of temporal affairs, had greatly impoverished the owner. And with the furniture of peace, the implements of war had likewise disappeared; the sword was broken, the helm and cuirass were cast away forever; the soldier had done with battles, and might not lift so much as his naked hand to guard his head. But the Holy Book remained, and the table on which it rested was drawn before the fire, while two of the persecuted sect sought comfort from its pages.

He who listened, while the other read, was the [115] master of the house, now emaciated in form, and altered as to the expression and healthiness of his countenance; for his mind had dwelt too long among visionary thoughts, and his body had been worn by imprisonment and stripes. The hale and weather-beaten old man who sat beside him had sustained less injury from a far longer course of the same mode of life. In person he was tall and dignified, and, which alone would have made him hateful to the Puritans, his gray locks fell from beneath the broad-brimmed hat, and rested on his shoulders. As the old man read the sacred page the snow drifted against the windows, or eddied in at the crevices of the door, while a blast kept laughing in the chimney, and the blaze leaped fiercely up to seek it. And sometimes, when the wind struck the hill at a certain angle, and swept down by the cottage across the wintry plain, its voice was the most doleful that can be conceived; it came as if the Past were speaking, as if the Dead had contributed each a whisper, as if the Desolation of Ages were breathed in that one lamenting sound.

The Quaker at length closed the book, retaining however his hand between the pages which he had been reading, while he looked stead-fastly at Pearson. The attitude and features of the latter might have indicated the endurance of bodily pain; he leaned his forehead on his hands, his teeth were firmly closed, and his frame was tremulous at intervals with a nervous agitation.

"Friend Tobias," inquired the old man, compassionately, "hast thou found no comfort in these many blessed passages of Scripture?"

"Thy voice has fallen on my ear like a sound afar off and indistinct," replied Pearson without lifting his [116] eyes. "Yea, and when I have hearkened carefully the words seemed cold and lifeless, and intended for another and a lesser grief than mine. Remove the book," he added, in a tone of sullen bitterness. "I have no part in its consolations, and they do but fret my sorrow the more."

"Nay, feeble brother, be not as one who hath never known the light," said the elder Quaker earnestly, but with mildness. "Art thou he that wouldst be content to give all, and endure all, for conscience' sake; desiring even peculiar trials, that thy faith might be purified and thy heart weaned from worldly desires? And wilt thou sink beneath an afflic-tion which happens alike to them that have their portion here below, and to them that lay up treasure in heaven? Faint not, for thy burden is yet light."

"It is heavy! It is heavier than I can bear!" exclaimed Pearson, with the impatience of a variable spirit. "From my youth upward I have been a man marked out for wrath; and year by year, yea, day after day, I have endured sorrows such as others know not in their lifetime. And now I speak not of the love that has been turned to hatred, the honor to ignominy, the ease and plentifulness of all things to danger, want, and nakedness. All this I could have borne, and counted myself blessed. But when my heart was desolate with many losses I fixed it upon the child of a stranger, and he became dearer to me than all my buried ones; and now he too must die as if my love were poison. Verily, I am an accursed man, and I will lay me down in the dust and lift up my head no more."

"Thou sinnest, brother, but it is not for me to rebuke thee; for I also have had my hours of darkness,[117] wherein I have murmured against the cross," said the old Quaker. He continued, perhaps in the hope of distracting his companion's thoughts from his own sorrows. "Even of late was the light obscured within me, when the men of blood had banished me on pain of death, and the constables led me onward from village to village towards the wilderness. A strong and cruel hand was wielding the knotted cords; they sunk deep into the flesh, and thou mightst have tracked every reel and totter of my footsteps by the blood that followed. As we went on"—

"Have I not borne all this; and have I murmured?" interrupted Pearson impatiently.

"Nay, friend, but hear me," continued the other. "As we journeyed on, night darkened on our path, so that no man could see the rage of the persecutors or the constancy of my endurance, though Heaven forbid that I should glory therein. The lights began to glimmer in the cottage windows, and I could discern the inmates as they gathered in comfort and security, every man with his wife and children by their own evening hearth. At length we came to a tract of fertile land; in the dim light, the forest was not visible around it; and behold! there was a straw-thatched dwelling, which bore the very aspect of my home, far over the wild ocean, far in our own England. Then came bitter thoughts upon me; yea, remembrances that were like death to my soul. The happiness of my early days was painted to me; the disquiet of my manhood, the altered faith of my declining years. I remembered how I had been moved to go forth a wanderer when my daughter, the youngest, the dearest of my flock, lay on her dying bed, and"—

"Couldst thou obey the command at such a moment?" exclaimed Pearson, shuddering.[118]

"Yea, yea," replied the old man hurriedly. "I was kneeling by her bedside when the voice spoke loud within me; but immediately I rose, and took my staff, and gat me gone. Oh! that it were permitted me to forget her woful look when I thus withdrew my arm, and left her journeying through the dark valley alone! for her soul was faint, and she had leaned upon my prayers. Now in that night of horror I was assailed by the thought that I had been an erring Christian and a cruel parent; yea, even my daughter, with her pale, dying features, seemed to stand by me and whisper, 'Father, you are deceived; go home and shelter your gray head.' O Thou, to whom I have looked in my farthest wanderings," continued the Quaker, raising his agitated eyes to heaven, "inflict not upon the bloodiest of our persecutors the unmitigated agony of my soul, when I believed that all I had done and suffered for Thee was at the instigation of a mocking fiend! But I yielded not; I knelt down and wrestled with the tempter, while the scourge bit more fiercely into the flesh. My prayer was heard, and I went on in peace and joy towards the wilderness."

The old man, though his fanaticism had generally all the calmness of reason, was deeply moved while reciting this tale; and his unwonted emotion seemed to rebuke and keep down that of his companion. They sat in silence, with their faces to the fire, imagining, perhaps, in its red embers new scenes of persecution yet to be encountered. The snow still drifted hard against the windows, and sometimes, as the blaze of the logs had gradually sunk, came down the spacious chimney and hissed upon the hearth. A cautious footstep might now and then be heard in a neighboring apartment, and the sound invariably drew the eyes [119] of both Quakers to the door which led thither. When a fierce and riotous gust of wind had led his thoughts, by a natural association, to homeless travellers on such a night, Pearson resumed the conversation.

"I have well-nigh sunk under my own share of this trial," observed he, sighing heavily; "yet I would that it might be doubled to me, if so the child's mother could be spared. Her wounds have been deep and many, but this will be the sorest of all."

"Fear not for Catharine," replied the old Quaker, "for I know that valiant woman, and have seen how she can bear the cross. A mother's heart, indeed, is strong in her, and may seem to contend mightily with her faith; but soon she will stand up and give thanks that her son has been thus early an accepted sacrifice. The boy hath done his work, and she will feel that he is taken hence in kindness both to him and her. Blessed, blessed are they that with so little suffering can enter into peace!"

The fitful rush of the wind was now disturbed by a portentous sound; it was a quick and heavy knocking at the outer door. Pearson's wan countenance grew paler, for many a visit of persecution had taught him what to dread; the old man, on the other hand, stood up erect, and his glance was firm as that of the tried soldier who awaits his enemy.

"The men of blood have come to seek me," he observed with calmness. "They have heard how I was moved to return from banishment; and now am I to be led to prison, and thence to death. It is an end I have long looked for. I will open unto them, lest they say, 'Lo, he feareth!'"

"Nay, I will present myself before them," said Pearson, with recovered fortitude. "It may be that [120] they seek me alone, and know not that thou abidest with me."

"Let us go boldly, both one and the other," rejoined his companion. "It is not fitting that thou or I should shrink."

They therefore proceeded through the entry to the door, which they opened, bidding the applicant "Come in, in God's name!" A furious blast of wind drove the storm into their faces, and extinguished the lamp; they had barely time to discern a figure, so white from head to foot with the drifted snow that it seemed like Winter's self, come in human shape, to seek refuge from its own desolation.

"Enter, friend, and do thy errand, be it what it may," said Pearson. "It must needs be pressing, since thou comest on such a bitter night."

"Peace be with this household," said the stranger, when they stood on the floor of the inner apartment.

Pearson started, the elder Quaker stirred the slumbering embers of the fire till they sent up a clear and lofty blaze; it was a female voice that had spoken; it was a female form that shone out, cold and wintry, in that comfortable light.

"Catharine, blessed woman!" exclaimed the old man, "art thou come to this darkened land again? art thou come to bear a valiant testimony as in former years? The scourge hath not prevailed against thee, and from the dungeon hast thou come forth triumphant; but strengthen, strengthen now thy heart, Catharine, for Heaven will prove thee yet this once, ere thou go to thy reward."

"Rejoice, friends!" she replied. "Thou who hast long been of our people, and thou whom a little child hath led to us, rejoice! Lo! I come, the messenger [121] of glad tidings, for the day of persecution is overpast. The heart of the king, even Charles, hath been moved in gentleness towards us, and he hath sent forth his letters to stay the hands of the men of blood. A ship's company of our friends hath arrived at yonder town, and I also sailed joyfully among them."

As Catharine spoke, her eyes were roaming about the room, in search of him for whose sake security was dear to her. Pearson made a silent appeal to the old man, nor did the latter shrink from the painful task assigned him.

"Sister," he began, in a softened yet perfectly calm tone, "thou tellest us of His love, manifested in temporal good; and now must we speak to thee of that selfsame love, displayed in chastenings. Hitherto, Catharine, thou hast been as one journeying in a darksome and difficult path, and leading an infant by the hand; fain wouldst thou have looked heaven-ward continually, but still the cares of that little child have drawn thine eyes and thy affections to the earth. Sister! go on rejoicing, for his totter-ing footsteps shall impede thine own no more."

But the unhappy mother was not thus to be consoled; she shook like a leaf, she turned white as the very snow that hung drifted into her hair. The firm old man extended his hand and held her up, keeping his eye upon hers, as if to repress any outbreak of passion.

"I am a woman, I am but a woman; will He try me above my strength?" said Catharine very quickly, and almost in a whisper. "I have been wounded sore: I have suffered much; many things in the body; many in the mind; crucified in myself, and in them that were dearest to me. Surely," added she, with a [122] long shudder, "He hath spared me in this one thing." She broke forth with sudden and irrepressible violence. "Tell me, man of cold heart, what has God done to me? Hath He cast me down, never to rise again? Hath He crushed my very heart in his hand? And thou, to whom I committed my child, how hast thou fulfilled thy trust? Give me back the boy, well, sound, alive, alive; or earth and Heaven shall avenge me!"

The agonized shriek of Catharine was answered by the faint, the very faint, voice of a child.

On this day it had become evident to Pearson, to his aged guest, and to Dorothy, that Ilbrahim's brief and troubled pilgrimage drew near its close. The two former would willingly have remained by him, to make use of the prayers and pious discourses which they deemed appropriate to the time, and which, if they be impotent as to the departing traveller's reception in the world whither it goes, may at least sustain him in bid-ding adieu to earth. But though Ilbrahim uttered no complaint, he was disturbed by the faces that looked upon him; so that Dorothy's entreat-ies, and their own conviction that the child's feet might tread heaven's pavement and not soil it, had induced the two Quakers to remove. Ilbra-him then closed his eyes and grew calm, and, except for now and then a kind and low word to his nurse, might have been thought to slumber. As nightfall came on, however, and the storm began to rise, something seemed to trouble the repose of the boy's mind, and to render his sense of hearing active and acute. If a passing wind lingered to shake the casement, he strove to turn his head towards it; if the door jarred to and fro upon its hinges, he looked long and anxiously [123] thitherward; if the heavy voice of the old man, as he read the Scriptures, rose but a little higher, the child almost held his dying breath to listen; if a snow-drift swept by the cottage, with a sound like the trailing of a garment, Ilbrahim seemed to watch that some visitant should enter.

But, after a little time, he relinquished whatever secret hope had agitated him, and with one low, complaining whisper, turned his cheek upon the pillow. He then addressed Dorothy with his usual sweetness, and besought her to draw near him; she did so, and Ilbrahim took her hand in both of his, grasping it with a gentle pressure, as if to assure himself that he retained it. At intervals, and without disturbing the repose of his countenance, a very faint trembling passed over him from head to foot, as if a mild but somewhat cool wind had breathed upon him, and made him shiver. As the boy thus led her by the hand, in his quiet progress over the borders of eternity, Dorothy almost imagined that she could discern the near, though dim, delightfulness of the home he was about to reach; she would not have enticed the little wanderer back, though she bemoaned herself that she must leave him and return. But just when Ilbrahim's feet were pressing on the soil of Paradise he heard a voice behind him, and it recalled him a few, few paces of the weary path which he had travelled. As Dorothy looked upon his features, she perceived that their placid expression was again disturbed; her own thoughts had been so wrapped in him, that all sounds of the storm, and of human speech, were lost to her; but when Catharine's shriek pierced through the room, the boy strove to raise himself.

"Friend, she is come! Open unto her!" cried he.[124]

In a moment his mother was kneeling by the bedside; she drew Ilbrahim to her bosom, and he nestled there, with no violence of joy, but contentedly, as if he were hushing himself to sleep. He looked into her face, and reading its agony, said, with feeble earnestness, "Mourn not, dearest mother. I am happy now." And with these words the gentle boy was dead.

The king's mandate to stay the New England persecutors was effectual in preventing further martyrdoms; but the colonial authorities, trusting in the remoteness of their situation, and perhaps in the supposed instability of the royal government, shortly renewed their severities in all other respects. Catharine's fanaticism had become wilder by the sundering of all human ties; and wherever a scourge was lifted there was she to receive the blow; and whenever a dungeon was unbarred thither she came, to cast herself upon the floor. But in process of time a more Christian spirit—a spirit of forbearance, though not of cordiality or approbation —began to pervade the land in regard to the persecuted sect. And then, when the rigid old Pilgrims eyed her rather in pity than in wrath; when the matrons fed her with the fragments of their children's food, and offered her a lodging on a hard and lowly bed; when no little crowd of schoolboys left their sports to cast stones after the roving enthusiast; then did Catharine return to Pearson's dwelling and made that her home.

As if Ilbrahim's sweetness yet lingered round his ashes; as if his gentle spirit came down from heaven to teach his parent a true religion, her fierce and vindictive nature was softened by the same griefs which had once irritated it. When the course of years had [125] made the features of the unobtrusive mourner familiar in the settlement, she became a subject of not deep, but general, interest; a being on whom the otherwise superflous sympathies of all might be bestowed. Every one spoke of her with that degree of pity which it is pleasant to experience; every one was ready to do her the little kindnesses which are not costly, yet manifest good will; and when at last she died, a long train of her once bitter persecutors followed her, with decent sadness and tears that were not painful, to her place by Ilbrahim's green and sunken grave.[126]

Hawthorne's Revision of "The Gentle Boy" *

When Hawthorne selected "The Gentle Boy" for inclusion in his 1837 edition of *Twice-Told Tales*, he deemed it necessary to revise that tale from the form in which it had first appeared in Samuel Griswold Goodrich's *Token* of 1832. That this was a consciously artistic revision, rather than a mere "worrying" of material, can be seen in part from the fact that the three other tales [1] which appeared in the same annual were

[1] "Roger Malvin's Burial" (*Mosses*, 1846); "My Kinsman, Major Molineux" and "The Wives of the Dead" (*Snow Image*, 1852).
* Seymour Gross, "Hawthorne's Revision of 'The Gentle Boy,'" *American Literature*, XXVI (May, 1954), 196–208. Reprinted by permission.

unrevised when subsequently incorporated into his collections. The tale, however, continued to disturb Hawthorne artistically even after his revision. In his preface to a separate reprint of the tale in 1839, he wrote, ". . . there are several among his TWICE TOLD TALES which on re-perusal, affect him less painfully with a sense of imperfect and ill-wrought conception, than THE GENTLE BOY." [2] He took refuge, however, in the cliché of nature-over-art, by concluding "that Nature here led him deeper into the Universal heart than Art has been able to follow." [3]

Some consideration of his changes in the tale should prove profitable, inasmuch as "The Gentle Boy" is the only tale of Hawthorne's in which we have abundant evidence of artistic revision.[4] These revisions are for the most part deletions. And when these deletions are viewed in their totality, they exhibit how Hawthorne has managed to give his piece a firmer point of view through the solidifying of a remarkably perilous balance between Puritan and Quaker. In short, he has clarified the terms of his tragedy.

Hawthorne introduces his tale with an expository sketch of the [196] historical position of the Quakers in seventeenth-century Massachusetts Bay.[5] With a calm objectivity Hawthorne points up the self-castigating nature of the Quakers, their maniacal courting of "the cross," and their deliberate choice of Massachusetts Bay as a most eligible place to invite martyrdom. As a consequence of these aberrations, an intrinsically holy feeling has been converted into a mad enthusiasm that has driven the Quakers beyond "rational religion." But there is a deliberate counterbalance. The Puritans' vicious reaction in the form of torture, even though terribly provoked, is not absolved of moral culpability. Irony lashes out at them in such a phrase as "The fines, imprisonments, and stripes liberally distributed by our pious forefathers." [6] Further, no matter what theoretical argument Hawthorne could summon up to

---

[2] Nathaniel Hawthorne, *The Gentle Boy: A Thrice Told Tale* (Boston, 1839), p. 4.

[3] *Ibid.*

[4] Hawthorne's revisions in other short pieces were, for the most part, matters of eradicating tasteless references to contemporaries, or simple word changes. For an analysis of the changes in "The Hall of Fantasy," see Harold P. Miller, "Hawthorne Surveys His Contemporaries," *American Literature*, XII, 228–235 (May, 1940).

[5] For a very thorough discussion of the historical sources of this tale, see G. Harrison Orians, "The Sources and Themes of Hawthorne's 'The Gentle Boy,' " *New England Quarterly*, XIV, 664–678 (Dec., 1941).

[6] George Parsons Lathrop, ed., *The Works of Nathaniel Hawthorne* (Boston, 1883), I, 85. (Hereinafter cited as *Works*.)

justify the Puritans (and, indeed, the first deletion is just such a justification), he could not bring himself to accept emotionally the cruelty of torture. Whenever he speaks of the Puritan devices for physical and mental torture, as for example in "Endicott and the Red Cross" and "Main Street," it is with fascinated horror. In fact, one of Hawthorne's most personal remarks is on this subject. In "Main Street," after discussing his own ancestor's guilty responsibility for the whipping of the Quaker Ann Coleman, he prayerfully hopes, with a touch of the inherited guilt he was always to feel, that "as the rain of so many years has wept upon it [the bloody trail of the whip], time after time, and washed it all away, so there may have been a dew of mercy to cleanse this cruel blood-stain out of the record of the persecutor's life!" [7]

The most Hawthorne could concede was that the Quakers' "indecorous exhibitions . . . *abstractly* considered, well deserved the moderate chastisement of the rod." [8] For Hawthorne, then, there was only an *abstract* justification in moderate punishment—no more. But the Puritans' justice was not abstract, and its concrete manifestations were hardly moderate.[197]

Once having recognized that Hawthorne has, at the very outset, set up a balance of two evils, abstract guilt and unreasonable retribution, which, as will be seen, is a necessary condition for the subsequent tragedy, the reason for the following deletion becomes evident.

That those who were active in, or consenting to, this measure [the killing of two Quakers in 1659], made themselves responsible for innocent blood, is not to be denied: yet the extenuating circumstances of their conduct are more numerous than can generally be pleaded by persecutors. The inhabitants of New England were a people, whose original bond of union was their peculiar religious principles. For the peaceful exercise of their own mode of worship, an object, the very reverse of universal liberty of conscience, they had hewn themselves a home in the wilderness: they had exposed themselves to the peril of death, and to a life which rendered the accomplishment of that peril almost a blessing. They had found no city of refuge prepared for them, but, with Heaven's assistance, they had created one; and it would be hard to say whether justice did not authorize their determination, to guard its gate against all who were destitute of the prescribed title to admittance. The principle of their foundation was such, that to destroy the unity of religion, might have been to subvert the government, and break up the colony, espe-

---

[7] *Works*, III, 463.
[8] *Ibid.*, I, 86. I am using *abstractly* of *The Token* rather than *abstractedly* of the Riverside edition, since the latter is obviously a misprint.

cially at a period when the state of affairs in England had stopped the tide of emigration, and drawn back many of the pilgrims to their native homes. The magistrates of Massachusetts Bay were, moreover, most imperfectly informed respecting the real tenets and character of the Quaker sect. They had heard of them, from various parts of the earth, as opposers of every known opinion, and enemies of all established governments; they had beheld extravagances which seemed to justify these accusations; and the idea suggested by their own wisdom may be gathered from the fact, that the persons of many individuals were searched, in the expectation of discovering witch-marks. But after all allowances, it is to be feared that the death of the Quakers was principally owing to the polemic fierceness, that distinct passion of human nature, which has so often produced frightful guilt in the most sincere and zealous advocates of virtue and religion.[9]

This is a very curious passage. That this is a rather convincing plea for historical necessity (motivated perhaps by Hawthorne's unconscious need to rationalize his ancestral guilt) seems fairly obvious. But Hawthorne the artist could see in its general tenor a threat to the balanced backdrop of the tale. Even the final sentence,[198] in which Hawthorne with characteristic sanity cuts down his seemingly logical argument, was best left unsaid. For after all, the rightness or wrongness of the situation makes little difference here. Caught between forces beyond their control, Ilbrahim and Tobias, like Romeo and Juliet, are tragically destroyed. What ultimately arrests us in both Shakespeare's and Hawthorne's tragedies is not the force itself, the existence of evil, but the tragic waste of decent human beings trapped by life itself.

The next deletion of real importance [10] is somewhat more difficult to explain. After Tobias's good heart has finally conquered his inherited

[9] Nathaniel Hawthorne, "The Gentle Boy," *The Token* (Boston, 1832), pp. 194–195.

[10] An unimportant but interesting change occurs soon after the story proper begins. As Tobias enters the scene, Hawthorne comments that "a gloomy extent of nearly four miles lay between him and his *home*." In the *Token* edition the final word is *house*. Ordinarily, such a minor change would be attributed to the kind of misprintings one finds in many of Hawthorne's stories, and about which he complained fairly often. But here, where there is ample evidence of close revision, it seems reasonable to attribute the change to artistic scrupulousness. The word *home* has richer, warmer connotations than does *house*, and is therefore substituted. When Tobias asks Ilbrahim where he belongs, the child, pointing to his father's grave, says, "Here is my home." And when Tobias later points to his own "home," "a thrill passed through the child's frame." And finally, Ilbrahim's acceptance of his new parents is complete when he considers "their house as home." Hawthorne's change, then, gives consistency to the distinction.

misgivings about the Quaker child whom he has found standing forlornly on his executed father's grave, he takes the boy home to his wife Dorothy, having decided to accept him as their own. After Tobias tells Dorothy to be kind to the child even as she would have been to their own children now dead, the following passage is deleted.

The wife's eyes filled with tears; she inquired neither who little Ilbrahim was, nor whence he came, but kissed his cheek and led the way into the dwelling. The sitting-room, which was also the kitchen, was lighted by a cheerful fire upon the large stone-laid hearth, and a confused variety of objects shone out and disappeared in the unsteady blaze. There were the household articles, the many wooden trenchers, the one large pewter dish, and the copper kettle whose inner surface was glittering like gold. There were the lighter implements of husbandry, the spade, the sickle, and the scythe, all hanging by the door, and the axe before which a thousand trees had bowed themselves. On another part of the wall were the steel cap and iron breast plate, the sword and the matchlock gun. There, in a corner, was a little chair, the memorial of a brood of children whose place by the fire-side was vacant forever. And there, on a table near the window, among all those tokens of labor, war, and mourning, was the Holy Bible, the book of life, an emblem of the blessed comforts which [199] it offers, to those who can receive them, amidst the toil, the strife, and sorrow of this world. Dorothy hastened to bring the little chair from its corner; she placed it on the hearth, and, seating the poor orphan there, addressed him in words of tenderness, such as only a mother's experience could have taught her. At length, when he had timidly begun to taste his warm bread and milk, she drew her husband apart.[11]

There is nothing in this passage which would contradict Dorothy's character as we come to know her: a warm, considerate, instinctively loving mother. In fact, the inclusion of the passage would have lent something to Hawthorne's portrayal of her as the ideal of "rational piety" and sensitive motherhood. Further, the description of the Puritans' household is effective. The rather casual cataloguing of the items, deftly accentuating the austerity of the entire setting, summons up for the reader the experimental gamut of Puritan life: husbandry, war, domesticity, piety, and death. Perhaps it might be suggested that the over-all effect of the scene with its emphasis on purity and cheerful utility would have run counter to the barbarity that the Puritans are later to exhibit. But the Pearsons are in no way representative of the Puritans in the tale; in fact, they are to be the victims, not the perpetrators, of the "cold sect's"

[11] *Token*, pp. 202–203.

persecutions. The omission of the passage also weakens a later passage in the tale,[12] in which the Pearson home is pictured now destitute of its "homely wealth." Without the previous passage the Pearsons' loss is not dramatically visualized, somewhat vitiating the pathos of their situation. However, Hawthorne must have felt that the warmth of the scene in the home of Puritans, even ones who are later to prove highly unrepresentative, might, unwittingly, upset the precarious balance he felt he needed. The first foreshadowing of Tobias's ultimate rejection of Puritanism comes when Dorothy asks her husband if the Indians had orphaned the child. "No," he answers, "the heathen savage would have given him to eat of his scanty morsel, and to drink of his birchen cup; but Christian men, alas! had cast him out to die." [13] After Dorothy with an even quicker tenderness than her husband accepts the child as her own, the following description of Ilbrahim is deleted: "She drew near to Ilbrahim, who, having finished his repast,[200] sat with the tears hanging upon his long eyelashes, but with a singular and unchildlike composure on his little face." [14] The key to the deletion is in the words "singular and unchildlike." Although Hawthorne could just as well have kept the rest of the passage, the final words contradict the quiet and lovely childishness of the boy. The two paragraphs which follow the deletion emphasize the pained helplessness of the child: tears that gush forth at the word "mother," the simple and affecting Quaker prayer he insists upon, his pale and spiritual countenance. The "singular and unchildlike composure" would have indicated, not the wretched bewilderment of a child buffeted by circumstances it could but imperfectly understand, but rather an almost premature recognition and acceptance of suffering as a part of the human condition.

The following pages of the tale deal with the Puritans' reaction to the Pearsons' act of Christian charity. They are adamant in their hatred of the child, whose very beauty and winning manners are ascribed to Satanic influences. Their antipathy is increased by their inability to convert the gentle Quaker to the tenets of Calvinism—to them a certain sign of invincible depravity. But more important, Tobias, once a respected member of the community, is now hooted and threatened as a "backslider."

On the second Sabbath after Ilbrahim has become a member of the family, the three Pearsons go to the meetinghouse. Hawthorne's treatment of the scene is stingingly ironic. The signal for commencement is a thundering drum—"a martial call to the place of holy and quiet

[12] *Works,* I, 115.   [13] *Ibid.,* I, 92.   [14] *Token,* p. 203.

thoughts." [15] The parishioners on the way to the holy place are full of hate, avoiding the "two parents linked together by the infant of their love." [16] They form a "formidable phalanx," so as to wither the Pearsons with gazes of disapproval. But even in this passage of the scathing contrast between theoretical piety and actual impiety, Hawthorne deleted a passage, which, on the face of it, would have served the vehicle of his critical comment, the military metaphor, very well: ". . . in connexion with which peculiarity [the use of a military drum as the commencement signal], it may be mentioned, that an apartment of the meetinghouse served the purposes of a powder magazine and armory." [17] [201]

Although this deletion would have served Hawthorne's purpose beautifully, he probably could not bring himself to be so unfair as to insinuate, even for artistic purposes, that the whole of the Puritans' religion was one monstrous distortion. He knew that the arsenal was for defense, not aggression, and that the meetinghouse was the most logical place to store arms. Whereas the use of a military drum is explained as being due to the absence of a bell, and carries only a subtle implication, the deleted passage is both too obvious and too baldly unextenuated.

Hawthorne's next deletion is motivated by a desire for unity of effect. Immediately following his description of the rude, unplastered, naked, and drab meetinghouse, there appears in the original version of the tale this obviously inappropriate passage.

On one side of the house sat the women, generally in sad-colored and most unfanciful apparel, although there were a few high head-dresses, on which the "Cobbler of Agawam" would have lavished his empty wit of words. There was no veil to be seen among them all, and it must be allowed that the November sun, shining brightly through the windows, fell upon many a demure but pretty set of features, which no barbarity of art could spoil. The masculine department of the house presented somewhat more variety than that of the women. Most of the men, it is true, were clad in black or dark-grey broadcloth, and all coincided in the short, ungraceful, and ear-displaying cut of their hair. But those who were in martial authority, having arrayed themselves in their embroidered buff-coats, contrasted strikingly with the remainder of the congregation, and attracted many youthful thoughts which should have been otherwise employed. [18]

This passage individualizes and humanizes the otherwise abstract and faceless force which is ultimately to crush Tobias and Ilbrahim. The

[15] *Works*, I, 96.   [16] *Ibid.*   [17] *Token*, p. 207.   [18] *Ibid.*, p. 208.

figures depicted here seem hardly the same ones who with barbarous self-righteousness had put Ilbrahim's father to death, or shouted after Tobias, "What shall be done to the backslider? Lo! the scourge is knotted for him, even the whip of nine cords, and every cord three knots!" [19] Nor is it possible to imagine these rather attractive people, a moment later, turning their "repulsive and unheavenly countenance[s] upon the gentle boy," and drawing back [202] their "earth-soiled garments from his touch," as if to say, "We are holier than thou." [20]

The description of the Puritan minister is also tempered in the final version. Although Hawthorne stresses the minister's having forgotten the lesson of persecution taught by the grim Archbishop Laud, by having the old divine condemn heretics even though but "little children" or "sucking babes," he deletes the aspersions he had originally cast upon the minister's intellectual capabilities. After describing the old man's countenance as "pale and thin," [21] Hawthorne deletes "yet not intellectual." [22] And following his résumé of the minister's sermon, Hawthorne strikes out the following passage as well:

Into this discourse was worked much learning, both sacred and profane, which, however, came forth not digested into its original elements, but in short quotations, as if the preacher were unable to amalgamate his own mind with that of the author. His own language was generally plain, even to affectation, but there were frequent specimens of a dull man's efforts to be witty—little ripples fretting the surface of a stagnant pool.[23]

The deletion here is extremely significant. Hawthorne in deleting this satiric passage is underlining the fact that the invidious mantle of evil that is settling down upon the shoulders of the three central characters stems not from a stupid man's pietistic aberrations, but rather is the outgrowth, necessary and indomitable, of the sect's metaphysic, whose self-sufficient righteousness must inevitably doom the tangential believer, be he ever so innocent and intrinsically good. Hawthorne's treatment of the minister's stupidity is amusing; but the Puritans are not a laughing matter. The minister, as a grim symbol of the Puritan force, cannot be, at the same time, an object for Popean satire.

The balance of evils is next affected by the return of Ilbrahim's mother, Catharine, to the meetinghouse. Garbed in the sackcloth and ashes of the conspicuous martyr, she delivers a countersermon. Haw-

[19] *Works*, I, 95.   [20] *Ibid.*, I, 97.   [21] *Ibid.*, I, 98.   [22] *Token*, p. 209.
[23] *Ibid.*, p. 210.

thorne's sharp comment on her impassioned rantings is, "Having thus given vent to the flood of malignity which she mistook for inspiration, the speaker was silent." [24] The only deletion is that of the irrevelant remark, "Having thus usurped a station to which [203] her sex can plead no title. . . ." [25] This deletion is somewhat allied to the previous one in that the particularity of the criticism detracts from the general evil which Hawthorne felt to be inherent in seventeenth-century Quakerism. For a woman to preach, as Hawthorne could see, was at most a violation of a convention; but for Hawthorne the deepest and most fundamental evil in Quakerism was the "unbridled fanaticism" that destroyed "the duties of the present life" and broke the bonds of natural affection—for Hawthorne the unpardonable sin. Finally, after a tortured struggle, Catharine leaves her son with the Pearsons, and wanders off again to carry out what she believes is her mission. In cataloguing her self-imposed suffering at the hands of other bigots, Hawthorne changes one phrase so as to emphasize the Puritans' cruelty: "For her voice had been already heard in many lands of Christendom; and she had pined in the cells of a Catholic Inquisition before she felt the lash and lay in the dungeons ["ate the bread" in the *Token*] of the Puritans." [26]

So Ilbrahim becomes a part of the "immovable furniture" of the Pearson household. The child under the consciousness of being loved blossoms into a delighted and delightful boy, although, as Hawthorne observes, "the disordered imaginations of both his father and mother had perhaps propagated a certain unhealthiness in the mind of the boy." [27] Ilbrahim is acutely sensitive both to pleasure and pain, and although his is a prevailingly sweet temperament, the slightest rebuke steeps him in an almost unnatural depression. The Puritans are unrelenting. It is with scorn and bitterness that they view the child, whose innocent spirits constantly offend their sense of propriety. But it is the children of the settlement who most hate Ilbrahim—the very children whom he needs for the exercise of his yet "unappropriated love." [28] When chance has it that one of these children is injured and has to be confined to the Pearson home for medical reasons, Ilbrahim's tragedy rises to its climax. Ilbrahim woos the injured boy, who is significantly misshapen, with the consideration, patience, and gentleness of an unworthy lover. When the boy is well enough to leave, Ilbrahim imagines that his natural [204] affection has overcome the inherited malice of the community. One day, completely trusting, Ilbrahim approaches a group of Puritan boys. But with

---

[24] *Works,* I, 101.   [25] *Token,* p. 211.   [26] *Works,* I, 107.
[27] *Ibid.,* I, 108.   [28] "Unappropriate love" in *Token.*

the "devil of their fathers" in their hearts the children attack him mercilessly. The boy whom Ilbrahim had befriended stands apart on crutches. He calls coaxingly to the besieged boy and Ilbrahim drags his bruised body towards the friend to "take his hand." When the Quaker child is close enough, the boy strikes him across the mouth with his crutch. It is all over with the child. Where before he had struggled against the battering of his body, he now, more deeply damaged, turns over to die. The Puritan force in its most elemental state—the children —has done its work. Ilbrahim is saved from actual death by some older people.

Back at the Pearsons' the child, his soul withered, awaits death. But Hawthorne forces us to remember that although the Puritan force has beat its unrelenting hate against the child's fragile being, the soul was crushed against the rock of the Quaker woman's unholy neglect of a mother's duty. Ilbrahim in his agony cries out "Mother, Mother," which "admitted of no substitute in his extreme affliction." [29]

The tragedy of Ilbrahim is complete. Caught between two abstract forces, which the gentle boy could only feel but never understand, he is ironically mangled between a pious love masquerading as hate, and pious hate masquerading as love. His physical death in the arms of his agonized mother later is an anticlimax. When the soul is dead the body will not long endure.

But before Ilbrahim's death Hawthorne had shifted his focus of interest to Tobias. Tobias had always yearned for a more fervid faith than Calvinism, although he had little doubt of its doctrinarian validity. His love for Ilbrahim had softened his attitude towards Quakers, but his contempt for the sect's tenets and outrageous practices remained firm. His struggle for metaphysical values is tortured by the paradox of the head and the heart. Whereas his intellect rejected the spiritual extravagances of the Quakers, his emotional nature was revolted by the Calvinists' torture and castigation, even in the name of a Truth whose theoretical basis he accepted. Even as he becomes assimilated to the "enthusiasts," his contempt for them is not lessened, and he resolves the problem by turning the [205] scorn upon himself. At this point in Tobias's religious predicament Hawthorne deletes this passage.

At length, when the change in his belief was fully accomplished, the contest grew very terrible between the love of the world, in its thousand shapes, and the power which moved him to sacrifice all for the one pure

---

[29] *Works*, I, 113.

faith; to quote his own words, subsequently uttered at a meeting of Friends, it was as if "Earth and Hell had garrisoned the fortress of his miserable soul, and Heaven came battering against it to storm the walls." [30]

The reason for this deletion is obvious. First, Hawthorne realized that by projecting Tobias's ultimate spiritual peace into the future he was vitiating, even nullifying, the tragedy which was still to be dramatized. "It is heavy! It is heavier than I can bear!" exclaims the tortured Tobias somewhat later, as he awaits the death of his new-found son.[31] Second, and more important, the passage seems to insinuate that Tobias's choice was the "correct" one: that his conversion enabled him finally to grasp The Truth ("the one pure faith"). But this is not what the form of the tale indicates. The quest for The Truth is not here Hawthorne's concern; on the contrary, it is the ruthless conviction that *the truth* is The Truth which activates the forces of the tragedy. Tobias is not the happy martyr whose anguished pain eventually gains for him the gift of certainty; he "acts according to the simplest Christian ethic, in an impulse of pure generosity and loving-kindness. And . . . the very pillars of the Christian temple . . . shatter about him and crush him." [32] Ultimately, Tobias's conversion was not toward the dogma of the Quakers, but away from the cruel inhumanity of the Puritans—a desperate and despairing escape, without sweetness or light. It is the tragedy of Ilbrahim that incites the tragedy of Tobias.

The revision of the following passage achieves the same effect as the previous deletion.

Such was his state of warfare at the period of Ilbrahim's misfortune; and the emotions consequent upon that event enlisted with the beseiging army, and decided the victory. There was a triumphant shout within him, and from that moment all was peace. Dorothy had not been the [206] subject of a similar process, for her reason was as clear as her heart was tender. (*Token*, pp. 227–228.)

Such was his state of mind at the period of Ilbrahim's misfortune; and the emotions consequent upon that event completed the change, of which the child had been the original instrument. (*Works*, I, 114.)

The original version indicates a spiritual peace, which is wholly absent from the final one. In revising his original passage, Hawthorne escaped

[30] *Token*, p. 227.   [31] *Works*, I, 117.
[32] Louise Dauner, "The 'Case' of Tobias Pearson: Hawthorne and the Ambiguities," *American Literature*, XXI, 468–469 (Jan., 1950).

the predicament of the Miracle Plays: the audience's knowledge that the "tragic" happenings of this world would be, at the end, recompensed with Infinite Bliss. The Miracle Plays, therefore, are never tragedies; but Hawthorne's tale is a tragedy.

The final scene of the tale introduces a new character: an old Quaker whose suffering, unlike Tobias's, has gained him the happy acceptance of the convinced martyr. The old man, as Catharine had, deserted a child to follow the compelling inner light. Although the old Quaker is an affecting figure, and his sincere suffering arouses the reader's sympathy, there runs through this section an unmistakable undertone of criticism. For Hawthorne, the inner light which causes an unnatural neglect of duties is, in reality, an inner darkness, and, so as not to mitigate the basic fanaticism which lay beneath the old man's actions, Hawthorne deleted this piece of description: "His features were strong and well connected, and seemed to express firmness of purpose and sober understanding, although his actions had frequently been at variance with this last attribute." [33]

Catharine returns to her final agony: Ilbrahim dies in her arms. And after still more years of even more "unbridled fanaticism," heightened by the absence of any earthly ties, she finally returns to the Pearson household, "her fierce and vindictive nature . . . softened by the same griefs which had once irritated it." [34] In time, her transformation wins over the Puritans, and when she dies many mourners follow her to her grave beside her son's. Both forces have spent themselves.

There remains but one final deletion to consider. Originally Hawthorne had closed his tale with these words: "My heart is glad of this triumph of our better nature; it gives me a kindlier feeling [207] for the fathers of my native land; and with it I will close the tale." [35] Perhaps Hawthorne omitted this extraneous "story-teller's" comment so as better to preserve the effect of imaginative reality; however, he closed so many another tale in a similar manner that such a conclusion would be extremely tenuous. But it does seem reasonable to assume that he deleted the passage because it would have tended to cast the greatest burden of guilt upon the Puritans; however, as I have attempted to demonstrate, Hawthorne manipulated his material, especially through his revisions, so as to point up the mutuality of guilt. Therefore, it seems to me, the theme of this tale is more than just a dramatized social tract—"a mature study of bigotry and persecution" [36]—although it is that too. Haw-

[33] *Token*, p. 229.   [34] *Works*, I, 125.   [35] *Token*, p. 240.
[36] Mark Van Doren, *Nathaniel Hawthorne* (New York, 1949), p. 77.

thorne's revisions in this tale so generalize and equalize the terms of the guilt, that, in its final effect, the thematic implication of the story transcends any particular manifestation of evil. For Hawthorne, more than for any of his contemporaries except Melville, the existence of an Evil Principle was a reality; [37] and this tale, ultimately, contemplates the tragedy of an innocent child and a Christian adult caught up by this elemental condition of existence, of which the historical act of persecution is but a grim reflection.[208]

"The Fruit of That Forbidden Tree": A Reading of "The Gentle Boy" *

"Courage, man; the hurt cannot be much."
"No, 'tis not so deep as a well, nor so wide as a church door; but 'tis enough, 'twill serve."   *Romeo and Juliet*

Even in Ilbrahim, Hawthorne's gentle boy, "sweet infant of the skies," the mortal taste of the fruit of that forbidden tree corrupts his heavenly nature and makes his heart elect as friend a "foul hearted little villain." Nowhere does Hawthorne's obsession with the enigma of original sin show itself more poignantly than in his story of "this poor broken-hearted infant." "The Gentle Boy" was written off by critics as an early and simple work, a work patently a "study of bigotry and martyrdom." [1] More recently it has been considered a tale showing the simplest Christian ethic—pure generosity and loving-kindness—pulling down the pillars of the Christian temple to crush and shatter [2] *or* the tragedy of Ilbrahim caught between two abstract forces, Puritanism and Quakerism.[3] My reading of the story indicates that in "The Gentle Boy" Hawthorne is

---

[37] "There is evil in every human heart," he wrote in his notebook for 1836 (*Works,* IX, 43).

[1] Mark Van Doren, *Nathaniel Hawthorne* (New York: Viking Press, 1957), p. 72.

[2] Louise Dauner, "The 'Case' of Tobias Pearson: Hawthorne and the Ambiguities," *American Literature,* XXI (January, 1950), 464–72.

[3] Seymour Gross, "Hawthorne's Revision of 'The Gentle Boy,'" *American Literature,* XXVI (May, 1954), 196–208.

* This essay by Agnes McNeill Donohue is published here for the first time.

making yet another pilgrimage into blighted human nature and post-lapsarian frailty. The journey is recorded in mordant irony, Hawthorne's birthmark, a birthmark always there, even though its outline is drawn in the faint lines of ambiguity.

Hawthorne's acute psychological intuition of the ironic way in which mankind's Eden-wounds lead to heartbreak shapes all the characters in the story. Ilbrahim's father and mother, the Pearsons, and the old Quaker are victimized by a hostile society, and in turn they seek a victim—the archetypal victim—Adamic Ilbrahim. Caught in the dualism of masochism and sadism, Ilbrahim is "used" by the self-seekers. Damned to be their sweating selves, the isolated ones fasten on the innocent, who is led into evil by his own flawed nature. Implicit in the theme of fallen nature are the other favorite Hawthorne leitmotivs: isolation and estrangement; secret guilt; the historical past universalized; the search for a father and a home; the initiation into evil; and the loss of innocence.

The story is deceptively simple, but the irony is never more specific and plangent. After an historical introduction which sets the exact time (1656) of the Puritan persecution of the Quakers in New England, Hawthorne opens the action on the evening of an autumn day. Tobias Pearson, a Puritan settler returning to his home, hears crying coming from the place in the wilderness where that morning two Quakers had been hanged by the Puritans in a frenzy of religious zeal. He finds a beautiful six-year-old boy clinging to the fresh grave. The child tells him: "they call me Ilbrahim, and my home is here." Pearson compassionately pleads with the child to come home with him after first conquering his revulsion in discovering that the child is the son of one of the murdered Quakers. The child finally yields and Pearson carries him home and gives him over to the kind ministrations of his wife Dorothy. The Pearsons' own children have died in the New World, and Ilbrahim is welcomed in their place. Despite the hostility of the neighbors, the Pearsons bring Ilbrahim to the meetinghouse where the minister preaches eloquently on the horrors of Quakerism. After the sermon a fanatic Quaker woman mounts the platform and delivers imprecations against her persecutors. She is Ilbrahim's mother, Catharine, sentenced to exile, and she gives Ilbrahim to the care of the Pearsons. Ilbrahim then lives quietly with the Pearsons until a "residue of unappropriated love" causes him to attempt friendship with a deformed Puritan boy who was injured in the neighborhood and is being nursed by Dorothy Pearson. After the boy has returned to his home, Ilbrahim, one summer day, attempts to join a group of children of which the invalid is one. They turn on him and beat him brutally; the "friend" strikes him on the mouth while pretending to help him. Ilbrahim is finally rescued and slowly regains his physical health; but his soul is stricken. On a winter night some months later, Pearson, whose religious sympathies have been more and more with the Quakers but who hates himself for his "heresy," is reading the Bible with an elderly Quaker exile. Dorothy is watching over the dying Ilbrahim. In the wind and storm Catharine returns for a deathbed farewell to Ilbrahim. After the death of the gentle boy, Catharine is more frenzied than ever, but the persecutions abate by decree and she gradually becomes milder. At her death she is spoken of with pity by her former persecutors.

The story is divided into six sections—opening and closing with an historical account of New England religious history which provides a patterned beginning and end. The second scene occurs in the forest. The third section, in the meetinghouse, occurs two weeks later. A forest-crowned amphitheater behind the meetinghouse is the setting of the fourth scene wherein the brutality to Ilbrahim takes place. Some months later the Pearson household is the setting for the penultimate horror of Ilbrahim's death. Symbolically, the early scene of Ilbrahim clinging to his father's grave is repeated when the story ends with a vision of Catharine's new grave and Ilbrahim's "green and sunken grave."

The significant physical violence in the tale occurs in the forest, the forest of primitive, unleashed malevolent forces. Ilbrahim's father has been hanged in the forest, and in the forest-crowned amphitheater Ilbrahim is attacked by "the brood of baby-fiends." The "civilized" violence takes place in the clearing—the town—where hypocrisy and sham mask the bestial behavior. It is in the meetinghouse that the minister incites the Puritans to persecution of the Quakers, that Catharine hurls imprecations at her persecutors, and that Ilbrahim is given away by his mother to the Pearsons. In the Pearson home in the clearing, Ilbrahim dies brokenhearted. There is constant movement in the story; the characters go from the forest to the clearing, the wilderness, the desert, the prison. All places seem to be not a home but a prison, a prison of human misery, and all the characters are on a pilgrimage.

All of the characters bear wounds: Catharine is persecuted in mind and body; Pearson is wounded by his dead children, his uneasy religious convictions, his loss of position and money; Dorothy is bereft of her children and persecuted because of Ilbrahim and Pearson; Ilbrahim dies of his wounds, not physical but psychic. But all are stricken with the fatal wound of humanity, and this wound is congenital.

A close analysis of the sections of the tale is necessary before the subtle meaning of the story is clear. The historical opening and closing is a favorite Hawthorne device. It becomes evident upon examination that Hawthorne is far less interested in the historical foundations of any given story than he is in using the device to create a superficial verisimilitude. Hawthorne establishes the links with the past but once that has been done, his intention is not historical but psychological. Most source studies of Hawthorne stories usually throw light only on the first paragraphs, because Hawthorne uses the historical event to provide a stepping-off place into the realms of his art: dark fantasy; brooding imagination; and universal human guilt. Thus the historical opening and closing serve only ironically to emphasize the unhistorical, timeless world where Hawthorne's "constant care is not to please but to remind of our, and Adam's curse."

The forest scene opens in the autumn twilight. A strong wind buffets the lonely figure of Ilbrahim clinging to his father's grave and it even plagues the strong characters driven by their own fanaticism and bigotry. The wind moans through the story and howls at Ilbrahim's death. Around all the violence of the tale roars the wind of desolation, a primary and consistent symbol in the story.

The grave is the symbolic center of the story as is the gravestone in "Roger Malvin's Burial," and the pillory in *The Scarlet Letter*. Ilbrahim attaches himself to his father's grave and says, "My home is here." (As in so many of Hawthorne's stories, the characters adumbrate their own fate.) Pearson promises Ilbrahim a new life and home; paradoxically, Ilbrahim in going to Pearson's home, finds not life but death. When Tobias and Ilbrahim reach the Pearson home, the description of the house is more the description of a shut, warm grave than a living home: it is "situated in the nook of a wood-covered hill, whither it seemed to have crept for protection"; the door is barred and must be opened. The meetinghouse too is described in burial-house terms: "the pine-built and undecorated house of prayer"; "the interior aspect of the meeting house was rude. . . . low ceiling, the unplastered walls, the naked wood work." The attack on Ilbrahim occurs in the ampitheater behind the meetinghouse-grave and the death of Ilbrahim occurs back in the home-grave, even more coffin-like because of the diminished and impoverished state of the Pearsons. The last scene is the grave of Catharine and the "green and sunken grave" of Ilbrahim.

In the second scene Tobias takes Ilbrahim home to Dorothy because he has been moved by compassion. But unlike the Biblical Tobias, his motives are not entirely pure. Pearson has been having religious difficulties; he has felt guilty about his own children whose deaths his neighbors imputed to his worldly motives in coming to New England; he has tired of religious war under Cromwell; he has responded to an inward voice in rescuing Ilbrahim, an imperceptible stirring of Quaker feelings; and he feels half convinced that he is a backslider, as his Puritan neighbors say he is, for befriending a Quaker heretic. These conflicts in Pearson lead him to a spiritual blindness as the Biblical Tobias was subjected to physical blindness; Pearson is attracted to Quaker belief, and because he is, he hates himself and turns inward in a rage of self-attack. If, like the Biblical Tobias, Pearson's blindness is a test of his virtue, he fails the test. Pearson grows bitter under his persecution; his son does not restore his sight. Pearson broods inwardly, his son perishes, and Pearson's "sight" is never recovered.

In the third section of the story—the events at the meetinghouse—imagery that was just suggested in part two is made explicit. We have learned that Pearson had fought in the religious wars with Cromwell as a cornet of dragoons and was presently a lieutenant in the trainbands. Pearson's role as a military man in the strife of religious war with devils and heretics is adopted and expanded by Hawthorne into an elaborate military metaphor to symbolize the bellicose and contentious nature of Puritanism that brings not peace but the sword. Biblical authority sanctions the imaginative concept of actual warfare with the devil, and Calvin complacently expands and accentuates it.[4] Hawthorne, however, uses the military imagery to suggest the psychological subtleties of religious belief clothed in a uniform of external authority which conceals ravening doubts and compulsions to sadistic behavior. The worshippers are summoned to religious exercises by the beat of a drum. The people respond at once in a disciplined, mechanical way. "At the

---

[4] *Calvin: Institutes of the Christian Religion*, ed. John T. McNeill (Philadelphia: The Westminster Press, 1960), Vol. I, p. 173. "And Paul, after he has warned us that our struggle is not with flesh and blood, but with the princes of the air, with the powers of darkness, and spiritual wickedness [Eph. 6:12], forthwith bids us put on that armor capable of sustaining so great and dangerous a contest [Eph. 6:13 ff.]. We have been forewarned that an enemy relentlessly threatens us, an enemy who is the very embodiment of rash boldness, of military prowess, of crafty wiles, of untiring zeal and haste, of every conceivable weapon and of skill in the science of warfare. We must, then, bend our every effort to this goal: that we should not let ourselves be overwhelmed by carelessness or faintheartedness, but on the contrary, with courage rekindled stand our ground in combat. Since this military service ends only at death, let us urge ourselves to perseverance. Indeed, conscious of our weakness and ignorance, let us especially call upon God's help, relying upon him alone in whatever we attempt, since it is he alone who can supply us with counsel and strength, courage and armor."

first sound of that martial call to the place of holy and quiet thoughts, Tobias and Dorothy set forth. . . ." Hawthorne's irony is apparent in the juxtaposition of "martial call" and "holy and quiet thoughts." With the "thundering summons" in their ears, the congregation forms a "formidable phalanx" at the door to indicate their fury at the Pearsons' audacity in bringing the little heretic Ilbrahim to church. The ploys of battle continue during the service; the Puritan minister denounces the Quakers and warns of the "danger of pity." Ilbrahim's mother emerges from her muffled cloak to hurl down imprecations at her persecutors; "hatred and revenge now wrapped themselves in the garb of piety." Religion is the name which fallen humanity has given to strife and warfare. If the Puritans are armored and equipped with weapons, then the Quakers are the eager martyrs goading them and seducing them into using their weapons. In the coffin-grave meetinghouse the vengeful, cruel, Calvinist Jehovah father figure in the guise of the Puritan minister wars with the fanatic, wild-eyed, unsexed, malignant mother figure in the guise of Catharine the Quakeress. Pearson, wrapped in uneasy doubts, turns in on himself; Dorothy's "rational piety" superficially comforts her. The congregation, like all Hawthorne's crowds, is devious, fickle, capricious, and protean. Everything takes place over the head and on the heart of little Ilbrahim, the forgotten victim, the lost cause. Catharine finally gives Ilbrahim away to the Pearsons and Hawthorne describes the scene: "The two females, as they held each a hand of Ilbrahim, formed a practical allegory; it was rational piety and unbridled fanaticism contending for the empire of a young heart." Ironically, neither side triumphs, but instead, the "young heart" is broken. The physical violence in the forest where Ilbrahim's father was hanged and the brutal attack made on Ilbrahim by the children is no worse than this civilized violence of the meetinghouse. The physical brutality is horrible in itself, but at least it cannot be totally disguised by hypocrisy and religious fraud.

Catharine leaves Ilbrahim with the Pearsons, cautioning them that he has been baptized in blood, and asking, "Will ye keep the mark fresh and ruddy upon his forehead?" Here Hawthorne prefigures the physical violence to be done to Ilbrahim. Catharine goes in search of further persecution, "the apostle of her own unquiet heart."

Hawthorne has described the battlefield, the combatants, the weapons of both sides; it is now necessary to recount the actual warfare in which the spoils become the victim. Up to this point, Ilbrahim has been "used" by adults; it is when he is "used" by his peers that his heart is completely broken.

When a neighbor child is injured in a fall from a tree and Dorothy undertakes to nurse him, Ilbrahim is tempted to bestow his "residue of unappropriated love." Hawthorne subtly endows the injured boy with the characteristics of the devil. The boy falls out of a tree; his "countenance impressed a beholder disagreeably" because the mouth is distorted and the eyebrows are irregular and close together; there is "an almost imperceptible twist of every joint"; the boy is sullen and is thought to be "obtuse in intellect," yet later in his life "evinced ambition and very peculiar [5] talents"; and finally Hawthorne suggests personal and moral irregularities, shrewdness and moral obliquity. Although Ilbrahim is appalled at the boy's moral deviousness and would have been deterred from making a friend of this boy in other circumstances, he is the victim of his own loving yet bent nature, and "nestled continually by the bedside of the little stranger."

Ilbrahim's giving of his love makes him totally vulnerable. Later, when he sees a group of Puritan children playing, he who had always before elected a more secure isolation approaches them "with a look of sweet confidence on his fair and spiritual face, as if, having manifested his love to one of them, he no longer had to fear a repulse from their society." Hawthorne's description of the attack upon Ilbrahim by the children is masterly. When Ilbrahim first sees the children, they are playing gleefully: "a heavenly little band," their "light and airy voices" coming from their "untainted bosoms," the "bliss of childhood" gushing "from its innocence." When Ilbrahim approaches, Hawthorne describes eloquently the fallen and depraved nature even of children, according to Puritan theology: [6]

All at once, the devil of their fathers entered into the unbreeched fanatics, and sending up a fierce, shrill cry, they rushed upon the poor Quaker child. In an instant, he was the centre of a brood of baby-fiends, who lifted sticks against him, pelted him with stones, and displayed an instinct of destruction far more loathsome than the bloodthirstiness of manhood.

Ilbrahim's "friend" calls to him to come and take his hand; Ilbrahim struggles to obey. Then is administered to the gentle boy the *coup de grace:*

[5] Hawthorne's use of this equivocal, neutral word is enormously suggestive.
[6] Calvin, *op. cit.,* Vol. I, p. 251. ". . . they have been enveloped in original sin and defiled by its stains. For that reason, even infants themselves, while they carry their condemnation along with them from their mother's womb, are guilty not of another's fault but of their own. For, even though the fruits of their iniquity have not yet come forth, they have the seed enclosed within them. Indeed their whole nature is a seed of sin; hence it can only be hateful and abhorrent to God. From this it follows that it is rightly considered sin in God's sight, for without guilt, there would be no accusation."

After watching the victim's struggling approach with a calm smile and unabashed eye, the foul-hearted little villain lifted his staff and struck Ilbrahim on the mouth so forcibly that the blood issued in a stream.

Ilbrahim no longer tries to defend himself and drops his arms. He is beaten down and trampled and finally rescued by a "few neighbors who put themselves to the trouble of rescuing the little heretic." Ilbrahim recovers physically after long and careful nursing, but spiritually he is broken and waits for death.

The sacrifice of the innocent victim occurs in a "forest-crowned amphitheater," a public place;[7] it is a public sacrifice ritually enacted. Ilbrahim is the human sacrifice demanded by the youthful fiends under the direction of the twisted child who delivers the mortal blow with his devil's staff.[8] The horrifying contrast Hawthorne makes between the innocent children at their guileless play and their devilish and obscene attack upon Ilbrahim is one of his most explicit statements of the capriciousness of man's fallen nature. Ilbrahim is misled by his own wounds to seek friendship with a devil; his encounter with the devil and his "brood of baby-fiends" gives him his mortal wounds. Ilbrahim is betrayed by his own misbegotten and misplaced love, betrayed by the Judas words of friendship, "Fear not, Ilbrahim, come hither and take my hand." Withered humanity cannot stand the affront of superior virtue; that virtue must be corrupted into shrewdness[9] or destroyed. Ilbrahim refuses to fight back or acquire guile and so, because the blows were delivered under the guise of love—although love betrayed—they are mortal and he must die.

Hawthorne could have found no more terrifying and moving symbol of the depravity of man than the hideous transfiguration of the children from blissful innocents to knowledgeable baby-fiends. Hawthorne's disciple James later shows he has learned his lesson well in *The Turn of the Screw*, and in our own time Tennessee Williams has given children in *Suddenly Last Summer* the final obscenity of cannibals. With terrible irony Hawthorne seems to be saying that we move from our blighted, isolated selves to love and social involvement; but in this movement away from isolation we either become armored and shrewd or like Ilbrahim, die.

The autumn wind of desolation that swept around Ilbrahim as he

---

[7] "As in *The Europeans*, there is always in Hawthorne's best writings the sense of a deeply significant public drama being enacted behind the deceptively simple apparent story." Q. D. Leavis, "Hawthorne as Poet—Part II," *Sewanee Review*, LIX (Summer, 1951), 457-58.

[8] Cf. the devil's staff in "Young Goodman Brown."

[9] Cf. Robin in "My Kinsman, Major Molineux," who finally becomes shrewd *after* his initiation into evil.

clung to his father's freshly turned grave becomes in the fifth section of the story a howling winter blizzard as Ilbrahim quietly seeks his own grave. The winter wind—not so unkind as man's ingratitude—blows home to Ilbrahim his wandering, distracted mother. The Pearson household has undergone changes since Ilbrahim became a tenant; the "implements of war" have disappeared, "the sword was broken, the helm and cuirass were cast away forever; the soldier had done with battles." Even though Tobias Pearson has resigned his office with the Puritan men of blood, the "furniture of peace" has likewise disappeared. Since Pearson's adoption of Quakerism, fines, imprisonments and "his own neglect of temporal affairs" have made him poor. But as his possessions waned, Pearson's spirit has not grown rich and comforted in his new-found religion. Pearson has only changed roles, not his heart; from the persecutor, he has become the persecuted, from the hunter, the hunted, and Hawthorne ironically suggests that even though this is an apparent reversal, it is difficult to tell the two states apart. Pearson still does not "belong"; he is isolated, estranged, embittered, full of self-pity. Like the Biblical Tobias, he has been blinded, but he can only lament; Pearson's son does not consort with an angel who will restore his sight.

The old Quaker who is lodging with the Pearsons provides an interesting contrast to the "brood of baby-fiends." As revolting as the children's viciousness is the noxious old man's "solacing" of Pearson with his story of the deathbed desertion of his child when the spirit summoned him. When Catharine knocks at the door, both Pearson and the old Quaker compete for the expected persecution. Since it is Catharine and not the men of blood, the old Quaker relinquishes masochism for sadism as he tells her of dying Ilbrahim whose "tottering footsteps shall impede thine own no more." In Catharine's return, Hawthorne allows us to take no comfort, for her "female form . . . shone out, cold and wintry." The paradox of the mother who is yet "cold and wintry" indicates a woman who has abdicated her role of mother and female for the role of prophet and fanatic. Ilbrahim dies in the wind, in this household of desolation, amid the self-seekers who have "used" him for their own purposes.

In the sixth section the historical narrative is resumed and we learn of Catharine's increased fanaticism after the death of her son. Gradually, however, the king's mandate has a mitigating effect upon the men of blood, and they begin to regard Catharine less in wrath than in pity. Less able to withstand pity than persecution, Catharine dies. Hawthorne's bitterest irony is reserved for the populace—all of selfish, blighted humanity is impaled on his final words:

When the course of years had made the features of the unobtrusive mourner familiar in the settlement, she became a subject of not deep, but general, interest; a being on whom the otherwise superfluous sympathies of all might be bestowed. Everyone spoke of her with that degree of pity which it is pleasant to experience; everyone was ready to do for her the little kindnesses which are not costly, yet manifest good will; and when at last she died, a long train of her once bitter persecutors followed her, with decent sadness and tears that were not painful, to her place by Ilbrahim's green and sunken grave.

Hawthorne's language is never more dispassionate and urbane as here where he damns all lukewarm unloving humanity to hell with his faint praise.

Ironically, the story of a gentle boy is a cruel and barbarous tale. Sadistic Puritans and masochistic Quakers—all are whited sepulchers using religion as a flail to enact primitive and primordial rites of chastisement and sacrifice. Both seek a victim—an Ilbrahim—to satisfy their lust for blood. But the victim must be as innocent as shriveled humanity can provide; and so it is a child, a lamb to be given to the slaughter, to be handed over to the bloody hands, the warped bodies and the contorted throats that demand his crucifixion. Hawthorne records in his notebooks in 1836 that "there is evil in every human heart" as if his own experience of life had only corroborated Calvin: "If these are the hereditary endowments of the human race, it is futile to seek anything good in our nature. Indeed, I grant that not all these wicked traits appear in every man; yet one cannot deny that this hydra lurks in the heart of each." [10] The idea of the hydra in the heart, this original sin in the Calvinistic damnatory theology that Hawthorne could not accept yet was unable to disavow, so conditioned his imagination that his brooding fancy produced at its best— as in "The Gentle Boy"—a tale forlorn and sorrowing, where mankind is caught "spitting from the mouth the withered apple-seed."

If this story is a saint's legend, as Harry Levin avers,[11] then how ironic that the sainted child Ilbrahim has no wholesome effect whatever upon any character in the tale. Tobias Pearson, although outwardly converted from a man of blood to a man of light, is left stumbling in the darkness of self-pity and the pride of self-attack. His worldly prosperity consumed, it might follow dogmatically that his spiritual well-being would prosper; but Tobias confesses himself "an accursed man . . . I will lay me down

---

[10] Calvin, Vol. I, p. 291.
[11] ". . . this saint's legend of an infant martyr. . . ." Harry Levin, *The Power of Blackness* (New York: Alfred A. Knopf, Inc., 1958), p. 54.

in the dust and lift up my head no more." Catharine, the child's mother, deserts him and continues her frantic pursuit of persecution. She attains gentleness only when her persecutors have wearied of their work. Dorothy Pearson, bereft of her own children, is further deprived and tormented by the victimizing of Ilbrahim. Catharine abdicates motherhood but Dorothy, the would-be mother, is never permitted a maternal role. Ilbrahim in his need and misery calls pitifully for his natural mother and disregards Dorothy except in her capacity as nurse. The old Quaker is as inflexible at Ilbrahim's deathbed as he was callous at the deathbed of his own daughter. The fanatic is so insulated within himself that the lives of others impinge on his consciousness only to the extent that they can be useful to him. Both the old Quaker and Catharine use the grief associated with the death of their children for their private purposes of martyrdom. The young invalid-devil whom Ilbrahim loves is remarkably unchanged by his association with the gentle boy. He is quick to betray Ilbrahim and, far from repenting or despairing like Judas, is said by Hawthorne to have evinced at a later period in his life "ambition and very peculiar talents." During the lifetime of the gentle boy, Ilbrahim aroused only antipathy from the general populace; if they were touched by his beauty and winning manners, they ascribed it to some kind of witchcraft, "for the bigots, when the outer surfaces of their iron hearts had been softened and again grew hard, affirmed that no merely natural cause could have so worked upon them." The lessening of their hatred toward the Quakers in general, which finally came about some years later, could not be ascribed to the influence of Ilbrahim, but to the abatement of persecution through the process of time.

"The Gentle Boy" is told in a rather more leisurely fashion than most of Hawthorne's tales. The style is always superficially limpid and pellucid, the ambiguities wreathed round with neutral words, vague hints and guesses to lull the reader into the belief that he understands everything that Hawthorne is saying. The dialogue is sparse and controlled, therefore far less offensive and astral than some of the speeches of little Pearl in *The Scarlet Letter*. Hawthorne's irony is never more explicit or astringent, and one wonders why this rhetorical excellence is absent from some of the later works.

In most Hawthorne stories, the characters are not particularly memorable because they carry too much of the burden of the symbolism. This is not true in "The Gentle Boy." The characters are not full-blooded human beings; rather they are somewhat asthenic and attenuated, yet they successfully carry the burden of Hawthorne's intention and are not drowned in the symbolism. Tobias Pearson is a bruised and doubting man filled with religious unease, betrayed by his compassion for Ilbrahim, yet using the boy to ward off complete isolation and emotional sterility. Our sympathies for him fail when he becomes totally self-absorbed and miserable. Dorothy Pearson is one of Hawthorne's "good women," colorless, devoted, a woman of the hearth not of the head, full of "rational piety," a lukewarm virtue that is no match for fanaticism or bigotry. Catharine, Ilbrahim's mother, is a rich and complex character, one of Hawthorne's dark beauties whose luxuriance has been despoiled. In her fanaticism, she becomes cold and dry like the ashes in her hair; her feminine softness is lost in her sackcloth garment. Uneasy in her role as persecuted martyr, she has abdicated her vocation as a mother; at the end of the story she has diminished into an "unobtrusive mourner." The old Quaker and the boy-devil are types. The old Quaker, consumed alternately by zeal and hate, is a pathetic shell. The devil-child, Ilbrahim's erstwhile friend, is more subtly drawn as a malicious monster, shrewd and filled with guile. The Puritan minister is sketched briefly but devastatingly as a pompous, mean, and narrow bigot. Ilbrahim himself is Hawthorne's triumph. Not a total symbol like Pearl, the pathetic and fantastic "domesticated sun-beam" arouses the reader's pity for his isolation and his yearning to love. Sweet but not quite saccharine, little Ilbrahim in his defenselessness and submission emblemizes the blight man was born for—it is Ilbrahim you mourn for.

Each one of the characters is isolated in his little prison of self and is unable to communicate with anyone else. Tobias Pearson is unable to share his religious doubts with anyone; Dorothy Pearson is loving, but her love is not conveyed in any productive way; Catharine's fanatic enthusiasm has sealed off her heart and her genuine emotions; and little Ilbrahim's one tentative and disastrous excursion into love and communication only compels his total withdrawal. In Hawthorne's lonely and secluded world, *every* man is an island.

This analysis has attempted to show that "The Gentle Boy" is not quite as simple as it appears to be. It seems to me that what most of the critics have missed in their treatment of this story is the emotional quality which gives the ambiguity and irony their power. It is only because Hawthorne yearns toward gentleness and innocence that his dry, remorseless indictment of universal human corruption is so moving. He is not resigned either emotionally or rationally to the effects of original sin, and his inquietude gives his work a deep, if negative, religious passion. What is it in the last paragraph of "The Gentle Boy" that makes his rhetoric so compelling but the juxtaposition of two ethics? Only one of these ethics is expressed—that of decent self-regard, in which compassion and love for others cross no threshold of pain. The implied ethic, which serves as ironic contrast, is of course the fundamental Christian ideal of love "costing not less than everything." The agony is that the Christian ethic appears impossible, so that the heart that desires it is forever frustrated.

"The Gentle Boy" is one more oblique statement of Hawthorne's tragic vision of deprived mankind in which even a little child—Ilbrahim,[12] the foreigner, the Samaritan—must die of the disease of humanity for which there is no cure. Hawthorne's horror and rejection of man's total depravity, and his faltering acknowledgment of it result in the ironic perfection of his art. The story is a wry and anguished cry, "Damn, damned Humanity!"

The Birthmark [*]

In the latter part of the last century there lived a man of science, an eminent proficient in every branch of natural philosophy, who not long before our story opens had made experience of a spiritual affinity more attractive than any chemical one. He had left his laboratory to the care of an assistant, cleared his fine countenance from the furnace smoke, washed the stain of acids from his fingers, and persuaded a beautiful woman to become his wife. In those days when the comparatively recent discovery of electricity and other kindred mysteries of Nature seemed to open paths into the region of miracle, it was not unusual for the love of science to rival the love of woman in its depth and absorbing energy.

---

[12] The name "Ilbrahim" is rather a puzzle. It is not a Turkish name as Hawthorne indicates; the nearest Turkish name is "Ibrahim" which may be what Hawthorne had in mind. "Ibrahim" is the Turkish equivalent of "Abraham." In the ninth century there were a group of Syrian heretics who denied the divinity of Christ and who were known as Abrahamites or Ibrahamites after their leader, Ibrahim of Antioch. Also, during Hawthorne's lifetime, there was a famous general of the Ottoman Empire named Ibrahim Pasha (1789–1848). However, the name of the gentle boy is not Ibrahim but Ilbrahim, speculate how we may.

[*] This story was printed in *The Pioneer* in March, 1843, and in *Mosses from an Old Manse* in 1846.

The higher intellect, the imagination, the spirit, and even the heart might all find their congenial aliment in pursuits which, as some of their ardent votaries believed, would ascend from one step of powerful intelligence to another, until the philosopher should lay his hand on the secret of creative force and perhaps make new worlds for himself. We know not whether Aylmer possessed this degree of faith in man's ultimate control over Nature. He had devoted himself, however, too unreservedly to scientific studies ever to be weaned from them by any second passion. His love for his young wife might prove the stronger of the two; but it could only be by intertwining itself with his love of science, and uniting the strength of the latter to his own.[47]

Such a union accordingly took place, and was attended with truly remarkable consequences and a deeply impressive moral. One day, very soon after their marriage, Aylmer sat gazing at his wife with a trouble in his countenance that grew stronger until he spoke.

"Georgiana," said he, "has it never occurred to you that the mark upon your cheek might be removed?"

"No, indeed," said she, smiling; but perceiving the seriousness of his manner, she blushed deeply. "To tell you the truth it has been so often called a charm that I was simple enough to imagine it might be so."

"Ah, upon another face perhaps it might," replied her husband; "but never on yours. No, dearest Georgiana, you came so nearly perfect from the hand of Nature that this slightest possible defect, which we hesitate whether to term a defect or a beauty, shocks me, as being the visible mark of earthly imperfection."

"Shocks you, my husband!" cried Georgiana, deeply hurt; at first reddening with momentary anger, but then bursting into tears. "Then why did you take me from my mother's side? You cannot love what shocks you!"

To explain this conversation it must be mentioned that in the centre of Georgiana's left cheek there was a singular mark, deeply interwoven, as it were, with the texture and substance of her face. In the usual state of her complexion—a healthy though delicate bloom—the mark wore a tint of deeper crimson, which imperfectly defined its shape amid the surrounding rosiness. When she blushed it gradually [48] became more indistinct, and finally vanished amid the triumphant rush of blood that bathed the whole cheek with its brilliant glow. But if any shifting motion caused her to turn pale there was the mark again, a crimson stain upon the snow, in what Aylmer sometimes deemed an almost fearful distinctness. Its shape bore not a little similarity to the human hand, though of the smallest pygmy size. Georgiana's lovers were wont to say that some fairy at her birth hour had laid her tiny hand upon the infant's cheek, and left this impress there in token of the magic endowments that were to give her such sway over all hearts. Many a desperate swain would have risked life for the privilege of pressing his lips to the mysterious hand. It must not be concealed, however, that the impression wrought by this fairy sign manual varied exceedingly, according to the difference of temperament in the beholders. Some fastidious persons—but they were exclusively of her own sex—affirmed that the bloody hand, as they chose to call it, quite destroyed the effect of Georgiana's beauty, and rendered her countenance even hideous. But it would be as reasonable to say that one of those small blue stains which sometimes occur in the purest statuary marble would convert the Eve of Powers to a monster. Masculine observers, if the birthmark did not heighten their admiration, contented themselves with wishing it away, that the world might possess one living specimen of ideal loveliness without the semblance of a flaw. After his marriage,—for he thought little or nothing of the matter before,—Aylmer discovered that this was the case with himself.

Had she been less beautiful,—if Envy's self could have found aught else to sneer at,—he might have [49] felt his affection heightened by the prettiness of this mimic hand, now vaguely portrayed, now lost, now stealing forth again and glimmering to and fro with every pulse of emotion that throbbed within her heart; but seeing her otherwise so perfect, he found this one defect grow more and more intolerable with every moment of their united lives. It was the fatal flaw of humanity which Nature, in one shape or another, stamps ineffaceably on all her productions, either to imply that they are temporary and finite, or that their perfection must be wrought by toil and pain. The crimson hand expressed the ineludible gripe in which mortality clutches the highest and purest of earthly mould, degrading them into kindred with the lowest, and even with the very brutes, like whom their visible frames return to dust. In this manner, selecting it as the symbol of his wife's liability to sin, sorrow, decay, and death, Aylmer's sombre imagination was not long in rendering the birthmark a frightful object, causing him more trouble and horror than ever Georgiana's beauty, whether of soul or sense, had given him delight.

At all the seasons which should have been their happiest, he invariably and without intending it, nay, in spite of a purpose to the contrary, reverted to this one disastrous topic. Trifling as it at first appeared, it so connected itself with innumerable trains of thought and modes of feeling that it became the central point of all. With the morning twilight Aylmer opened his eyes upon his wife's face and recognized the symbol of imperfection; and when they sat together at the evening hearth his eyes wandered stealthily to her cheek, and beheld, flickering with the blaze of the wood fire, the spectral hand that wrote mortality [50] where he would fain have worshipped. Georgiana soon learned to shudder at his gaze. It needed but a glance with the peculiar expression that his face often wore to change the roses of her cheek into a deathlike paleness, amid which the crimson hand was brought strongly out, like a bass-relief of ruby on the whitest marble.

Late one night when the lights were growing dim, so as hardly to betray the stain on the poor wife's cheek, she herself, for the first time, voluntarily took up the subject.

"Do you remember, my dear Aylmer," said she, with a feeble attempt at a smile, "have you any recollection of a dream last night about this odious hand?"

"None! none whatever!" replied Aylmer, starting; but then he added, in a dry, cold tone, affected for the sake of concealing the real depth of his emotion, "I might well dream of it; for before I fell asleep it had taken a pretty firm hold of my fancy."

"And you did dream of it?" continued Georgiana, hastily; for she dreaded lest a gush of tears should interrupt what she had to say. "A terrible dream! I wonder that you can forget it. Is it possible to forget this one expression?—'It is in her heart now; we must have it out!' Reflect, my husband; for by all means I would have you recall that dream."

The mind is in a sad state when Sleep, the all-involving, cannot confine her spectres within the dim region of her sway, but suffers them to break forth, affrighting this actual life with secrets that perchance belong to a deeper one. Aylmer now remembered his dream. He had fancied himself with his servant Aminadab, attempting an operation for the removal of [51] the birthmark; but the deeper went the knife, the deeper sank the hand, until at length its tiny grasp appeared to have caught hold of Georgiana's heart; whence, however, her husband was inexorably resolved to cut or wrench it away.

When the dream had shaped itself perfectly in his memory, Aylmer sat in his wife's presence with a guilty feeling. Truth often finds its way to the mind close muffled in robes of sleep, and then speaks with uncompromising directness of matters in regard to which we practise an unconscious self-deception during our waking moments. Until now he had not been aware of the tyrannizing influence acquired by one idea over his mind, and of the lengths which he might find in his heart to go for the sake of giving himself peace.

"Aylmer," resumed Georgiana, solemnly, "I know not what may be the cost to both of us to rid me of this fatal birthmark. Perhaps its removal may cause cureless deformity; or it may be the stain goes as deep as life itself. Again: do we know that there is a possibility, on any terms, of unclasping the firm gripe of this little hand which was laid upon me before I came into the world?"

"Dearest Georgiana, I have spent much thought upon the subject," hastily interrupted Aylmer. "I am convinced of the perfect practicability of its removal."

"If there be the remotest possibility of it," continued Georgiana, "let the attempt be made at whatever risk. Danger is nothing to me; for life, while this hateful mark makes me the object of your horror and disgust,—life is a burden which I would fling down with joy. Either remove this dreadful hand, or take my wretched life! You have deep science. All the world bears witness of it. You have achieved [52] great wonders. Cannot you remove this little, little mark, which I cover with the tips of two small fingers? Is this beyond your power, for the sake of your own peace, and to save your poor wife from madness?"

"Noblest, dearest, tenderest wife," cried Aylmer, rapturously, "doubt not my power. I have already given this matter the deepest thought—thought which might almost have enlightened me to create a being less perfect than yourself. Georgiana, you have led me deeper than ever into the heart of science. I feel myself fully competent to render this dear cheek as faultless as its fellow; and then, most beloved, what will be my triumph when I shall have corrected what Nature left imperfect in her fairest work! Even Pygmalion, when his sculptured woman assumed life, felt not greater ecstasy than mine will be."

"It is resolved, then," said Georgiana, faintly smiling. "And, Aylmer, spare me not, though you should find the birthmark take refuge in my heart at last."

Her husband tenderly kissed her cheek—her right cheek—not that which bore the impress of the crimson hand.

The next day Aylmer apprised his wife of a plan that he had formed whereby he might have opportunity for the intense thought and constant watchfulness which the proposed operation would require; while Georgiana, likewise, would enjoy the perfect repose essential to its success. They were to seclude themselves in the extensive apartments occupied by Aylmer as a laboratory, and where, during his toilsome youth, he had made discoveries in the elemental powers of Nature that had roused the admiration of all the learned societies in Europe. Seated calmly in this laboratory, the pale philosopher had investigated [53] the secrets of the highest cloud region and of the profoundest mines; he had satisfied himself of the causes that kindled and kept alive the fires of the volcano; and had explained the mystery of fountains, and how it is that they gush forth, some so bright and pure, and others with such rich medicinal virtues, from the dark bosom of the earth. Here, too, at an earlier period, he had studied the wonders of the human frame, and attempted to fathom the very process by which Nature assimilates all her precious influences from earth and air, and from the spiritual world, to create and foster man, her masterpiece. The latter pursuit, however, Aylmer had long laid aside in unwilling recognition of the truth—against which all seekers sooner or later stumble—that our great creative Mother, while she amuses us with apparently working in the broadest sunshine, is yet severely careful to keep her own secrets, and, in spite of her pretended openness, shows us nothing but results. She permits us, indeed, to mar, but seldom to mend, and, like a jealous patentee, on no account to make. Now, however, Aylmer resumed these half-forgotten investigations; not, of course, with such hopes or wishes as first suggested them; but because they involved much physiological truth and lay in the path of his proposed scheme for the treatment of Georgiana.

As he led her over the threshold of the laboratory, Georgiana was cold and tremulous. Aylmer looked cheerfully into her face, with intent to reassure her, but was so startled with the intense glow of the birthmark upon the whiteness of her cheek that he could not restrain a strong convulsive shudder. His wife fainted.

"Aminadab! Aminadab!" shouted Aylmer, stamping violently on the floor.[54]

Forthwith there issued from an inner apartment a man of low stature, but bulky frame, with shaggy hair hanging about his visage, which was grimed with the vapors of the furnace. This personage had been Aylmer's underworker during his whole scientific career, and was admirably fitted for that office by his great mechanical readiness, and the skill with which, while incapable of comprehending a single principle, he executed all the details of his master's experiments. With his vast strength, his shaggy hair, his smoky aspect, and the indescribable earthiness that incrusted him, he seemed to represent man's physical nature; while Aylmer's slender figure, and pale, intellectual face, were no less apt a type of the spiritual element.

"Throw open the door of the boudoir, Aminadab," said Aylmer, "and burn a pastil."

"Yes, master," answered Aminadab, looking intently at the lifeless form of Georgiana; and then he muttered to himself, "If she were my wife I'd never part with that birthmark."

When Georgiana recovered consciousness she found herself breathing an atmosphere of penetrating fragrance, the gentle potency of which had recalled her from her deathlike faintness. The scene around her looked like enchantment. Aylmer had converted those smoky, dingy, sombre rooms, where he had spent his brightest years in recondite pursuits, into a series of beautiful apartments not unfit to be the secluded abode of a lovely woman. The walls were hung with gorgeous curtains, which imparted the combination of grandeur and grace that no other species of adornment can achieve; and as they fell from the ceiling to the floor, their rich and ponderous folds, concealing all angles and straight lines, appeared to shut in the scene [55] from infinite space. For aught Georgiana knew, it might be a pavilion among the clouds. And Aylmer, excluding the sunshine, which would have interfered with his chemical processes, had supplied its place with perfumed lamps, emitting flames of various hue, but all uniting in a soft, impurpled radiance. He now knelt by his wife's side, watching her earnestly, but without alarm; for he was confident in his science, and felt that he could draw a magic circle round her within which no evil might intrude.

"Where am I? Ah, I remember," said Georgiana, faintly; and she placed her hand over her cheek to hide the terrible mark from her husband's eyes.

"Fear not, dearest!" exclaimed he. "Do not shrink from me! Believe me, Georgiana, I even rejoice in this single imperfection, since it will be such a rapture to remove it."

"Oh, spare me!" sadly replied his wife. "Pray do not look at it again. I never can forget that convulsive shudder."

In order to soothe Georgiana, and, as it were, to release her mind from the burden of actual things, Aylmer now put in practice some of the light and playful secrets which science had taught him among its profounder lore. Airy figures, absolutely bodiless ideas, and forms of unsubstantial beauty came and danced before her, imprinting their momentary footsteps on beams of light. Though she had some indistinct idea of the method of these optical phenomena, still the illusion was almost perfect enough to warrant the belief that her husband possessed sway over the spiritual world. Then again, when she felt a wish to look forth from her seclusion, immediately, as if her thoughts were answered, the procession of external existence [56] flitted across a screen. The scenery and the figures of actual life were perfectly represented, but with that bewitching, yet indescribable difference which always makes a picture, an image, or a shadow so much more attractive than the original. When wearied of this, Aylmer bade her cast her eyes upon a vessel containing a quantity of earth. She did so, with little interest at first; but was soon startled to perceive the germ of a plant shooting upward from the soil. Then came the slender stalk; the leaves gradually unfolded themselves; and amid them was a perfect and lovely flower.

"It is magical!" cried Georgiana. "I dare not touch it."

"Nay, pluck it," answered Aylmer,—"pluck it, and inhale its brief perfume while you may. The flower will wither in a few moments and leave nothing save its brown seed vessels; but thence may be perpetuated a race as ephemeral as itself."

But Georgiana had no sooner touched the flower than the whole plant suffered a blight, its leaves turning coal-black as if by the agency of fire.

"There was too powerful a stimulus," said Aylmer, thoughtfully.

To make up for this abortive experiment, he proposed to take her portrait by a scientific process of his own invention. It was to be effected by rays of light striking upon a polished plate of metal. Georgiana assented; but, on looking at the result, was affrighted to find the features of the portrait blurred and indefinable; while the minute figure of a hand appeared where the cheek should have been. Aylmer snatched the metallic plate and threw it into a jar of corrosive acid.

Soon, however, he forgot these mortifying failures.[57] In the intervals of study and chemical experiment he came to her flushed and exhausted, but seemed invigorated by her presence, and spoke in glowing language of the resources of his art. He gave a history of the long dynasty of the alchemists, who spent so many ages in quest of the universal solvent by which the golden principle might be elicited from all things vile and base. Aylmer appeared to believe that, by the plainest scientific logic, it was altogether within the limits of possibility to discover this long-sought medium; "but," he added, "a philosopher who should go deep enough to acquire the power would attain too lofty a wisdom to stoop to the exercise of it." Not less singular were his opinions in regard to the elixir vitæ. He more than intimated that it was at his option to concoct a liquid that should prolong life for years, perhaps interminably; but that it would produce a discord in Nature which all the world, and chiefly the quaffer of the immortal nostrum, would find cause to curse.

"Aylmer, are you in earnest?" asked Georgiana, looking at him with amazement and fear. "It is terrible to possess such power, or even to dream of possessing it."

"Oh, do not tremble, my love," said her husband. "I would not wrong either you or myself by working such inharmonious effects upon our lives; but I would have you consider how trifling, in comparison, is the skill requisite to remove this little hand."

At the mention of the birthmark, Georgiana, as usual, shrank as if a redhot iron had touched her cheek.

Again Aylmer applied himself to his labors. She could hear his voice in the distant furnace room giving [58] directions to Aminadab, whose harsh, uncouth, misshapen tones were audible in response, more like the grunt or growl of a brute than human speech. After hours of absence, Aylmer reappeared and proposed that she should now examine his cabinet of chemical products and natural treasures of the earth. Among the former he showed her a small vial, in which, he remarked, was contained a gentle yet most powerful fragrance, capable of impregnating all the breezes that blow across a kingdom. They were of inestimable value, the contents of that little vial; and, as he said so, he threw some of the perfume into the air and filled the room with piercing and invigorating delight.

"And what is this?" asked Georgiana, pointing to a small crystal globe containing a gold-colored liquid. "It is so beautiful to the eye that I could imagine it the elixir of life."

"In one sense it is," replied Aylmer; "or, rather, the elixir of immortality. It is the most precious poison that ever was concocted in this world. By its aid I could apportion the lifetime of any mortal at whom you might point your finger. The strength of the dose would determine whether he were to linger out years, or drop dead in the midst of a breath. No king on his guarded throne could keep his life if I, in my private station, should deem that the welfare of millions justified me in depriving him of it."

"Why do you keep such a terrific drug?" inquired Georgiana in horror.

"Do not mistrust me, dearest," said her husband, smiling; "its virtuous potency is yet greater than its harmful one. But see! here is a powerful cosmetic. With a few drops of this in a vase of water, freckles may be washed away as easily as the hands are cleansed.[59] A stronger infusion would take the blood out of the cheek, and leave the rosiest beauty a pale ghost."

"Is it with this lotion that you intend to bathe my cheek?" asked Georgiana, anxiously.

"Oh, no," hastily replied her husband; "this is merely superficial. Your case demands a remedy that shall go deeper."

In his interviews with Georgiana, Aylmer generally made minute inquiries as to her sensations and whether the confinement of the rooms and the temperature of the atmosphere agreed with her. These questions had such a particular drift that Georgiana began to conjecture that she was already subjected to certain physical influences, either breathed in with the fragrant air or taken with her food. She fancied likewise, but it might be altogether fancy, that there was a stirring up of her system— a strange, indefinite sensation creeping through her veins, and tingling, half painfully, half pleasurably, at her heart. Still, whenever she dared to look into the mirror, there she beheld herself pale as a white rose and with the crimson birthmark stamped upon her cheek. Not even Aylmer now hated it so much as she.

To dispel the tedium of the hours which her husband found it necessary to devote to the processes of combination and analysis, Georgiana turned over the volumes of his scientific library. In many dark old tomes she met with chapters full of romance and poetry. They were the works of the philosophers of the middle ages, such as Albertus Magnus, Cornelius Agrippa, Paracelsus, and the famous friar who created the prophetic Brazen Head. All these antique naturalists stood in advance of their centuries, yet were imbued with some of their credulity, and therefore were [60] believed, and perhaps imagined themselves to have acquired from the investigation of Nature a power above Nature, and from physics a sway over the spiritual world. Hardly less curious and imaginative were the early volumes of the Transactions of the Royal Society, in which the members, knowing little of the limits of natural possibility, were continually recording wonders or proposing methods whereby wonders might be wrought.

But to Georgiana the most engrossing volume was a large folio from her husband's own hand, in which he had recorded every experiment of his scientific career, its original aim, the methods adopted for its development, and its final success or failure, with the circumstances to which either event was attributable. The book, in truth, was both the history and emblem of his ardent, ambitious, imaginative, yet practical and laborious life. He handled physical details as if there were nothing beyond them; yet spiritualized them all, and redeemed himself from materialism by his strong and eager aspiration towards the infinite. In his grasp the veriest clod of earth assumed a soul. Georgiana, as she read, reverenced Aylmer and loved him more profoundly than ever, but with a less entire dependence on his judgment than heretofore. Much as he had accomplished, she could not but observe that his most splendid successes were almost invariably failures, if compared with the ideal at which he aimed. His brightest diamonds were the merest pebbles, and felt to be so by himself, in comparison with the inestimable gems which lay hidden beyond his reach. The volume, rich with achievements that had won renown for its author, was yet as melancholy a record as ever mortal hand had penned. It was the sad confession [61] and continual exemplification of the shortcomings of the composite man, the spirit burdened with clay and working in matter, and of the despair that assails the higher nature at finding itself so miserably thwarted by the earthly part. Perhaps every man of genius in whatever sphere might recognize the image of his own experience in Aylmer's journal.

So deeply did these reflections affect Georgiana that she laid her face upon the open volume and burst into tears. In this situation she was found by her husband.

"It is dangerous to read in a sorcerer's books," said he with a smile, though his countenance was uneasy and displeased. "Georgiana, there are pages in that volume which I can scarcely glance over and keep my senses. Take heed lest it prove as detrimental to you."

"It has made me worship you more than ever," said she.

"Ah, wait for this one success," rejoined he, "then worship me if you will. I shall deem myself hardly unworthy of it. But come, I have sought you for the luxury of your voice. Sing to me, dearest."

So she poured out the liquid music of her voice to quench the thirst of his spirit. He then took his leave with a boyish exuberance of gayety, assuring her that her seclusion would endure but a little longer, and that the result was already certain. Scarcely had he departed when Georgiana felt irresistibly impelled to follow him. She had forgotten to inform Aylmer of a symptom which for two or three hours past had begun to excite her attention. It was a sensation in the fatal birthmark, not painful, but which induced a restlessness throughout her system. Hastening after her [62] husband, she intruded for the first time into the laboratory.

The first thing that struck her eye was the furnace, that hot and feverish worker, with the intense glow of its fire, which by the quantities of soot clustered above it seemed to have been burning for ages. There was a distilling apparatus in full operation. Around the room were retorts, tubes, cylinders, crucibles, and other apparatus of chemical research. An electrical machine stood ready for immediate use. The atmosphere felt oppressively close, and was tainted with gaseous odors which had been tormented forth by the processes of science. The severe and homely simplicity of the apartment, with its naked walls and brick pavement, looked strange, accustomed as Georgiana had become to the fantastic elegance of her boudoir. But what chiefly, indeed almost solely, drew her attention, was the aspect of Aylmer himself.

He was pale as death, anxious and absorbed, and hung over the furnace as if it depended upon his utmost watchfulness whether the liquid which it was distilling should be the draught of immortal happiness or misery. How different from the sanguine and joyous mien that he had assumed for Georgiana's encouragement!

"Carefully now, Aminadab; carefully, thou human machine; carefully, thou man of clay!" muttered Aylmer, more to himself than his assistant. "Now, if there be a thought too much or too little, it is all over."

"Ho! ho!" mumbled Aminadab. "Look, master! look!"

Aylmer raised his eyes hastily, and at first reddened, then grew paler than ever, on beholding Georgiana.[63] He rushed towards her and seized her arm with a gripe that left the print of his fingers upon it.

"Why do you come hither? Have you no trust in your husband?" cried he, impetuously. "Would you throw the blight of that fatal birthmark over my labors? It is not well done. Go, prying woman, go!"

"Nay, Aylmer," said Georgiana with the firmness of which she possessed no stinted endowment, "it is not you that have a right to complain. You mistrust your wife; you have concealed the anxiety with which you watch the development of this experiment. Think not so unworthily of me, my husband. Tell me all the risk we run, and fear not that I shall shrink; for my share in it is far less than your own."

"No, no, Georgiana!" said Aylmer, impatiently; "it must not be."

"I submit," replied she calmly. "And, Aylmer, I shall quaff whatever draught you bring me; but it will be on the same principle that would induce me to take a dose of poison if offered by your hand."

"My noble wife," said Aylmer, deeply moved, "I knew not the height and depth of your nature until now. Nothing shall be concealed. Know, then, that this crimson hand, superficial as it seems, has clutched its grasp into your being with a strength of which I had no previous conception. I have already administered agents powerful enough to do aught except to change your entire physical system. Only one thing remains to be tried. If that fail us we are ruined."

"Why did you hesitate to tell me this?" asked she.

"Because, Georgiana," said Aylmer, in a low voice, "there is danger."

"Danger? There is but one danger—that this horrible stigma shall be left upon my cheek!" cried [64] Georgiana. "Remove it, remove it, whatever be the cost, or we shall both go mad!"

"Heaven knows your words are too true," said Aylmer, sadly. "And now, dearest, return to your boudoir. In a little while all will be tested."

He conducted her back and took leave of her with a solemn tenderness which spoke far more than his words how much was now at stake. After his departure Georgiana became rapt in musings. She considered the character of Aylmer, and did it completer justice than at any previous moment. Her heart exulted, while it trembled, at his honorable love— so pure and lofty that it would accept nothing less than perfection nor miserably make itself contented with an earthlier nature than he had dreamed of. She felt how much more precious was such a sentiment than that meaner kind which would have borne with the imperfection for her sake, and have been guilty of treason to holy love by degrading its perfect idea to the level of the actual; and with her whole spirit she prayed that, for a single moment, she might satisfy his highest and deepest conception. Longer than one moment she well knew it could not be; for his spirit was ever on the march, ever ascending, and each instant required something that was beyond the scope of the instant before.

The sound of her husband's footsteps aroused her. He bore a crystal goblet containing a liquor colorless as water, but bright enough to be the draught of immortality. Aylmer was pale; but it seemed rather the consequence of a highly-wrought state of mind and tension of spirit than of fear or doubt.

"The concoction of the draught has been perfect," [65] said he, in answer to Georgiana's look. "Unless all my science have deceived me, it cannot fail."

"Save on your account, my dearest Aylmer," observed his wife, "I might wish to put off this birthmark of mortality by relinquishing mortality itself in preference to any other mode. Life is but a sad possession to those who have attained precisely the degree of moral advancement at which I stand. Were I weaker and blinder it might be happiness. Were I stronger, it might be endured hopefully. But, being what I find myself, methinks I am of all mortals the most fit to die."

"You are fit for heaven without tasting death!" replied her husband. "But why do we speak of dying? The draught cannot fail. Behold its effect upon this plant."

On the window seat there stood a geranium diseased with yellow blotches, which had overspread all its leaves. Aylmer poured a small quantity of the liquid upon the soil in which it grew. In a little time, when the roots of the plant had taken up the moisture, the unsightly blotches began to be extinguished in a living verdure.

"There needed no proof," said Georgiana, quietly. "Give me the goblet. I joyfully stake all upon your word."

"Drink, then, thou lofty creature!" exclaimed Aylmer, with fervid admiration. "There is no taint of imperfection on thy spirit. Thy sensible frame, too, shall soon be all perfect."

She quaffed the liquid and returned the goblet to his hand.

"It is grateful," said she with a placid smile. "Methinks it is like water from a heavenly fountain; for it [66] contains I know not what of unobtrusive fragrance and deliciousness. It allays a feverish thirst that had parched me for many days. Now, dearest, let me sleep. My earthly senses are closing over my spirit like the leaves around the heart of a rose at sunset."

She spoke the last words with a gentle reluctance, as if it required almost more energy than she could command to pronounce the faint and lingering syllables. Scarcely had they loitered through her lips ere she was lost in slumber. Aylmer sat by her side, watching her aspect with the emotions proper to a man the whole value of whose existence was involved in the process now to be tested. Mingled with this mood, however, was the philosophic investigation characteristic of the man of science. Not the minutest symptom escaped him. A heightened flush of the cheek, a slight irregularity of breath, a quiver of the eyelid, a hardly perceptible tremor through the frame,—such were the details which, as the moments passed, he wrote down in his folio volume. Intense thought had set its stamp upon every previous page of that volume, but the thoughts of years were all concentrated upon the last.

While thus employed, he failed not to gaze often at the fatal hand, and not without a shudder. Yet once, by a strange and unaccountable impulse, he pressed it with his lips. His spirit recoiled, however, in the very act; and Georgiana, out of the midst of her deep sleep, moved uneasily and murmured as if in remonstrance. Again Aylmer resumed his watch. Nor was it without avail. The crimson hand, which at first had been strongly visible upon the marble paleness of Georgiana's cheek, now grew more faintly outlined. She remained not less pale than ever; but the birthmark, [67] with every breath that came and went, lost somewhat of its former distinctness. Its presence had been awful; its departure was more awful still. Watch the stain of the rainbow fading out of the sky, and you will know how that mysterious symbol passed away.

"By Heaven! it is well-nigh gone!" said Aylmer to himself, in almost irrepressible ecstasy. "I can scarcely trace it now. Success! success! And now it is like the faintest rose color. The lightest flush of blood across her cheek would overcome it. But she is so pale!"

He drew aside the window curtain and suffered the light of natural day to fall into the room and rest upon her cheek. At the same time he heard a gross, hoarse chuckle, which he had long known as his servant Aminadab's expression of delight.

"Ah, clod! ah, earthly mass!" cried Aylmer, laughing in a sort of frenzy, "you have served me well! Matter and spirit—earth and heaven —have both done their part in this! Laugh, thing of the senses! You have earned the right to laugh."

These exclamations broke Georgiana's sleep. She slowly unclosed her eyes and gazed into the mirror which her husband had arranged for that purpose. A faint smile flitted over her lips when she recognized how barely perceptible was now that crimson hand which had once blazed forth with such disastrous brilliancy as to scare away all their happiness. But then her eyes sought Aylmer's face with a trouble and anxiety that he could by no means account for.

"My poor Aylmer!" murmured she.

"Poor? Nay, richest, happiest, most favored!" exclaimed he. "My peerless bride, it is successful! You are perfect!" [68]

"My poor Aylmer," she repeated, with a more than human tenderness, "you have aimed loftily; you have done nobly. Do not repent that with so high and pure a feeling, you have rejected the best the earth could offer. Aylmer, dearest Aylmer, I am dying!"

Alas! it was too true! The fatal hand had grappled with the mystery of life, and was the bond by which an angelic spirit kept itself in union with a mortal frame. As the last crimson tint of the birthmark—that sole token of human imperfection—faded from her cheek, the parting breath of the now perfect woman passed into the atmosphere, and her soul, lingering a moment near her husband, took its heavenward flight. Then a hoarse, chuckling laugh was heard again! Thus ever does the gross fatality of earth exult in its invariable triumph over the immortal essence which, in this dim sphere of half development, demands the completeness of a higher state. Yet, had Aylmer reached a profounder wisdom, he need not thus have flung away the happiness which would have woven his mortal life of the selfsame texture with the celestial. The momentary circumstance was too strong for him; he failed to look beyond the shadowy scope of time, and, living once for all in eternity, to find the perfect future in the present.[69]

Interpretation of "The Birthmark" *

This story amounts to a sort of *parable*. . . . Indeed, Hawthorne frankly applies the term "parable" to one or two of his other stories of this kind. In the second paragraph of this story, Hawthorne says quite explicitly that the story of Aylmer and Georgiana has a "deeply impressive moral." But if we as readers are deeply impressed with the moral, we will be so because the presentation has been sufficiently concrete and sufficiently dramatic to impress us: the moral will hardly be "deeply impressive" in isolation. Even if we grant that Hawthorne is primarily interested here in the theme and does not hesitate to bring his theme to the fore, we are still compelled to ask the same questions with regard to this story which we have had to ask with regard to other stories. We may well begin with the problem which will probably present itself early to any reader: the problem of motivation.

Why is Aylmer anxious to remove the birthmark from his wife's cheek? She herself is frankly shocked when her husband first suggests removing it. She had not thought of it as a blemish; she had actually been complimented on it as something which was rather charming; and obviously, the birthmark had not prevented Aylmer from thinking her very beautiful, or from marrying her. Indeed, we are told, only a few women, jealous of her surpassing beauty, had ever regarded it as a disfigurement.

It is ironical that even Aylmer would not have come to regard the birthmark as a blemish if Georgiana had been less beautiful. As it is, the birthmark arrests his attention and gradually provokes his desire to remove it from the very fact that it remains the only possible blemish [103] upon otherwise perfect beauty: ". . . his eyes wandered stealthily

* From *Understanding Fiction* by Cleanth Brooks and Robert Penn Warren. Copyright, 1943, F. S. Crofts & Co., Inc. By permission of Appleton-Century-Crofts, Inc.

to her cheek, and beheld, flickering with the blaze of the wood fire, the spectral hand that wrote mortality where he would fain have worshiped."

Even so, had Aylmer not been a scientist, a daring experimenter, the birthmark on his wife's cheek would hardly have come to obsess him; for it was neither so large nor so prominent that it might not have been dismissed from mind, had not the thought that it lay within his power to remove it insinuated itself into Aylmer's imagination. That this is a very prominent part of his motivation is indicated in his remark to Georgiana: "I feel myself fully competent to render this cheek as fault-less as its fellow; and then, most beloved, what will be my triumph when I shall have corrected what Nature left imperfect in her fairest work!"

We are not, of course, to conceive of Aylmer as a monster, a man who would experiment on his own wife for his own greater glory. Hawthorne does not mean to suggest that Aylmer is depraved and heartless. The triumph of which Aylmer speaks will not be for vulgar display and self-advertisement. It will be a triumph which his wife will share and a triumph to be won for her sake. And he *is* confident that he will be successful. The element of pride is there, but the kind of pride, it is suggested, is that which enters into and colors many of man's nobler purposes. What the story emphasizes is not Aylmer's self-conceit but rather his possession of the questing spirit which will not resign itself to the limitations and imperfections of nature. Nature itself is to be corrected, to be made perfect.

The decision to attempt to remove the birthmark is, of course, not arrived at in a moment, but by stages. Aylmer, before he allows the experiment to become a part of his conscious purpose, finds himself dreaming of it. His wife, who had paid no attention to her birthmark, soon begins to become self-conscious about it, and finally the mark becomes something hateful to her. Moreover, when she finds how much the thought of its removal has come to mean to her husband, she urges him on as a proof of her love for him. Others had counted the blemish charming, and other lovers would have risked life to kiss it; but just before the final experiment is to be made Georgiana can say that she fears only one thing—not death, but "that this horrible stigma shall be left upon my cheek!" As for Aylmer, the enterprise, which at the begin-ning was little more than a fantastic notion, has become a "rapture." [104]

Aminadab, Aylmer's assistant, provides a sort of measuring stick for the folly and nobility of the husband and wife. He is, as Aylmer calls him, a "man of clay." He lacks the imagination for the noble enterprise of daring to surpass nature. The tiny blemish in a woman so beautiful as Georgiana would cause him no uneasiness at all, and he says, with a shrewd and solid common sense, "If she were my wife, I'd never part with that birthmark."

The birthmark is removed. Aylmer has his "peerless bride" in entire perfection for a moment, but the birthmark, symbol of the earthy, the mortal, can be eradicated only at the price of life itself. Aylmer has not realized that perfection is something never achieved on earth and in terms of mortality.

Here, of course, appears the theme of the story, the "impressive moral" which we have been told the story contains. But if the story is to be merely the vehicle for this moral, why has Hawthorne chosen to use the method of fiction at all? It is true that the story, as he has constructed it, is a rather transparent symbol for the basic idea, and that the characters have a rather obvious symbolic reference: Aminadab stands for the earthy, gross side of man's nature: Aylmer, for the aspiring and imaginative element in man. But, even so, why has Hawthorne written a story at all rather than an essay, say, or a sermon?

An obvious reason in favor of the story, of course, is our basic interest as human beings in a story, even a story which is closely tied to an idea. The story allows the author to develop suspense, to provide a dramatic form for the situation, to engage our interests more intensely. But there are other things which Hawthorne gains from his use of fiction here, matters usually overlooked but perhaps more important ultimately than the added interest and intensity. We shall see what these things are if we consider Hawthorne's attitude toward the situation which he has described. What, for example, is Hawthorne's attitude toward the various characters and toward the decisions which they make? Aminadab, for instance, would seem to support Hawthorne's moral, but does Hawthorne consider him to be a higher type than Aylmer? Hardly. Aminadab is for the author, too, a "man of clay," gross, animal-like, easily satisfied. Aylmer tries to achieve what is impossible and thus commits a folly; but it would be misreading the story to infer that Hawthorne dismisses him as merely a foolish man. The author is sympathetic to him, and obviously sees in his ruinous experiment a certain nobility.

What is the author's attitude toward the moral itself? Is man to give [105] up all his attempts to conquer nature? Would Hawthorne have men settle down into a supine and passive acceptance of what nature gives? A careful reading of the story will suggest that Hawthorne himself does not take his own moral in these terms. There are many qualifications to be made, one would gather—matters of emphasis and matters of application to be taken into account. One cannot range the characters into two absolute categories, the good and the bad, the right and the wrong; and the moral itself is not a rule to be applied absolutely and without qualification.

Most important of all, it should be apparent that Hawthorne is *not interested in having us apply a rule*—he is not interested merely in trying to win our assent to a particular generalization, or in trying to make us adopt a certain course of action. His story, even with its heavy emphasis on a particular theme, is something more than a sermon or a lawyer's brief. His total intention, like that of any writer of fiction, is wider than this.

. . . . .[106]

Hawthorne's "The Birthmark":
Science as Religion *

Hawthorne's "The Birthmark" has been called, not inappropriately, a parable. The "truth" which it aims to set forth can be disengaged from the narrative: in a rational attempt to "perfect" nature man may destroy the organic life from which the imperfection is inseparable. But, as Messrs. Brooks and Warren have made clear, it is necessary to guard against an oversimplification of what the story says, to guard particularly against converting even a parabolic drama into melodrama. Aylmer, the overweening scientist, resembles less the villain than the tragic hero: in his catastrophic attempt to improve on human actuality there is not only pride and a deficient sense of reality but also disinterested aspiration. The story does not advocate total resignation or a flat acquiescence in the immediate state of affairs. Despite its firm expository conclusion, "The Birthmark" hardly advocates at all; it enters the neighborhood of greatness because it has a great theme, but is not tempted into pat answers. The theme which Hawthorne explores may be defined as the problem of mediating between irrational passivity and a hyperrational

* R. B. Heilman, "Hawthorne's 'The Birthmark': Science as Religion," *The South Atlantic Quarterly*, XLVIII (October, 1949), 575–83. Reprinted by permission.

reorganization of life. Failure in this problem, as in others, may coincide with urgent good will; this is the formulation of the tragic actor which Hawthorne adopts, in contrast with the tragic structure in which an evil or perverted will is joined to saving qualities such as the capacity for repentance. But Hawthorne makes a more precise definition of the tragic error—one which is worth a brief examination.

This definition is made implicitly in the language of the story—language which may be either literal or figurative but in either case has influential overtones. What we find recurrently in "The Birthmark," and therefore insistently asking to be taken into account, is the terminology and imagery of religion. Specifically religious problems are not overtly introduced into the story, but the language of religion is there so unfailingly that, like iterative imagery in drama [575] and poetry, it must be closely inspected if a final reading of the story is to be complete. What it does is create a story that transcends the parabolic: the foreground parable concerns man's relations with nature, but the immanent story is about man's conceptions of evil. The further we trace the implications of language, the less simple we discover Hawthorne's tale to be.

The scientific progress of Aylmer's day, we are told, "seemed to open paths into the region of *miracle*"; scientists are called *votaries;* Aylmer may have shared their "*faith* in man's ultimate control over Nature." The subjects of their study are called *secrets,* but also, repeatedly, *mysteries;* at the end, the "*mysterious* symbol had passed away," but it had been inseparable from the very "*mystery* of life." When Georgiana's and Aylmer's union has been virtually identified with the scientific effort to remove the birthmark, Georgiana thinks of Aylmer's devotion to her —to the perfected her—as "*holy* love." What is made clear by such terms, which function precisely like poetic images, is that science itself has become religion, able to provide an ultimate account of reality and therefore to exact complete human dedication. It has become religion not only for Aylmer but also for Georgiana—". . . she *prayed* that, for a single moment, she might satisfy his highest and deepest conception." Indeed, her taking of Aylmer's final potion, which is to effect her transformation, is recorded in terms which make it virtually a Christian act. The drink is "bright enough to be the draught of *immortality*"; to Georgiana it is "like water from a *heavenly* fountain," and it will allay "a feverish thirst that had parched me for many days." Since Biblical language makes frequent use of metaphors of thirst to express spiritual yearnings, it is difficult not to read in such a passage a reminiscence of

John 4:14—". . . whosoever drinketh of the waters that I shall give him shall never thirst; but the water that I shall give him shall be in him a well of water springing up into everlasting life."

The question, of course, is whether Georgiana's draught is really heavenly and has the power to allay the thirst that from the soul doth rise; whether, in other words, the auspices under which she drinks are spiritual principles. The irony of her illusion is subtly carried on by her blunt command, "Give me the goblet." At one [576] level the analogy with communion is amplified; but *goblet* also has a metaphorical value, and we are inevitably reminded of the cup which is an ordeal: ". . . the cup which my Father hath given me, shall I not drink it?" Georgiana has overcome her dread and has come to conceive of herself, at least in part, as a sacrifice. The end is the secular salvation of mortal man.

The cup has been given by Aylmer. The language-pattern of the story indicates that in the religion of science Aylmer is less priest than God. The votaries believed, Hawthorne records, that the scientist would "lay his hands on the *secret of creative force* and perhaps *make new worlds* for himself." The word *wonders* is used repeatedly to describe what Aylmer and other scientists achieved. Aylmer, though he speaks jokingly, does apply the term *sorcerer* to himself; a laboratory exploit of his is *magical;* he is confident that he can "draw a *magic* circle around her within which no evil might intrude." He could make, he intimates, "an *immortal* nostrum"; he has created an "elixir of *immortality*"; the potion which he prepares for Georgiana may be the draught "of *immortal* happiness or misery." Aylmer has given to the problems offered by the birthmark such deep thought that he feels almost able "to *create* a being less perfect" than Georgiana. He is sure that he can make her cheek *faultless.* And then he makes an allusion which contributes importantly to this part of the meaning: "Even Pygmalion, when his sculptured woman assumed life, felt not greater ecstasy than mine will be." Formally, Aylmer rarely fails to exhibit a consciousness of human limitations; but still he cannot discipline that part of himself which aspires to infinite power. At the conclusion of the experiment he exclaims spontaneously, "By *Heaven!* it is well nigh gone!" What is this Heaven? Has a superhuman power aided him? Or has his power itself seemed to go beyond the terrestrial? A minute later he lets "the light of *natural* day" enter the room, and Aminadab, "the *earthly* mass," chuckles grossly. It is as though Aylmer has descended for a moment into another kind of reality from that which is proper to him. Indeed, he distinguishes two kinds of force which he declares have been at work: "Matter and spirit—

earth and heaven—have both done their part in this!" But the question is whether Aylmer really accepts the dualism to which his words give expression.[577]

In fact, we have almost a parody of the Father who gives the bitter cup to drink. Aylmer, as we have seen, is virtually translated into the godhead: His *"sorcerer's* book," Georgiana insists to him, "has made me *worship* you more than ever." The confusion of values has spread to Georgiana. Aylmer's own confusion is shown further in his paradoxical inclination to adore as well as create: "the spectral hand wrote mortality where he would fain have *worshiped.*" Yet later, in a context which shows that his evaluation is moral, he assures her, "You are fit for heaven without tasting death!" Perhaps, then, she ought to be almost suitable for adoration, and the hand itself should seem a negligible flaw. Yet over it Aylmer is almost hysterical, while, as we shall see, he is blind to more serious flaws closer to home.

That Aylmer is a confused man has always been plain to readers of the story. But, when we examine it in detail, we discover that the language of the story defines his confusion very precisely—defines it as the mistaking of science for religion. The essential story, I have said, is about man's conception of evil: Aylmer does not, in the long run, regard evil as real. Without actually denying its reality, Aylmer in effect simplifies and attenuates it by treating it as manageable, subject to human control, indeed removable. Aylmer's religion reverses the Christian sense of the reality of evil—a reality which can ultimately be dealt with only by divine grace. Aylmer is a romantic perfectibilitarian, who suffers from a dangerous fastidiousness in the presence of complex actuality. "You are perfect!" he assures Georgiana—as she is dying. He believes in perfectibility without retaining the modifying concept of damnability. Man's confidence in his ability to deal with evil by some physical or psychological or social surgery makes him an earthly god: in his presumption he proposes to establish a heaven on earth. Thus, like Aylmer, man becomes committed to a hyperrational—that is, a shallowly grounded —reorganization of life. Hawthorne brilliantly summarizes the metaphysics of the scientific religion in Aylmer's explication of the series of steps in his rehabilitation of Georgiana. He tells her, "I have already administered agents powerful enough to change your entire physical system. Only one thing remains to be tried." ". . . to change your entire physical system" is, in this cosmology, the [578] equivalent of regeneration or conversion. Aylmer's faith becomes, in effect: improve the body, and you save the soul.

Hawthorne repeatedly underlines the error of Aylmer's ways. His confusion of values shows in the fact that his husbandly love can have strength only "by intertwining itself with his love of science." The birthmark which he proposes to remove is "fairy," "mysterious," "magic"— terms which indicate how much more is at stake than Aylmer suspects at his most acute. He accepts uncritically Georgiana's assurance that from his hand she is willing "to take a dose of poison," in ironic anticipation of the way in which his elixir actually does work. He demands complete "trust" and is angry when, following him into the laboratory, she throws "the blight of that fatal birthmark over my labors"—his own word, *blight*, having a summary accuracy of which he is ironically innocent. Aylmer accepts entirely his wife's passionate exclamation that if the birthmark is not removed "we shall both go mad!" What the reader must see in this madness is a simple inability to accept the facts of life. It is precisely this inability of which Hawthorne, throughout the story, keeps reminding us, almost overwhelmingly.

Hawthorne could hardly have found a better symbol than the birthmark, which speaks of the imperfection born with man, with man as a race. Here is original sin in fine imaginative form. Aylmer does not altogether fail to see what is involved; he is not crudely stupid; but his sense of power leads him to undervalue the penalties of life. His tragedy is that he lacks the tragic sense; he is, we may say, a characteristic modern, the exponent of an age which has deified science and regards it as an irresistibly utopianizing force. His tragic flaw is to fail to see the tragic flaw in humanity. Hawthorne never lets the reader forget the deep significance of the "human hand" which scars Georgiana. He comments ironically on the lovers who hoped to see "one living specimen of ideal loveliness without the semblance of a flaw," a suggestion of a common attitude for which Aylmer speaks. The birthmark is a "symbol of imperfection," "the spectral hand that wrote mortality," the "sole token of human imperfection." This "fatal flaw of humanity"—the terms are virtually Christian—implies that all the productions of nature are "temporary and finite" and that "their perfection must be wrought by toil [579] and pain." For spiritual discipline Aylmer wants to substitute magic— not quite pushbutton magic perhaps, but still a shortcut, a kind of prestidigitation. It is not that he is ignorant in a gross way; he sees much, but his premises stop him at the threshold of wisdom. He recognizes that the blemish on Georgiana's face is a "mark of earthly imperfection"; he even selects it "as the symbol of his wife's liability to sin, sorrow, decay, and death." The frequency of images of death in the story is a thematic reminder of the reality from which Aylmer doggedly turns away. Although here he actually puts his finger upon the realities which the mature man must come to terms with, his faith leads him to feel, as we have seen, "that he could draw a magic circle round her within which no evil might intrude." Evil is manageable: the symbol itself has become the reality.

What we finally come to is the problem of spirit, and the test of Aylmer's creed is the kind of spiritual values it embodies. We hear repeatedly about Aylmer's spirit and his interest in the spiritual. He had "attempted to fathom," we learn, "the very process by which Nature assimilates all her precious influences from earth and air, and from the *spiritual* world, to create and foster man, her masterpiece." Aminadab represents "man's physical nature"; in Aylmer we see "the *spiritual* element." Georgiana is almost convinced "that her husband possessed sway over the *spiritual* world." As she reads his record of experiments, the author, apparently speaking for her, comments: "He handled physical details as if there were nothing beyond them; yet *spiritualized* them all, and redeemed himself from materialism by his strong and eager aspiration towards the *infinite*. In his grasp the veriest clod of earth assumed a *soul*." His failures are those of "the *spirit* burdened with clay and working in matter"; "his *spirit* was ever on the march, ever ascending"—the spirit, one is tempted to say, of progress. But as a result of this spiritual yearning of his, another's "angelic spirit" leaves on its "heavenward flight."

At the end Hawthorne, distinguishing "mortal" and "celestial," reaffirms a dualism which he has insisted upon throughout the story and which, as various words of theirs make clear, is formally assented to also by Georgiana and Aylmer. But the first defect of Aylmer's religion, as the drama makes clear, is that in practice he [580] does not accept dualism at all: for him, spirit is not distinct from matter but is the perfecting of matter. The material stigma that shocks him he is said, just once, to regard as symbol; but his efforts at amelioration are directed wholly at the symbol, not at its antecedent substance. Aylmer is actually symptom-doctoring and is unaware that the locus of the disease is elsewhere. His creed is secular and monistic. All the talk about spirit is an ironic commentary upon his essential lack of insight into real problems of spirit.

The story specifies what level of spiritual comprehension Aylmer does reach. He aspires, and his aspiration is presented with a good deal of sympathy, as is just; as between aspiration and passivity, the choice is, in the main, clear; but a judgment must be made between one kind of aspiration and another. So the question becomes: how, and toward what, does Aylmer actually aspire? Does he, for instance, aspire toward better insight? Toward charity? Toward wisdom? Or is it not rather that his aspiration is inextricably involved with the exercise of power? "There is no taint of imperfection on thy spirit," he tells Georgiana. Why? Because Georgiana has just indicated an unreserved willingness to accept his potion; her faith in him is total. He is not content with her perfection of "spirit." For him, immense knowledge is a means of doing things, of achieving physical, visible ends. We see in him no evidence of concern with the quality of his own life, or perception, or thought.

In this man of science divine discontent is with others; as Georgiana puts it, his love "would accept nothing less than perfection nor miserably make itself contented with an earthlier nature than he had dreamed of." It is of course Georgiana who shall be "all perfect." The romantic scientist has no thought of the problem of perfecting himself; indeed, his spiritual perception is very close to that of uplift and do-good-ism. He begs the real problem of spirit and is fanatical about the shortcomings of the world. Hawthorne is very acute in analyzing further the especial quality of Aylmer's outward-bound perfectionism and in discerning in it a core of intense fastidiousness. This hypersensitivity rushes in, indeed, at the very moment at which Aylmer fleetingly achieves a kind of wholeness of response to Georgiana, an acceptance of her which implies a spiritual modification of himself. "Yet once, by a strange and unaccountable [581] impulse, he pressed it [the birthmark] with his lips." Here is virtually a redefinition of his love. But immediately his fastidiousness reasserts itself and gives the parting tone to the action: "His *spirit* recoiled, however, in the very act. . . ." That is his spirit: a primary awareness of the flaws of others and of the demand which they appear to make for remedy from without.

The heir of Prometheus kills his beneficiary, not by conferring a single blessing, but by endeavoring to eradicate the imperfections humanity is heir to. Upon this aspiration to divinity Hawthorne comments in his account of Aylmer's library, of the works of "these antique naturalists" who "perhaps imagined themselves to have acquired from the investigation of Nature a power above Nature, and from physics a sway over the spiritual world." Hawthorne has already remarked that the "great creative Mother . . . is yet severely careful to keep her own secrets." What Hawthorne has done, really, is to blueprint the course of science in modern imagination, to dramatize its persuasive faith in its omnipotence, and thus its taking on the colors of religion.

This very formulation commits Hawthorne to a critique—a critique which he makes by disclosing the false spirituality of Aylmer. It is the false spirituality of power conjoined with fastidiousness, of physical improvement, of external remedy, of *ad hoc* prescriptions, of reform: Aylmer's surgery is a fine symbol for a familiar code. Yet the code would have only an innocuous life in a museum-case if it did not gain converts. Thus we have Georgiana's very important role in the story: she is less the innocent victim than the fascinated sharer in magic who conspires in her own doom. Georgiana, the woman killed with kindness by the man who would be god, is really humanity—with its share of the heroic, its common sense, which enables it to question heroes, and yet its capacity for being beguiled, for combining good intention, devotion, and destructive delusion. In the marriage of science and humanity we see the inevitably catastrophic interaction of a mechanical perfectionism and the "birthmark of mortality." Science has no way of coming to terms with human imperfection, and humanity, tutored by science, can no longer accept its liability to sin and death.

Ironically, it is Georgiana who cuts off, or at least helps cut off,[582] a final path of spiritual rectification for Aylmer. "Do not *repent*," she says, "that . . . you have rejected the best earth could offer." Not only is Aylmer's definition of "the best" inadequate, but he is encouraged in a hardening of spirit which precludes his entering upon a reconsideration of values. His religion offers no way of dealing with his pride. And his pride—with its intense demand that the world submit itself to his limited criteria—gives us another definition of the spiritual defect of this man who is so convinced that spirit is his concern. When Georgiana confesses her desire to worship him more fully, he scarcely bothers to be deprecatory: "Ah, wait for this one success, . . . then *worship* me if you will. I shall deem myself hardly unworthy of it." These are the ultimate marks of his moral infatuation.

The critical problem in "The Birthmark" has to do with the kind of mistake Aylmer makes. Hawthorne's language tells us, subtly but insistently, that Aylmer has apotheosized science; and the images and drama together define the spiritual shortcoming of this new revelation—its belief in the eradicability of evil, its Faustian proneness to love power, its incapacity to bring about renunciation or self-examination, its pride. I once thought that Hawthorne had stopped short of the proper goal of the story by not including the next phase of Aylmer's experience—the phase in which, if the tragic view of Aylmer were to prevail, Aylmer would entertain the Furies. But the summation of Aylmer's defects is that he cannot see the Furies. The story stops where it must.[583]

Young Goodman Brown *

Young Goodman Brown came forth at sunset into the street at Salem village; but put his head back, after crossing the threshold, to exchange a parting kiss with his young wife. And Faith, as the wife was aptly named, thrust her own pretty head into the street, letting the wind play with the pink ribbons of her cap while she called to Goodman Brown.

"Dearest heart," whispered she, softly and rather sadly, when her lips were close to his ear, "prithee put off your journey until sunrise and sleep in your own bed to-night. A lone woman is troubled with such dreams and such thoughts that she's afeard of herself sometimes. Pray tarry with me this night, dear husband, of all nights in the year."

"My love and my Faith," replied young Goodman Brown, "of all nights in the year, this one night must I tarry away from thee. My journey, as thou callest it, forth and back again, must needs be done 'twixt now and sunrise. What, my sweet, pretty wife, dost thou doubt me already, and we but three months married?"

"Then God bless you!" said Faith, with the pink ribbons; "and may you find all well when you come back."

"Amen!" cried Goodman Brown. "Say thy prayers, dear Faith, and go to bed at dusk, and no harm will come to thee."

So they parted; and the young man pursued his [89] way until, being about to turn the corner by the meeting-house, he looked back and saw the head of Faith still peeping after him with a melancholy air, in spite of her pink ribbons.

"Poor little Faith!" thought he, for his heart smote him. "What a wretch am I to leave her on such an errand! She talks of dreams, too. Methought as she spoke there was trouble in her face, as if a dream had warned her what work is to be done to-night. But no, no; 't would kill her to think it. Well, she's a blessed angel on earth; and after this one night I'll cling to her skirts and follow her to heaven."

With this excellent resolve for the future, Goodman Brown felt him-

* This story appeared in *The New England Magazine* in April, 1835, and in *Mosses from an Old Manse* in 1846.

self justified in making more haste on his present evil purpose. He had taken a dreary road, darkened by all the gloomiest trees of the forest, which barely stood aside to let the narrow path creep through, and closed immediately behind. It was all as lonely as could be; and there is this peculiarity in such a solitude, that the traveller knows not who may be concealed by the innumerable trunks and the thick boughs overhead; so that with lonely footsteps he may yet be passing through an unseen multitude.

"There may be a devilish Indian behind every tree," said Goodman Brown to himself; and he glanced fearfully behind him as he added, "What if the devil himself should be at my very elbow!"

His head being turned back, he passed a crook of the road, and, looking forward again, beheld the figure of a man, in grave and decent attire, seated at the foot of an old tree. He arose at Goodman Brown's approach and walked onward side by side with him.

"You are late, Goodman Brown," said he. "The [90] clock of the Old South was striking as I came through Boston, and that is full fifteen minutes agone."

"Faith kept me back a while," replied the young man, with a tremor in his voice, caused by the sudden appearance of his companion, though not wholly unexpected.

It was now deep dusk in the forest, and deepest in that part of it where these two were journeying. As nearly as could be discerned, the second traveller was about fifty years old, apparently in the same rank of life as Goodman Brown, and bearing a considerable resemblance to him, though perhaps more in expression than features. Still they might have been taken for father and son. And yet, though the elder person was as simply clad as the younger, and as simple in manner too, he had an indescribable air of one who knew the world, and who would not have felt abashed at the governor's dinner table or in King William's court, were it possible that his affairs should call him thither. But the only thing about him that could be fixed upon as remarkable was his staff, which bore the likeness of a great black snake, so curiously wrought that it might almost be seen to twist and wriggle itself like a living serpent. This, of course, must have been an ocular deception, assisted by the uncertain light.

"Come, Goodman Brown," cried his fellow-traveller, "this is a dull pace for the beginning of a journey. Take my staff, if you are so soon weary."

"Friend," said the other, exchanging his slow pace for a full stop, "having kept covenant by meeting thee here, it is my purpose now to return whence I came. I have scruples touching the matter thou wot'st of."

"Sayest thou so?" replied he of the serpent, smiling apart. "Let us walk on, nevertheless, reasoning as [91] we go; and if I convince thee not thou shalt turn back. We are but a little way in the forest yet."

"Too far! too far!" exclaimed the goodman, unconsciously resuming his walk. "My father never went into the woods on such an errand, nor his father before him. We have been a race of honest men and good Christians since the days of the martyrs; and shall I be the first of the name of Brown that ever took this path and kept"—

"Such company, thou wouldst say," observed the elder person, interpreting his pause. "Well said, Goodman Brown! I have been as well acquainted with your family as with ever a one among the Puritans; and that's no trifle to say. I helped your grandfather, the constable, when he lashed the Quaker woman so smartly through the streets of Salem; and it was I that brought your father a pitch-pine knot, kindled at my own hearth, to set fire to an Indian village, in King Philip's war. They were my good friends, both; and many a pleasant walk have we had along this path, and returned merrily after midnight. I would fain be friends with you for their sake."

"If it be as thou sayest," replied Goodman Brown, "I marvel they never spoke of these matters; or, verily, I marvel not, seeing that the least rumor of the sort would have driven them from New England. We are a people of prayer, and good works to boot, and abide no such wickedness."

"Wickedness or not," said the traveller with the twisted staff, "I have a very general acquaintance here in New England. The deacons of many a church have drunk the communion wine with me; the selectmen of divers towns make me their chairman; and a majority of the Great and General Court are firm supporters [92] of my interest. The governor and I, too—But these are state secrets."

"Can this be so?" cried Goodman Brown, with a stare of amazement at his undisturbed companion. "Howbeit, I have nothing to do with the governor and council; they have their own ways, and are no rule for a simple husbandman like me. But, were I to go on with thee, how should I meet the eye of that good old man, our minister, at Salem village? Oh, his voice would make me tremble both Sabbath day and lecture day."

Thus far the elder traveller had listened with due gravity; but now burst into a fit of irrepressible mirth, shaking himself so violently that his snake-like staff actually seemed to wriggle in sympathy.

"Ha! ha! ha!" shouted he again and again; then composing himself, "Well, go on, Goodman Brown, go on; but, prithee, don't kill me with laughing."

"Well, then, to end the matter at once," said Goodman Brown, considerably nettled, "there is my wife, Faith. It would break her dear little heart; and I'd rather break my own."

"Nay, if that be the case," answered the other, "e'en go thy ways, Goodman Brown. I would not for twenty old women like the one hobbling before us that Faith should come to any harm."

As he spoke he pointed his staff at a female figure on the path, in whom Goodman Brown recognized a very pious and exemplary dame, who had taught him his catechism in youth, and was still his moral and spiritual adviser, jointly with the minister and Deacon Gookin.

"A marvel, truly, that Goody Cloyse should be so far in the wilderness at nightfall," said he. "But [93] with your leave, friend, I shall take a cut through the woods until we have left this Christian woman behind. Being a stranger to you, she might ask whom I was consorting with and whither I was going."

"Be it so," said his fellow-traveller. "Betake you to the woods, and let me keep the path."

Accordingly the young man turned aside, but took care to watch his companion, who advanced softly along the road until he had come within a staff's length of the old dame. She, meanwhile, was making the best of her way, with singular speed for so aged a woman, and mumbling some indistinct words—a prayer, doubtless—as she went. The traveller put forth his staff and touched her withered neck with what seemed the serpent's tail.

"The devil!" screamed the pious old lady.

"Then Goody Cloyse knows her old friend?" observed the traveller, confronting her and leaning on his writhing stick.

"Ah, forsooth, and is it your worship indeed?" cried the good dame. "Yea, truly is it, and in the very image of my old gossip, Goodman Brown, the grandfather of the silly fellow that now is. But—would your worship believe it?—my broomstick hath strangely disappeared, stolen, as I suspect, by that unhanged witch, Goody Cory, and that, too, when I was all anointed with the juice of smallage, and cinquefoil, and wolf's bane"—

"Mingled with fine wheat and the fat of a new-born babe," said the shape of old Goodman Brown.

"Ah, your worship knows the recipe," cried the old lady, cackling aloud. "So, as I was saying, being all ready for the meeting, and no horse to ride on, I made up my mind to foot it; for they tell me there is a nice [94] young man to be taken into communion to-night. But now your good worship will lend me your arm, and we shall be there in a twinkling."

"That can hardly be," answered her friend. "I may not spare you my arm, Goody Cloyse; but here is my staff, if you will."

So saying, he threw it down at her feet, where, perhaps, it assumed life, being one of the rods which its owner had formerly lent to the Egyptian magi. Of this fact, however, Goodman Brown could not take cognizance. He had cast up his eyes in astonishment, and, looking down again, beheld neither Goody Cloyse nor the serpentine staff, but his fellow-traveller alone, who waited for him as calmly as if nothing had happened.

"That old woman taught me my catechism," said the young man; and there was a world of meaning in this simple comment.

They continued to walk onward, while the elder traveller exhorted his companion to make good speed and persevere in the path, discoursing so aptly that his arguments seemed rather to spring up in the bosom of his auditor than to be suggested by himself. As they went, he plucked a branch of maple to serve for a walking stick, and began to strip it of the twigs and little boughs, which were wet with evening dew. The moment his fingers touched them they became strangely withered and dried up as with a week's sunshine. Thus the pair proceeded, at a good free pace, until suddenly, in a gloomy hollow of the road, Goodman Brown sat himself down on the stump of a tree and refused to go any farther.

"Friend," said he, stubbornly, "my mind is made up. Not another step will I budge on this errand.[95] What if a wretched old woman do choose to go to the devil when I thought she was going to heaven: is that any reason why I should quit my dear Faith and go after her?"

"You will think better of this by and by," said his acquaintance, composedly. "Sit here and rest yourself a while; and when you feel like moving again, there is my staff to help you along."

Without more words, he threw his companion the maple stick, and was as speedily out of sight as if he had vanished into the deepening gloom. The young man sat a few moments by the roadside, applauding himself greatly, and thinking with how clear a conscience he should meet the minister in his morning walk, nor shrink from the eye of good old Deacon Gookin. And what calm sleep would be his that very night, which was to have been spent so wickedly, but so purely and sweetly now, in the arms of Faith! Amidst these pleasant and praiseworthy meditations, Goodman Brown heard the tramp of horses along the road, and deemed it advisable to conceal himself within the verge of the forest, conscious of the guilty purpose that had brought him thither, though now so happily turned from it.

On came the hoof tramps and the voices of the riders, two grave old voices, conversing soberly as they drew near. These mingled sounds appeared to pass along the road, within a few yards of the young man's hiding-place; but, owing doubtless to the depth of the gloom at that particular spot, neither the travellers nor their steeds were visible. Though their figures brushed the small boughs by the wayside, it could not be seen that they intercepted, even for a moment, the faint gleam from the strip of bright sky athwart [96] which they must have passed. Goodman Brown alternately crouched and stood on tiptoe, pulling aside the branches and thrusting forth his head as far as he durst without discerning so much as a shadow. It vexed him the more, because he could have sworn, were such a thing possible, that he recognized the voices of the minister and Deacon Gookin, jogging along quietly, as they were wont to do, when bound to some ordination or ecclesiastical council. While yet within hearing, one of the riders stopped to pluck a switch.

"Of the two, reverend sir," said the voice like the deacon's, "I had rather miss an ordination dinner than to-night's meeting. They tell me that some of our community are to be here from Falmouth and beyond, and others from Connecticut and Rhode Island, besides several of the Indian pow-wows, who, after their fashion, know almost as much deviltry as the best of us. Moreover, there is a goodly young woman to be taken into communion."

"Mighty well, Deacon Gookin!" replied the solemn old tones of the minister. "Spur up, or we shall be late. Nothing can be done, you know, until I get on the ground."

The hoofs clattered again; and the voices, talking so strangely in the empty air, passed on through the forest, where no church had ever been gathered or solitary Christian prayed. Whither, then, could these holy men be journeying so deep into the heathen wilderness? Young Goodman Brown caught hold of a tree for support, being ready to sink down on the ground, faint and overburdened with the heavy sickness of his heart. He looked up to the sky, doubting whether there really was a heaven above him. Yet [97] there was the blue arch, and the stars brightening in it.

"With heaven above and Faith below, I will yet stand firm against the devil!" cried Goodman Brown.

While he still gazed upward into the deep arch of the firmament and had lifted his hands to pray, a cloud, though no wind was stirring, hurried across the zenith and hid the brightening stars. The blue sky was still visible, except directly overhead, where this black mass of cloud was sweeping swiftly northward. Aloft in the air, as if from the depths of the cloud, came a confused and doubtful sound of voices. Once the listener fancied that he could distinguish the accents of towns-people of his own, men and women, both pious and ungodly, many of whom he had met at the communion table, and had seen others rioting at the tavern. The next moment, so indistinct were the sounds, he doubted whether he had heard aught but the murmur of the old forest, whispering without a wind. Then came a stronger swell of those familiar tones, heard daily in the sunshine at Salem village, but never until now from a cloud of night. There was one voice, of a young woman, uttering lamentations, yet with an uncertain sorrow, and entreating for some favor, which, perhaps, it would grieve her to obtain; and all the unseen multitude, both saints and sinners, seemed to encourage her onward.

"Faith!" shouted Goodman Brown, in a voice of agony and desperation; and the echoes of the forest mocked him, crying, "Faith! Faith!" as if bewildered wretches were seeking her all through the wilderness.

The cry of grief, rage, and terror was yet piercing the night, when the unhappy husband held his breath [98] for a response. There was a scream, drowned immediately in a louder murmur of voices, fading into far-off laughter, as the dark cloud swept away, leaving the clear and silent sky above Goodman Brown. But something fluttered lightly down through the air and caught on the branch of a tree. The young man seized it, and beheld a pink ribbon.

"My Faith is gone!" cried he, after one stupefied moment. "There is no good on earth; and sin is but a name. Come, devil; for to thee is this world given."

And, maddened with despair, so that he laughed loud and long, did Goodman Brown grasp his staff and set forth again, at such a rate that he seemed to fly along the forest path rather than to walk or run. The road grew wilder and drearier and more faintly traced, and vanished at length, leaving him in the heart of the dark wilderness, still rushing onward with the instinct that guides mortal man to evil. The whole forest was peopled with frightful sounds—the creaking of the trees, the howling of wild beasts, and the yell of Indians; while sometimes the wind tolled like a distant church bell, and sometimes gave a broad roar around the traveller, as if all Nature were laughing him to scorn. But he was himself the chief horror of the scene, and shrank not from its other horrors.

"Ha! ha! ha!" roared Goodman Brown when the wind laughed at him. "Let us hear which will laugh loudest. Think not to frighten me with your deviltry. Come witch, come wizard, come Indian powwow, come devil himself, and here comes Goodman Brown. You may as well fear him as he fear you."

In truth, all through the haunted forest there could be nothing more frightful than the figure of Goodman Brown. On he flew among the black pines, brandishing [99] his staff with frenzied gestures, now giving vent to an inspiration of horrid blasphemy, and now shouting forth such laughter as set all the echoes of the forest laughing like demons around him. The fiend in his own shape is less hideous than when he rages in the breast of man. Thus sped the demoniac on his course, until, quivering among the trees, he saw a red light before him, as when the felled trunks and branches of a clearing have been set on fire, and throw up their lurid blaze against the sky, at the hour of midnight. He paused, in a lull of the tempest that had driven him onward, and heard the swell of what seemed a hymn, rolling solemnly from a distance with the weight of many voices. He knew the tune; it was a familiar one in the choir of the village meeting-house. The verse died heavily away, and was lengthened by a chorus, not of human voices, but of all the sounds of the benighted wilderness pealing in awful harmony together. Goodman Brown cried out, and his cry was lost to his own ear by its unison with the cry of the desert.

In the interval of silence he stole forward until the light glared full upon his eyes. At one extremity of an open space, hemmed in by the dark wall of the forest, arose a rock, bearing some rude, natural resemblance either to an altar or a pulpit, and surrounded by four blazing pines, their tops aflame, their stems untouched, like candles at an evening meeting. The mass of foliage that had overgrown the summit of the rock was all on fire, blazing high into the night and fitfully illuminating the whole field. Each pendent twig and leafy festoon was in a blaze. As the red light arose and fell, a numerous congregation alternately shone forth, then disappeared in shadow, and [100] again grew, as it were, out of the darkness, peopling the heart of the solitary woods at once.

"A grave and dark-clad company," quoth Goodman Brown.

In truth they were such. Among them, quivering to and fro between gloom and splendor, appeared faces that would be seen next day at the council board of the province, and others which, Sabbath after Sabbath, looked devoutly heavenward, and benignantly over the crowded pews, from the holiest pulpits in the land. Some affirm that the lady of the governor was there. At least there were high dames well known to her, and wives of honored husbands, and widows, a great multitude, and ancient maidens, all of excellent repute, and fair young girls, who trembled lest their mothers should espy them. Either the sudden gleams of light flashing over the obscure field bedazzled Goodman Brown, or he recognized a score of the church members of Salem village famous for their especial sanctity. Good old Deacon Gookin had arrived, and waited at the skirts of that venerable saint, his revered pastor. But, irreverently consorting with these grave, reputable, and pious people, these elders of the church, these chaste dames and dewy virgins, there were men of dissolute lives and women of spotted fame, wretches given over to all mean and filthy vice, and suspected even of horrid crimes. It was strange to see that the good shrank not from the wicked, nor were the sinners abashed by the saints. Scattered also among their pale-faced enemies were the Indian priests, or powwows, who had often scared their native forest with more hideous incantations than any known to English witchcraft.

"But where is Faith?" thought Goodman Brown; and, as hope came into his heart, he trembled.[101]

Another verse of the hymn arose, a slow and mournful strain, such as the pious love, but joined to words which expressed all that our nature can conceive of sin, and darkly hinted at far more. Unfathomable to mere mortals is the lore of fiends. Verse after verse was sung; and still the chorus of the desert swelled between like the deepest tone of a mighty organ; and with the final peal of that dreadful anthem there came a sound, as if the roaring wind, the rushing streams, the howling beasts, and every other voice of the unconcerted wilderness were mingling and according with the voice of guilty man in homage to the prince of all. The four blazing pines threw up a loftier flame, and obscurely discovered shapes and visages of horror on the smoke wreaths above the impious assembly. At the same moment the fire on the rock shot redly forth and formed a glowing arch above its base, where now appeared a figure. With reverence be it spoken, the figure bore no slight similitude, both in garb and manner, to some grave divine of the New England churches.

"Bring forth the converts!" cried a voice that echoed through the field and rolled into the forest.

At the word, Goodman Brown stepped forth from the shadow of the trees and approached the congregation, with whom he felt a loathful brotherhood by the sympathy of all that was wicked in his heart. He could have well-nigh sworn that the shape of his own dead father beckoned him to advance, looking downward from a smoke wreath, while a woman, with dim features of despair, threw out her hand to warn him back. Was it his mother? But he had no power to retreat one step, nor to resist, even in thought, when the minister and good old Deacon Gookin seized his [102] arms and led him to the blazing rock. Thither came also the slender form of a veiled female, led between Goody Cloyse, that pious teacher of the catechism, and Martha Carrier, who had received the devil's promise to be queen of hell. A rampant hag was she. And there stood the proselytes beneath the canopy of fire.

"Welcome, my children," said the dark figure, "to the communion of your race. Ye have found thus young your nature and your destiny. My children, look behind you!"

They turned; and flashing forth, as it were, in a sheet of flame, the fiend worshippers were seen; the smile of welcome gleamed darkly on every visage.

"There," resumed the sable form, "are all whom ye have reverenced from youth. Ye deemed them holier than yourselves, and shrank from your own sin, contrasting it with their lives of righteousness and prayerful aspirations heavenward. Yet here are they all in my worshipping assembly. This night it shall be granted you to know their secret deeds: how hoary-bearded elders of the church have whispered wanton words to the young maids of their households; how many a woman, eager for widows' weeds, has given her husband a drink at bedtime and let him sleep his last sleep in her bosom; how beardless youths have made haste to inherit their fathers' wealth; and how fair damsels—blush not, sweet ones—have dug little graves in the garden, and bidden me, the sole guest, to an infant's funeral. By the sympathy of your human hearts for sin ye shall scent out all the places—whether in church, bed-chamber, street, field, or forest—where crime has been committed, and shall exult to behold the whole earth one stain of guilt, one [103] mighty blood spot. Far more than this. It shall be yours to penetrate, in every bosom, the deep mystery of sin, the fountain of all wicked arts, and which inexhaustibly supplies more evil impulses than human power—than my power at its utmost—can make manifest in deeds. And now, my children, look upon each other."

They did so; and, by the blaze of the hell-kindled torches, the wretched man beheld his Faith, and the wife her husband, trembling before that unhallowed altar.

"Lo, there ye stand, my children," said the figure, in a deep and solemn tone, almost sad with its despairing awfulness, as if his once angelic nature could yet mourn for our miserable race. "Depending upon one another's hearts, ye had still hoped that virtue were not all a dream. Now are ye undeceived. Evil is the nature of mankind. Evil must be your only happiness. Welcome again, my children, to the communion of your race."

"Welcome," repeated the fiend worshippers, in one cry of despair and triumph.

And there they stood, the only pair, as it seemed, who were yet hesitating on the verge of wickedness in this dark world. A basin was hollowed, naturally, in the rock. Did it contain water, reddened by the lurid light? or was it blood? or, perchance, a liquid flame? Herein did the shape of evil dip his hand and prepare to lay the mark of baptism upon their foreheads, that they might be partakers of the mystery of sin, more conscious of the secret guilt of others, both in deed and thought, than they could now be of their own. The husband cast one look at his pale wife, and Faith at him. What polluted wretches would the next [104] glance show them to each other, shuddering alike at what they disclosed and what they saw!

"Faith! Faith!" cried the husband, "look up to heaven, and resist the wicked one."

Whether Faith obeyed he knew not. Hardly had he spoken when he found himself amid calm night and solitude, listening to a roar of the wind which died heavily away through the forest. He staggered against the rock, and felt it chill and damp; while a hanging twig, that had been all on fire, besprinkled his cheek with the coldest dew.

The next morning young Goodman Brown came slowly into the street of Salem village, staring around him like a bewildered man. The good old minister was taking a walk along the graveyard to get an appetite for breakfast and meditate his sermon, and bestowed a blessing, as he passed, on Goodman Brown. He shrank from the venerable saint as if to avoid an anathema. Old Deacon Gookin was at domestic worship, and the holy words of his prayer were heard through the open window. "What God doth the wizard pray to?" quoth Goodman Brown. Goody Cloyse, that excellent old Christian, stood in the early sunshine at her own lattice, catechizing a little girl who had brought her a pint of morning's milk. Goodman Brown snatched away the child as from the grasp of the fiend himself. Turning the corner by the meeting-house, he spied the head of Faith, with the pink ribbons, gazing anxiously forth, and bursting into such joy at sight of him that she skipped along the street and almost kissed her husband before the whole village. But Goodman Brown looked sternly and sadly into her face, and passed on without a greeting.

Had Goodman Brown fallen asleep in the forest and only dreamed a wild dream of a witch-meeting? [105]

Be it so if you will; but, alas! it was a dream of evil omen for young Goodman Brown. A stern, a sad, a darkly meditative, a distrustful, if not a desperate man did he become from the night of that fearful dream. On the Sabbath day, when the congregation were singing a holy psalm, he could not listen because an anthem of sin rushed loudly upon his ear and drowned all the blessed strain. When the minister spoke from the pulpit with power and fervid eloquence, and, with his hand on the open Bible, of the sacred truths of our religion, and of saint-like lives and triumphant deaths, and of future bliss or misery unutterable, then did Goodman Brown turn pale, dreading lest the roof should thunder down upon the gray blasphemer and his hearers. Often, awaking suddenly at midnight, he shrank from the bosom of Faith; and at morning or eventide, when the family knelt down at prayer, he scowled and muttered to himself, and gazed sternly at his wife, and turned away. And when he had lived long, and was borne to his grave a hoary corpse, followed by Faith, an aged woman, and children and grandchildren, a goodly procession, besides neighbors not a few, they carved no hopeful verse upon his tombstone, for his dying hour was gloom.[106]

Ambiguity and Clarity in Hawthorne's "Young Goodman Brown" *

"Young Goodman Brown" is generally felt to be one of Hawthorne's more difficult tales, from the ambiguity of the conclusions which may be drawn from it. Its hero, a naïve young man who accepts both society in general and his fellowmen as individuals at their own valuation, is in one terrible night presented with the vision of human Evil, and is ever afterwards "A stern, a sad, a darkly meditative, a distrustful, if not a desperate man . . . ," whose "dying hour was gloom." So far we are clear enough, but there are confusing factors. In the first place, are the events

* Richard H. Fogle, "Ambiguity and Clarity in Hawthorne's 'Young Goodman Brown,'" *New England Quarterly*, XVIII (December, 1943), 448–65. Reprinted by permission.

of the night merely subjective, a dream; or do they actually occur? Again, at the crucial point in his ordeal Goodman Brown summons the strength to cry to his wife Faith, "look up to heaven, and resist the evil one." It would appear from this that he has successfully resisted the supreme temptation—but evidently he is not therefore saved. Henceforth, "On the Sabbath day, when the congregation were singing a holy psalm, he could not listen because an anthem of sin rushed loudly upon his ear and drowned all the blessed strain." On the other hand, he is not wholly lost, for in the sequel he is only at intervals estranged from "the bosom of Faith." Has Hawthorne himself failed to control the implications of his allegory?

I should say rather that these ambiguities of meaning are intentional, an integral part of his purpose. Hawthorne wishes to propose, not flatly that man is primarily evil, but instead the gnawing doubt lest this should indeed be true. "Come, devil; for to thee is this world given," exclaims Goodman Brown at the height of his agony, but he finds strength to resist the devil, and in the ambiguous conclusion he does not entirely reject his former faith. His trial, then, comes not from the certainty but the dread of Evil. Hawthorne poses the dangerous question of [448] the relations of Good and Evil in man, but withholds his answer. Nor does he permit himself to settle whether the events of the night of trial are real or the mere figment of a dream.

These ambiguities he conveys and fortifies by what Yvor Winters has called "the formula of alternative possibilities," [1] and F. O. Matthiessen "the device of multiple choice," [2] in which are suggested two or more interpretations of a single action or event. Perhaps the most striking instance of the use of this device in "Young Goodman Brown" is the final word on the reality of the hero's night experience:

Had Goodman Brown fallen asleep in the forest and only dreamed a wild dream of a witch-meeting?

Be it so if you will; [3] but alas! it was a dream of evil omen for young Goodman Brown.

This device of multiple choice, or ambiguity, is the very essence of Hawthorne's tale. Nowhere does he permit us a simple meaning, a merely single interpretation. At the outset, young Goodman Brown leaves the arms of his wife Faith and the safe limits of Salem town to keep a

---

[1] *Maule's Curse* (Norfolk, Connecticut, 1938), 18. Mr. Winters limits his discussion of the device to Hawthorne's novels.

[2] *American Renaissance* (New York, 1941), 276.

[3] These and all subsequent italics are mine.

mysterious appointment in the forest. Soon he encounters his conductor, a man "in grave and decent attire," commonplace enough save for an indefinable air of acquaintanceship with the great world. ". . . the only thing about him that could be fixed upon as remarkable was his staff, which bore the likeness of a great black snake, so curiously wrought that it might almost be seen to twist and wriggle itself like a living serpent. *This, of course, must have been an ocular deception, assisted by the uncertain light.*" 4 [449]

This man is, of course, the Devil, who seeks to lure the still-reluctant goodman to a witch-meeting. In the process he progressively undermines the young man's faith in the institutions and the men whom he has heretofore revered. First Goody Cloyse, "a very pious and exemplary dame, who had taught him his catechism in youth, and was still his moral and spiritual adviser," is shown to have more than casual acquaintance with the Devil—to be, in fact, a witch. Goodman Brown is shaken, but still minded to turn back and save himself. He is then faced with a still harder test. Just as he is about to return home, filled with self-applause, he hears the tramp of horses along the road:

On came the hoof tramps and the voices of the riders, two grave old voices, conversing soberly as they drew near. These mingled sounds appeared to pass along the road, within a few yards of the young man's hiding-place; *but, owing doubtless to the depth of the gloom at that particular spot, neither the travellers nor their steeds were visible. Though their figures brushed the small boughs by the wayside, it could not be seen that they intercepted, even for a moment, the faint gleam from the strip of bright sky athwart which they must have passed.* It vexed him the more, because he could have sworn, *were such a thing possible,* that he recognized the voices of the minister and Deacon Gookin, jogging along quietly, as they were wont to do, when bound to some ordination or ecclesiastical council.

The conversation of the minister and the deacon makes it only too clear that they also are in league with the evil one. Yet Goodman Brown, although now even more deeply dismayed, still resolves to stand firm,

⁴ Hawthorne may have taken this suggestion from the serpent-staff of Mercury. He later uses it for lighter purposes on at least two occasions in *A Wonder Book*. Mercury's staff is described by Epimetheus as "like two serpents twisting around a stick, and . . . carved so naturally that I, at first, thought the serpents were alive" ("The Paradise of Children"). Again, in "The Miraculous Pitcher," "Two snakes, carved in the wood, were represented as twining themselves about the staff, and were so very skilfully executed that old Philemon (whose eyes, you know, were getting rather dim) almost thought them alive, and that he could see them wriggling and twisting."

heartened by the blue arch of the sky and the stars brightening in it.[5] At that moment a cloud, "though no wind was stirring," hides the stars, and he hears a confused babble of voices. *"Once the listener fancied that he could distinguish* the accents of townspeople of his own . . .*[450]* The next moment, so indistinct were the sounds, *he doubted whether he had heard aught* but the murmur of the old forest, whispering without a wind."* But to his horror he believes that he hears the voice of his wife Faith, uttering only weak and insincere objections as she is borne through the air to the witch-meeting.

Now comes a circumstance which at first sight would appear to break the chain of ambiguities, for his suspicions seem concretely verified. A pink ribbon, which he remembers having seen in his wife's hair, comes fluttering down into his grasp. This ribbon, an apparently solid object like the fatal handkerchief in *Othello,* seems out of keeping with the atmosphere of doubt which has enveloped the preceding incidents.[6] Two considerations, however, make it possible to defend it. One is that if Goodman Brown is dreaming, the ribbon like the rest may be taken as part-and-parcel of his dream. It is to be noted that this pink ribbon appears in his wife's hair once more as she meets him at his return to Salem in the morning. The other is that for the moment the ribbon vanishes from the story, melting into its shadowy background. Its impact is merely temporary.

Be it as you will, as Hawthorne would say. At any rate the effect on Goodman Brown is instantaneous and devastating. Casting aside all further scruples, he rages through the wild forest to the meeting of witches, for the time at least fully accepting the domination of Evil. He soon comes upon a "numerous congregation," alternately shadowy and clear in the flickering red light of four blazing pines above a central rock.

Among them, *quivering to and fro between gloom and splendor,* appeared faces that would be seen next day at the council board of the province, and others which, Sabbath after Sabbath, looked devoutly heavenward, and benignantly over the crowded pews, from the holiest pulpits in the land. *Some affirm that* the lady of [451] the governor was there. . . . *Either the sudden gleams of light flashing over the obscure field bedazzled*

[5] Cf. Bosola to the Duchess at a comparably tragic moment in Webster's *Duchess of Malfi:* "Look you, the stars shine still."
[6] "As long as what Brown saw is left wholly in the realm of hallucination, Hawthorne's created illusion is compelling. . . . Only the literal insistence on that damaging pink ribbon obtrudes the labels of a confining allegory, and short-circuits the range of association." Matthiessen, *American Renaissance,* 284.

Goodman Brown, or he recognized a score of the church members of Salem village famous for their especial sanctity.

Before this company steps out a presiding figure who bears "With reverence be it spoken . . . *no slight similitude,* both in garb and manner, to some grave divine of the New England churches," and calls forth the "converts." At the word young Goodman Brown comes forward. *"He could have well-nigh sworn that* the shape of his own dead father beckoned him to advance, looking downward from a smoke wreath, while a woman, with dim features of despair, threw out her hand to warn him back. *Was it his mother?"* But he is quickly seized and led to the rock, along with a veiled woman whom he dimly discerns to be his wife Faith. The two are welcomed by the dark and ambiguous leader into the fraternity of Evil, and the final, irretrievable step is prepared.

A basin was hollowed, naturally, in the rock. *Did it contain water, reddened by the lurid light? or was it blood? or, perchance, a liquid flame?* Herein did the shape of evil dip his hand and prepare to lay the mark of baptism upon their foreheads, that they might be partakers of the mystery of sin, more conscious of the secret guilt of others, both in deed and thought, than they could now be of their own. The husband cast one look at his pale wife, and Faith at him. What polluted wretches would the next glance show them to each other, shuddering alike at what they disclosed and what they saw!
"Faith! Faith!" cried the husband, "look up to heaven, and resist the wicked one."
Whether Faith obeyed he knew not.

Hawthorne then concludes with the central ambiguity, which we have already noticed, whether the events of the night were actual or a dream? The uses of this device, if so it may be called, are multiple in consonance with its nature. Primarily it offers opportunity for freedom and richness of suggestion. By [452] it Hawthorne is able to suggest something of the density and incalculability of life, the difficulties which clog the interpretation of even the simplest incidents, the impossibility of achieving a single and certain insight into the actions and motives of others. This ambiguity adds depth and tone to Hawthorne's thin and delicate fabric. It covers the bareness of allegory, imparting to its one-to-one equivalence of object and idea a wider range of allusiveness, a hint of rich meaning still untapped. By means of it the thesis of "Young Goodman Brown" is made to inhere firmly in the situation, whence the reader himself must extract it to interpret. Hawthorne the artist refuses to limit himself to a single and doctrinaire conclusion,[7] proceeding instead by indirection. Further, it permits him to make free with the two opposed worlds of actuality and of imagination without incongruity or the need to commit himself entirely to either; while avoiding a frontal attack upon the reader's feeling for everyday verisimilitude, it affords the author licence of fancy. It allows him to draw upon sources of legend and superstition which still strike a responsive chord in us, possessing something of the validity of universal symbols.[8] Hawthorne's own definition of Romance may very aptly be applied to his use of ambiguity: it gives him scope "so [to] manage his atmospherical medium as to bring out or mellow the lights and deepen and enrich the shadows of the picture." [9]

These scanty observations must suffice here for the general importance of Hawthorne's characteristic ambiguity. It remains to describe its immediate significance in "Young Goodman Brown." Above all, the separate instances of this "multiple [453] choice device" organically cohere to reproduce in the reader's mind the feel of the central ambiguity of theme, the horror of the hero's doubt. Goodman Brown, a simple and pious nature, is wrecked as a result of the disappearance of the fixed poles of his belief. His orderly cosmos dissolves into chaos as church and state, the twin pillars of his society, are hinted to be rotten, with their foundations undermined.[10] The yearning for certainty is basic to his spirit—and he is left without the comfort even of a firm reliance in the Devil.[11] His better qualities avail him in his desperation little more than the inner evil which

[7] "For Hawthorne its value consisted in the variety of explanations to which it gave rise." *American Renaissance*, 277. The extent of my indebtedness to Mr. Matthiessen is only inadequately indicated in my documentation.

[8] "It is only by . . . symbols that have numberless meanings beside the one or two the writer lays an emphasis upon, or the half-score he knows of, that any highly subjective art can escape from the barrenness and shallowness of a too conscious arrangement, into the abundance and depth of nature. . . ." W. B. Yeats, "The Philosophy of Shelley's Poetry," *Ideas of Good and Evil* (London, 1914), 90. Thus Hawthorne by drawing upon Puritan superstition and demonology is able to add another dimension to his story.

[9] Preface, *The House of the Seven Gables*.

[10] Goodman Brown is disillusioned with the church in the persons of Goody Cloyse, the minister, and Deacon Gookin, and it will be recalled that the figure of Satan at the meeting "bore no slight similitude . . . to some grave divine of the New England churches." As to the secular power, the devil tells Brown that ". . . the selectmen of divers towns make me their chairman; and a majority of the Great and General Court are firm supporters of my interest. The governor and I, too— But these are state secrets."

[11] The story could conceivably be read as intellectual satire, showing the pitfalls that lie in wait for a too-shallow and unquestioning faith. Tone and emphasis clearly show, however, a more tragic intention.

prompted him to court temptation, for they prevent him from seeking the only remaining refuge—the confraternity of Sin. Henceforth he is fated to a dubious battle with shadows, to struggle with limed feet toward a redemption which must forever elude him, since he has lost the vision of Good while rejecting the proffered opportunity to embrace Evil fully. Individual instances of ambiguity, then, merge and coalesce in the theme itself to produce an all-pervading atmosphere of uneasiness and anguished doubt.

Ambiguity alone, however, is not a satisfactory aesthetic principle. Flexibility, suggestiveness, allusiveness, variety—all these are without meaning if there is no pattern from which to vary, no center from which to flee outward. And, indeed, ambiguity of itself will not adequately account for the individual phenomenon of "Young Goodman Brown." The deliberate haziness and multiple implications of its meaning are counterbalanced by the firm clarity of its technique, in structure and in style.[454]

This clarity is embodied in the lucid simplicity of the basic action; in the skilful foreshadowing by which the plot is bound together; in balance of episode and scene; in the continuous use of contrast; in the firmness and selectivity of Hawthorne's pictorial composition; in the carefully arranged climactic order of incident and tone; in the detachment and irony of Hawthorne's attitude; and finally in the purity, the grave formality, and the rhetorical balance of the style. His amalgamation of these elements achieves an effect of totality, of exquisite craftsmanship, of consummate artistic economy in fitting the means to the attempted ends.

The general framework of the story has a large simplicity. Goodman Brown leaves his wife Faith and the safe confines of Salem town at sunset, spends the night in the forest, and at dawn returns a changed man. Within this simple pattern plot and allegory unfold symmetrically and simultaneously. The movement of "Young Goodman Brown" is the single revolution of a wheel, which turns full-circle upon itself. As by this basic structure, the action is likewise given form by the device of foreshadowing, through which the entire development of the plot is already implicit in the opening paragraph. Thus Faith is troubled by her husband's expedition, and begs him to put it off till sunrise. "A lone woman is troubled with such dreams and such thoughts that she's afeard of herself sometimes," says she, hinting the ominous sequel of her own baptism in sin. " 'My love and my Faith,' replied young Goodman Brown, 'of all nights in the year, this one night must I tarry away from thee. My journey . . . forth and back again, must needs be done 'twixt now and sunrise.' " They part, but Brown looking back sees "the head of Faith still peeping after him with a melancholy air, in spite of her pink ribbons."

"Poor little Faith!" thought he, for his heart smote him. "What a wretch am I to leave her on such an errand! She talks of dreams, too. Methought as she spoke there was trouble in her face, as if a dream had warned her what work is to be done to-night. But no,[455] no; 'twould kill her to think of it. Well, she's a blessed angel on earth; and after this one night I'll cling to her skirts and follow her to heaven."

This speech, it must be confessed, is in several respects clumsy, obvious, and melodramatic;[12] but beneath the surface lurks a deeper layer. The pervasive ambiguity of the story is foreshadowed in the subtle emphasizing of the dream-motif, which paves the way for the ultimate uncertainty whether the incidents of the night are dream or reality; and in his simpleminded aspiration to "cling to her skirts and follow her to heaven," Goodman Brown is laying an ironic foundation for his later horror of doubt. A broader irony is apparent, in the light of future events, in the general emphasis upon Faith's angelic goodness.

Hawthorne's seemingly casual references to Faith's pink ribbons, which are mentioned three times in the opening paragraphs, are likewise far from artless. These ribbons, as we have seen, are an important factor in the plot; and as an emblem of heavenly Faith their color gradually deepens into the liquid flame or blood of the baptism into sin.[13]

Another instance of Hawthorne's careful workmanship is his architectural balance of episodes or scenes. The encounter with Goody Cloyse, the female hypocrite and sinner, is set off against the conversation of the minister and Deacon Gookin immediately afterward. The exact correspondence of the two episodes is brought into high relief by two balancing speeches. Goody Cloyse has lost her broomstick, and must perforce walk to the witch-meeting—a sacrifice she is willing to make since "they [456] tell me there is a nice young man to be taken into com-

---

[12] It has the earmarks of the set dramatic soliloquy, serving in this case to provide both information about the plot and revelation of character. Mr. Matthiessen attributes Hawthorne's general use of theatrical devices to the influence of Scott, who leads in turn to Shakespeare. *American Renaissance*, 203.

[13] Further, in welcoming the two candidates to the communion of Evil, the Devil says, "By the sympathy of your human hearts for sin ye shall scent out all the places . . . where crime has been committed, and shall exult to behold the whole earth one stain of guilt, *one mighty blood spot*." For this discussion of the pink ribbons I am largely indebted to Leland Schubert, *Hawthorne, the Artist* (Chapel Hill, 1944), 79–80.

munion to-night." A few minutes later Deacon Gookin, in high anticipation remarks that "there is a goodly young woman to be taken into communion." A still more significant example of this balance is contained in the full swing of the wheel—in the departure at sunset and the return at sunrise. At the beginning of the story Brown takes leave of "Faith with the pink ribbons," turns the corner by the meeting-house and leaves the town; in the conclusion

. . . Young Goodman Brown came slowly into the street of Salem village, staring around him like a bewildered man. The good old minister was taking a walk along the graveyard to get an appetite for breakfast and meditate his sermon, and bestowed a blessing, as he passed, on Goodman Brown. He shrank from the venerable saint as if to avoid an anathema. Old Deacon Gookin was at domestic worship, and the holy words of his prayer were heard through the open window. "What God doth the wizard pray to?" quoth Goodman Brown. Goody Cloyse, that excellent old Christian, stood in the early sunshine at her own lattice, catechizing a little girl who had brought her a pint of morning's milk.[14] Goodman Brown snatched the child away as from the grasp of the fiend himself. Turning the corner by the meeting-house, he spied the head of Faith, with the pink ribbons, gazing anxiously forth, and bursting into such joy at the sight of him that she skipped along the street and almost kissed her husband before the whole village. But Goodman Brown looked sternly and sadly into her face, and passed on without a greeting.

The exact parallel between the earlier and the later situation serves to dramatize intensely the change which the real or fancied happenings of the night have brought about in Goodman Brown.[15] [457]

Contrast, a form of balance, is still more prominent in "Young Goodman Brown" than the kind of analogy of scene and episode which I have mentioned. The broad antitheses of day against night, the town against the forest, which signify in general a sharp dualism of Good and Evil, are supplemented by a color-contrast of red-and-black at the witch-meeting, by the swift transition of the forest scene from leaping flame

[14] This touch takes on an ironic and ominous significance if it is noticed that Goody Cloyse has that night been Faith's sponsor, along with the "rampant hag" Martha Carrier, at the baptism into sin by blood and flame.

[15] Here we may anticipate a little in order to point out the steady and premeditated irony arising from the locutions "good old minister," "venerable saint," and "excellent old Christian"; and the climactic effect produced by the balance and repetition of the encounters, which are duplicated in the sentence-structure and the repetition of "Goodman Brown."

to damp and chill, and by the consistent cleavage between outward decorum and inner corruption in the characters.[16]

The symbols of Day and Night, of Town and Forest, are almost indistinguishable in meaning. Goodman Brown leaves the limits of Salem at dusk and reënters them at sunrise; the night he spends in the forest. Day and the Town are clearly emblematic of Good, of the seemly outward appearance of human convention and society. They stand for the safety of an unquestioning and unspeculative faith. Oddly enough, Goodman Brown in the daylight of the Salem streets is a young man too simple and straightforward to be interesting, and a little distasteful in his boundless reverence for such unspectacular worthies as the minister, the deacon, and Goody Cloyse. Night and the Forest are the domains of the Evil One, symbols of doubt and wandering, where the dark subterraneous forces of the human spirit riot unchecked.[17] By the dramatic necessities of the plot Brown is a larger figure in the Forest of Evil,[18] and as a chief actor at the witch-meeting, than within the safe bounds of the town.[458]

The contrast of the red of fire and blood against the black of night and the forest at the witch-meeting has a different import. As the flames rise and fall, the faces of the worshippers of Evil are alternately seen in clear outline and deep shadow, and all the details of the scene are at one moment revealed, the next obscured. It seems, then, that the red is Sin or Evil, plain and unequivocal; the black is that doubt of the reality either of Evil or Good which tortures Goodman Brown and is the central ambiguity of Hawthorne's story.[19]

A further contrast follows in the swift transformation of scene when young Goodman Brown finds himself "amid calm night and solitude.

[16] Epitomized by Brown's description of the assemblage at the meeting as "a grave and dark-clad company."

[17] "The conception of the dark and evil-haunted wilderness came to him [Hawthorne] from the days of Cotton Mather, who held that 'the New Englanders are a people of God settled in those which were once the devil's territories.'" Matthiessen, *American Renaissance*, 282–283. See also Matthiessen's remark of *The Scarlet Letter* that ". . . the forest itself, with its straggling path, images to Hester 'the moral wilderness in which she had so long been wandering'; and while describing it Hawthorne may have taken a glance back at Spenser's Wood of Errour." *American Renaissance*, 279–280. This reference to Spenser may as fitly be applied to the path of Young Goodman Brown, "darkened by all the gloomiest trees of the forest, which barely stood aside to let the narrow path creep through, and closed immediately behind."

[18] "But he was himself the chief horror of the scene, and shrank not from its other horrors."

[19] Hawthorne not infrequently uses color for symbol. See such familiar instances as *The Scarlet Letter* and "The Minister's Black Veil."

. . . He staggered against the rock, and felt it chill and damp; while a hanging twig, that had been all on fire, besprinkled his cheek with the coldest dew." [20]

Most pervasive of the contrasts in "Young Goodman Brown" is the consistent discrepancy between appearance and reality,[21] which helps to produce its heavy atmosphere of doubt and shadow. The church is represented by the highly respectable figures of Goody Cloyse, the minister, and Deacon Gookin, who in the forest are witch and wizards. The devil appears to Brown in the guise of his grandfather, "in grave and decent attire." As the goodman approaches the meeting, his ears are greeted by "the swell of what seemed a hymn, rolling solemnly from a distance with the weight of many voices. He knew the tune; it was a familiar one in the choir of the village meeting-house." The Communion of Sin is, in fact, the faithful counterpart of a grave and pious ceremony at a Puritan meeting-house. "At one extremity of an open space, hemmed in by the dark wall of the forest, arose a rock, bearing some rude, natural resemblance either to an altar or a pulpit, and surrounded by four blazing [459] pines, their tops aflame, their stems untouched, like candles at an evening meeting." The worshippers are "a numerous congregation," Satan resembles some grave divine, and the initiation into sin takes the form of a baptism.[22]

Along with this steady use of contrast at the Sabbath should be noticed its firmly composed pictorial quality. The rock, the center of the picture, is lighted by the blazing pines. The chief actors are as it were spotlighted in turn as they advance to the rock, while the congregation is generalized in the dimmer light at the outer edges. The whole composition is simple and definite, in contrast with the ambiguity occasioned by the rise and fall of the flame, in which the mass of the worshippers alternately shines forth and disappears in shadow.[23]

[20] See Schubert, *Hawthorne, the Artist*, 63. One would presume this device to be traditional in the story of the supernatural, where a return to actuality must eventually be made. An obvious example is the vanishing at cockcrow of the Ghost in *Hamlet*. See also the conclusion of Hawthorne's own "Ethan Brand."

[21] Evil must provisionally be taken for reality during the night in the forest, in spite of the ambiguity of the ending.

[22] The hint of the perverse desecration of the Black Mass adds powerfully here to the connotative scope of the allegory.

[23] The general effect is very like that of the famous Balinese Monkey Dance, which is performed at night, usually in a clearing of the forest, by the light of a single torch. The chief figures, the Monkey King and the King of the Demons, advance in turn to this central torch, while the chorus of dancers remains in the semi-obscurity of the background. This dance is allegorical, the Monkeys, as helpers of the Balinese, representing Good against the Evil of the Demons.

The clarity and simple structural solidity of "Young Goodman Brown" evinces itself in its tight dramatic framework. Within the basic form of the turning wheel it further divides into four separate scenes, the first and last of which, of course, are the balancing departure from and return to Salem. The night in the forest falls naturally into two parts: the temptation by the Devil and the witch-meeting. These two scenes, particularly the first, make full and careful use of the dramatic devices of suspense and climactic arrangement; and Hawthorne so manipulates his materials as to divide them as sharply as by a dropped curtain.

The temptation at first has the stylized and abstract delicacy of Restoration Comedy, or of the formalized seductions of Molière's *Don Juan*. The simple goodman, half-eager and half-reluctant, is wholly at the mercy of Satan, who leads him step by step to the inevitable end. The tone of the earlier part of this scene is lightly ironic: an irony reinforced by the inherent irony [460] of the situation, which elicits a double meaning at every turn.

"Come, Goodman Brown," cried his fellow-traveller, "this is a dull pace for the beginning of a journey. Take my staff, if you are so soon weary."

"Friend," said the other, exchanging his slow pace for a full stop, "having kept covenant by meeting thee here, it is my purpose now to return whence I came. I have scruples touching the matter thou wot'st of."

"Sayest thou so?" replied he of the serpent, smiling apart. "Let us walk on, nevertheless, reasoning as we go; and if I convince thee not thou shalt turn back. We are but a little way in the forest yet."

Then begins a skilful and relentless attack upon all the values which Goodman Brown has lived by. His reverence for his Puritan ancestors, "a people of prayer, and good works to boot," is speedily turned against him as the Devil claims them for tried and dear companions. Next comes the episode of Goody Cloyse, who taught the young man his catechism. Brown is sorely cast down, but at length sturdily concludes: "What if a wretched old woman do choose to go to the devil when I thought she was going to heaven: is that any reason why I should quit my dear Faith and go after her?" But no sooner has he rallied from this blow than he is beset by another, still more shrewdly placed: he hears the voices of the minister and Deacon Gookin, and from their conversation gathers that they are bound for the meeting, and eagerly anticipating it. This is nearly final, but he still holds out. " 'With heaven above, and Faith below, I will yet stand firm against the devil!' cried Goodman Brown"; only to be utterly overthrown by the sound of his wife's voice in the air, and the crushing evidence of the fatal pink ribbon.

The style has gradually deepened and intensified along with the carefully graduated intensity of the action, and now Hawthorne calls upon all his resources to seize and represent the immense significance of the moment. Nature itself is made at once to sympathize with and to mock the anguished chaos of [461] the young man's breast; in his rage he is both at one with and opposed to the forest and the wind.[24] The symphony of sound, which began with the confused babble of voices in the sky as Faith and her witch-attendants swept overhead, rises to a wild crescendo.[25]

And, maddened with despair, so that he laughed loud and long, did Goodman Brown grasp his staff and set forth again, at such a rate that he seemed to fly along the forest path rather than to walk or run. The road grew wilder and drearier and more faintly traced, and vanished at length, leaving him in the heart of the dark wilderness, still rushing onward with the instinct that guides mortal man to evil. The whole forest was peopled with frightful sounds—the creaking of the trees, the howling of wild beasts, and the yell of Indians; while sometimes the wind tolled like a distant church bell, and sometimes gave a broad roar around the traveller, as if all Nature were laughing him to scorn. But he was himself the chief horror of the scene, and shrank not from its other horrors.

After ascending to this climax, Hawthorne disengages himself and separates his scenes with the definiteness of the dropping of a curtain— by the simple expedient of shifting his view from the hero to his surroundings. Goodman Brown coming upon the witch-meeting is a mere onlooker until the moment comes for him to step forward for his baptism into sin. Up to that moment Satan usurps the stage. The eye is first directed to the central rock-altar, then to the four blazing pines which light it. Next there is the sense of a numerous assembly, vaguely seen in the fitful firelight. Finally the figure of Satan appears at the base of the rock, framed in an arch of flame. Only when he is summoned are we once more fully aware of Goodman Brown,[462] as he stands at the altar by his wife Faith. Then, a moment later, comes the second crashing

[24] "The intensity of the situation is sustained by all the devices Hawthorne had learned from the seventeenth century, for just as the heavens groaned in Milton's fall of the angels, the winds are made to whisper sadly at the loss of this man's faith." Matthiessen, *American Renaissance*, 284. The winds, however, roar rather than "whisper sadly."

[25] Cf. Schubert's account of the sound-effects in "Young Goodman Brown," *Hawthorne, the Artist*, 114–117. Mr. Schubert distorts the effect and purpose of Hawthorne's use of sound in the story by comparing it to "the last movement of Beethoven's Ninth Symphony"—description of sound is not the sound itself— but his perception is extremely valuable.

climax when Brown calls upon his wife to "look up to heaven, and resist the wicked one"—cut off abruptly by anticlimax as the meeting vanishes in a roaring wind, and Brown leaning against the rock finds it chill and damp to his touch.

The satisfaction one feels in the clean line of the structure of the story is enhanced by Hawthorne's steady detachment from his materials: an attitude which deepens the impression of classic balance, which in turn stands against the painful ambiguity of the theme. Even the full tone of the intensest scenes, as Goodman Brown rushing through the forest, is tempered by restraint. The participant is overweighted by the calm, impartial (though not unfeeling) spectator; Hawthorne does not permit himself to become identified with his hero. He displays young Goodman Brown not in and for himself, but always in relation to the whole situation and set of circumstances. This detachment of attitude is plainest in the almost continuous irony, unemphatic but nonetheless relentless: an irony organically related to the ever-present ambiguities of the situation, but most evident in sustained tone. Thus, after recording Goodman Brown's aspiration to "cling to Faith's skirts and follow her to heaven," the author adds with deadly calm, "With this excellent resolve for the future, Goodman Brown felt himself justified in making more haste on his present evil purpose."

This detachment is implicit in the quiet, the abstractness, and the exquisite gravity of Hawthorne's style, everywhere formal and exactly though subtly cadenced. It throws a light and idealizing veil over the action,[26] and as it were maintains an [463] aesthetic distance from it, while hinting at the ugliness it mercifully covers. The difference between the saying and the thing said, at times provides dramatic tension and a kind of ironic fillip. Note, for example, the grave decorum and eighteenth-century stateliness, the perverted courtliness, of Satan's welcome to young Brown and Faith:

This night it shall be granted you to know their secret deeds: how hoary-bearded elders of the church have whispered wanton words to the

[26] Hawthorne's notion of the ideality which art should lend to nature is apparent in his comment in the introductory essay to *Mosses from an Old Manse* upon the reflection of a natural scene in water: "Each tree and rock, and every blade of grass, is distinctly imaged, and however unsightly in reality, assumes ideal beauty in the reflection." And a few pages later—"Of all this scene, the slumbering river has a dream picture in its bosom. Which, after all was the most real—the picture, or the original? the objects palpable to our grosser senses, or their apotheosis in the stream beneath? Surely the disembodied images stand in closer relation to the soul."

young maids of their households; how many a woman, eager for widows' weeds, has given her husband a drink at bedtime and let him sleep his last sleep in her bosom; how beardless youths have made haste to inherit their fathers' wealth; and how fair damsels—blush not, sweet ones—have dug little graves in the garden, and bidden me, the sole guest, to an infant's funeral.

The steady procession of measured, ceremonious generalizations— "hoary-bearded elders," "wanton words," "beardless youths," and "fair damsels," is in radical contrast with the implication of the meaning; and the grisly archness of "blush not, sweet ones" is deeply suggestive in its incongruity.[27]

In "Young Goodman Brown," then, Hawthorne has achieved that reconciliation of opposites which Coleridge deemed the highest art. The combination of clarity of technique, embodied in simplicity and balance of structure, in firm pictorial composition, in contrast and climactic arrangement, in irony and detachment, with ambiguity of meaning as signalized by the "device of multiple choice," in its interrelationships produces the story's characteristic effect. By means of these two elements Hawthorne reconciles oneness of action with multiplicity [464] of suggestion, and enriches the bareness of systematic allegory. Contrarily, by them he holds in check the danger of lapsing into mere speculation without substance or form. The phantasmagoric light-and-shadow of the rising and falling fire, obscuring and softening the clear, hard outline of the witch-meeting, is an image which will stand for the essential effect of the story itself, compact of ambiguity and clarity harmoniously interfused.[465]

---

[27] I would not be understood to affirm that this adaptation of the eighteenth-century mock-heroic is the sole effect of Hawthorne's style in "Young Goodman Brown." The seventeenth century plays its part too. The agony of the goodman in the forest, and the sympathy of the elements, is Miltonic. And in this same scene of the witch-meeting Hawthorne twice touches upon Miltonic tenderness and sublimity: " 'Lo, there ye stand, my children,' said the figure, in a deep and solemn tone, almost sad with its despairing awfulness, as if his once angelic nature could yet mourn for our miserable race. . . . And there they stood, the only pair, as it seemed, who were yet hesitating on the verge of wickedness in this dark world."

Just Married!—In the Village of Witches *

O N E

Another of Hawthorne's newly married couples never had known care-free bliss as Lord and Lady of the May. For Young Goodman Brown, after a proper Puritan upbringing by his father, the deacon, the minister, and Goodwife Cloyse who taught him the catechism, was wedded in Salem village to pretty Faith, with pink ribbons on her cap. Young Goodman has a rendezvous to keep with a stranger in the forest, and although Faith importunes him to 'tarry with me this night . . . of all nights in the year,' he leaves her behind, dissembling his 'evil purpose.' Goodman's 'covenant' is kept with a dark-clad stranger whose staff 'might almost be seen to twist and wriggle itself like a living serpent.' Walking together, they 'might have been taken for father and son.' Reluctantly the youth penetrates the dreary forest where, though 'It was all as lonely as could be . . . the traveller knows not who may be concealed . . . he may be passing through an unseen multitude.'

They overtake old Goody Cloyse, who greets the stranger familiarly: 'And is it your worship indeed . . . in the very image of my old gossip, Goodman Brown, the grandfather of the silly fellow that now is.' Her broomstick has been stolen but she's off to the meeting afoot, 'for they tell me there is a nice young man to be taken into communion tonight.' She disappears on the stranger's 'writhing stick,' and a moment later the deacon and [149] minister ride by. 'There is a goodly young woman to be taken into communion,' says the deacon; the minister urges him to 'Spur up,' for 'Nothing can be done, you know, until I get on the ground.' Goodman Brown begins to understand toward what he is 'journeying so deep into the heathen wilderness.'

The rest of the story I shall discuss below, with closer attention to certain details. Brown's destination is a Witches' Sabbath—'of all nights in the year' this must be October 31, All Saints' Eve, and he finds, at a

* Daniel G. Hoffman, "Just Married!—In the Village of Witches," From *Form and Fable in American Fiction*, by Daniel G. Hoffman, pp. 149–68. © 1961 by Daniel G. Hoffman and reprinted by permission of Oxford University Press, Inc.

rock altar flanked by blazing pines, all the worthies of Salem in the coven of the Prince of Darkness. At the call, 'Bring forth the converts!' Brown steps forward—'he was himself the chief horror of the scene, and shrank not from its other horrors.' 'Thither came also the slender form of a veiled female.' The Devil addresses them: 'Depending upon one another's hearts, ye still had hoped that virtue were not all a dream. Now are ye undeceived. Evil is the nature of mankind. Evil must be your only happiness. Welcome again, my children, to the communion of your race.' At a natural basin in the rock, 'the shape of evil' dipped his hand and prepared 'to lay the mark of baptism upon their foreheads, that they might be partakers of the mystery of sin.' At this eleventh hour Young Goodman Brown cries in agony and terror, 'Faith! Faith! look up to heaven, and resist the wicked one.'

Young Goodman Brown never knew whether Faith obeyed him. The phantasmagoric tableau vanishes, and he finds himself alone in the dark forest. 'A hanging twig, that had been all on fire, besprinkled his cheek with the coldest dew.' Hawthorne's control of his powerfully ambivalent structural metaphors in this story—the synoptic *enjambement* of journey, initiation, and witchcraft—gives him the authority to ask at the end, without diminution of intensity, 'Had Goodman Brown fallen asleep in the forest and only dreamed a wild dream of a witch-meeting?' The author can even say, 'Be it so if you will; but alas! it was a dream of evil omen for young Goodman Brown.' His life henceforth leads not, like Edgar the May Lord's, toward heaven by [150] a difficult path; his heart has been blighted by this initiation into the coven of evil that binds mankind. 'They carved no hopeful verse upon his tombstone, for his dying hour was gloom.'

This tale is one of Hawthorne's masterpieces, and it has received its share of appreciative comment. Fogle sensitively explicates the delicate balance Hawthorne achieved between ambiguity of implication and clarity of form, while Roy R. Male finds the center of meaning in 'the fact that Faith's ambiguity is the ambiguity of womanhood and . . . the dark night in the forest is essentially a sexual experience, though it is also much more.' [1] My concern is to discover what imaginative possibilities Hawthorne found in his ancestral *donnée* of Salem witchcraft and how he realized them in 'Young Goodman Brown.'

All readers of course acknowledge that the Witches' Sabbath is one of Hawthorne's most memorable dramatizations of man's recognition of

[1] Fogle, *Hawthorne's Fiction*, pp. 15–32; Male, *Hawthorne's Tragic Vision*, pp. 76–80.

evil, and it is often remarked that Hawthorne did not forget that his own great-great-grandfather 'made himself so conspicuous in the martyrdom of the witches, that their blood may fairly be said to have left a stain upon him.' To do justice to Hawthorne's achievement we will do well to take as seriously as he did, for artistic purposes, the role of his Salem forebears in 1692. Speaking of the witch-condemning magistrate and of an earlier Hathorne who had scourged the Quakers, Hawthorne writes in the introductory chapter of *The Scarlet Letter*, 'I, the present writer, as their representative, hereby take shame upon myself for their sakes, and pray that any curse incurred by them—as I have heard, and as the dreary and unprosperous condition of the race, for many a long year back, would argue to exist—may now and henceforth be removed.'

Such a curse was in fact pronounced on Judge Hathorne. 'That God would take vengeance' was the cry of Goodwife Cary's husband, who had been forced to see her tortured and taunted by accusers whose cruelties that magistrate abetted in the names [151] of piety and justice.[2] The curse on the one hand identifies these antecedent Hathornes with the Pyncheons in *The House of the Seven Gables*; but on the other it identifies Nathaniel Hawthorne's sense of inherited guilt, of original sin, with their inhumanities.[3]

When a writer is truly prepossessed by the guilt of his pious ancestors in such affairs, we cannot dismiss the involvement of his fictional characters with curses and witchcraft as merely the Gothic machinery of romance, nor as artistic devices for producing ambiguities. Hawthorne *was* thus prepossessed by the part of his paternal forebears in Salem's season of horror. The zeal of those Puritans to discover satanism in their neighbors became for their descendant an emblem, an allegorical 'type,' of their particular tragic flaw—hypocritical pride. Endicott would serve as 'the Puritan of Puritans' in 'The Maypole,' but his iron rigidity would be manifested elsewhere in Hawthorne's work in contexts yet more destructive of man's capacity for bliss. When the Puritans had dealt with Morton's one dissident colony on the neighboring hill and turned instead upon each other, the consequences of their iron rule blighted both

---

[2] Nathaniel Cary's letter was printed by Robert Calef in *More Wonders of the Invisible World* (1692), reprinted in Burr, *Narratives of the Witchcraft Cases*, p. 351.

[3] The actual curse pronounced upon the Pyncheons, 'God will give you blood to drink,' were the dying words of Sarah Good to the Rev. Nicholas Noyes of Salem who was present at her execution. Judge Hathorne had committed Sarah Good's four-year-old child to prison, where she was fettered in irons. See Calef in *Narratives*, pp. 345, 358.

themselves and their posterity. In his historical sketch 'Main Street' Hawthorne without ambiguity presents their triumphs against the heretics and witches who threatened the Puritan commonwealth, and concludes,

It was impossible for the succeeding race to grow up, in heaven's freedom, beneath the discipline which their gloomy energy of character had established; nor, it may be, have we even yet thrown off all the unfavorable influences, which, among many good ones, were bequeathed us by our Puritan forefathers. Let us thank God for [152] having given us such ancestors; and let each successive generation thank Him, not less fervently, for being one step further from them in the march of ages.

The source of that balance between Hawthorne's clarity of design and ambiguity of meaning, which Fogle justly proposes as the key to his achievement, lies in his capacity to present the world of his Puritan forebears through a simultaneous double-exposure. We see old Salem both as they saw it, accepting their values, and as it appears from Hawthorne's very different view. Thus the Puritan values function both as absolutes (to the characters) and as one of several possible choices offered to the reader. Hawthorne so manages this doubleness that he can criticize Puritanism without destroying our suspension of disbelief in its premises. One of these which served his purposes especially well was witchcraft.

'It has also been made a doubt by some,' four New England clergymen wrote in 1689, introducing a book by Cotton Mather which Nathaniel Hawthorne would read, 'whether there are any such things as Witches, i.e., such as by Contract or Explicit Covenant with the Devil, improve, or rather are improved by him to the doing of things strange in themselves and besides their natural Course. But (besides that the Word of God assures us that there have been such, and gives order about them) no Age passes without some apparent Demonstration of it.'[4] Puritanism was perhaps as close to the Manichean as any Christian sect has come; the Power of Evil was acknowledged with the same fervor as the Power of Light. Indeed, it was a faith more pessimistic than that of the ancient dualists, for it made no provision for the goodness of man. The terrifying insecurity of each soul that it was not among the Elect produced those psychological tensions in Puritan culture which set the New England background apart from the heritage of the other colonies. One of those tensions reached the breaking-point in Salem,[153] where upright,

---

[4] *Memorable Providences, Relating to Witchcrafts and Possessions,* reprinted in *Narratives,* p. 95.

pious citizens like John Hathorne condemned their neighbors to death on evidence no stronger than this:

> These ten . . . did vehemently accuse [Goodwife Cory] of Afflicting them, by Biting, Pinching, Strangling, etc. And they said, they did in their Fits see her likeness coming to them, and bringing a Book for them to Sign; Mr. Hathorne, a Magistrate of Salem, asked her, why she Afflicted those Children? she said, she did not Afflict them; he asked her, who did then? she said, 'I don't know, how should I know?' she said, they were Poor Distracted Creatures, and no heed to be given to what they said; Mr. Hathorne and Mr. Noyes replied that it was the Judgement of all that were there present, that they were bewitched, and only she (the Accused) said they were Distracted; She was Accused by them, that the Black Man whispered to her in her Ear now (while she was upon Examination) and that she had a Yellow Bird, that did use to Suck between her fingers. . . . When the Accused had any motion of their Body, Hands or Mouth, the Accusers would cry out, as when she bit her Lip, they would cry out of being bitten . . . if she stirred her Feet, they would stamp and cry out of Pain there. After the Hearing the said Cory was committed to Salem Prison, and then their crying out of her abated.

The passage is from Calef's *More Wonders of the Invisible World* (1692), a book bitterly critical of the trials.[5] This same woman appears in 'Young Goodman Brown'; Goody Cloyse complains to the Black Man that her broomstick 'hath strangely disappeared, stolen, as I suspect, by that unhanged witch Goody Cory.' (Goody Cloyse, herself indicted for witchcraft, was the sister of two other witches, one whom Mr. Hathorne examined, the other whom he committed.[6])

Hawthorne found two means of taking witchcraft seriously as a way of revealing 'the truths of the human heart.' Accepting the reality of witchcraft as a sin, he would share the Puritans' abhorrence, as unredeemedly damned souls, of all who trafficked [154] in sortilege and necromancy. In his early story, 'The Hollow of the Three Hills,' a young woman meets a withered witch by such a spot, 'so gray tradition tells,' as was 'once the resort of the Power of Evil and his plighted subjects. . . . in the performance of an impious baptismal rite.' But this woman has long since received the Devil's baptism, and the role of the old witch is to bring to life before her the parents she has dishonored, the husband she has driven mad, the child she has killed. In her crimes

[5] Calef, in *Narratives*, p. 344. That Hawthorne read it we infer from the victims named in 'Main Street,' whose sufferings are reported by Calef alone among the chroniclers of Salem.

[6] Ibid., pp. 346–7.

against the human heart she, like Ethan Brand, is guilty of the Unpardonable Sin; still capable of remorse, she dies, the final victim of her own enormities. Some of the materials for 'Young Goodman Brown' are touched on here, but by the time Hawthorne conceived the later tale he had devised a far more radical means of employing them.

Suppose Hawthorne, for artistic purposes, to have taken witchcraft at exactly the value his great-great-grandsire put upon it; suppose him to have been able to believe that Goody Cory and others like her had really made covenants with the Black Man; suppose such Accusers as Abigail Williams were factually correct in reporting 'That she saw a great number of Persons in the Village at the Administration of a Mock Sacrament.' [7] What were the logical moral consequences of beliefs such as those Judge Hathorne had acted upon? It is obvious that no one was exempt from suspicion, that the hysterical seizures of the accusers might be produced by the 'spirit' of any member of the colony. Mistress Ann Hibbens, the sister of Governor Bellingham himself, had been executed for a witch in 1656. When the line between the damned witches and the accusing Christians became too fine to draw with certainty, even the avid Cotton Mather had to concede 'that some of those that were concerned grew amazed at the number and condition of those that were accused, and feared that Satan, by his wiles, had entrapped innocent persons under the imputation of that crime; and at last, as [155] was evidently seen, there must be a stop put, or the generation of the kingdom of God would fall under condemnation.' [8]

Suppose, then, that an innocent young Puritan, newly married, as yet unaware of his taint of original sin, should leave his faith just long enough, on one night, to follow the dark stranger into the forest—and find there the Witches' Sabbath where those who took the Devil's communion were all the members of his daylight world of piety. Hawthorne takes witchcraft more seriously, in fact, than had John Hathorne or Cotton Mather, for unlike them he does not flinch to acknowledge the covenant of the fallen nature of all mankind. Magistrate Hathorne seems not to have recanted or repented after the general amnesty, as did a more distinguished judge, Samuel Sewall. John Hathorne would seem to have made no connection between the state of his own soul in God's sight and his responsibility, say, for the sufferings of Giles Cory, whose wife he had committed for witchcraft. Cory, also accused and seeing that none had been cleared by trial, 'chose to undergo what Death they

[7] Calef, in *Narratives*, pp. 345-6.
[8] Mather, *Magnalia Christi Americani*, Book VI, chap. lxxxii.

would put him to . . . [The sentence was pressing, *peine forte et dure*]. His Tongue being prest out of his Mouth, the Sheriff with his Cane forced it in again when he was dying.' [9] No, Nathaniel Hawthorne could accept the guilt of alleged witches only as their individual share of the guilt of mankind. He must accept also the guilt of their accusers and tormentors. 'Young Goodman Brown' is one of his expiations for John Hathorne's guilt, as well as for his own.

Not only an expiation but a judgment upon his fathers, too. For what Young Goodman Brown learns at the Witches' Sabbath, while it is a knowledge more profound than that of the zealots who did the devil's work in 1692, is still but a partial knowledge. It is too incomplete to win him wisdom or happiness. He is so blinded by perception of evil that his life is ever after blighted. In this he is true to the Puritan past, as Hawthorne [156] envisaged it. In the struggle between jollity and gloom, Young Goodman Brown would seem to have had no choice. On his return to Salem he finds his wife Faith 'gazing anxiously forth, and bursting into such joy at the sight of him that she skipped along the street and almost kissed her husband before the whole village.' This would have been, for Brown, but to deepen their 'stain of guilt' in the eyes of their fellow-hypocrites. 'Goodman Brown looked sternly and sadly into her face, and passed on without a greeting.'

This tale, like 'The Maypole of Merry Mount,' presents the symbolistic development of details elaborated from within a frame of allegory. The names of the couple are as allegorical as any in Bunyan: The Puritan Everyman is the husband of Christian Faith. By the end of the tale he proves more Puritan than Christian, renouncing her larger vision for the 'distrustful,' 'desperate,' 'gloom' of his life and death. Faith, too, had been at the Witches' Sabbath; she can accept man even with full knowledge of his evil nature. But Goodman lacks her largesse, her charity, her balance. 'Often, awaking suddenly at midnight, he shrank from the bosom of Faith; . . . when the family knelt down at prayer, he scowled and muttered to himself, and gazed sternly at his wife, and turned away.' Faith remains true to him—she follows his 'hoary corpse' to the grave, but he has indeed been damned by his night among the witches.

T W O

The singular quality of Young Goodman Brown's adventure is the intensity with which the dramatic, theological, psychological, and cultural dimensions of the tale are fused together in the single structural

[9] Calef, in *Narratives*, p. 367.

metaphor of his journey into the dark forest and his return to the day-light world. Traditions of witchcraft served Hawthorne's complex pur-poses with extraordinary precision in each of these dimensions of mean-ing. If 'Young Goodman Brown' is the most profound work of fiction drawing [157] on those traditions in American writing,[10] one reason for this is that Hawthorne knew better than any author of his century what the traditions signified or could be made to signify. The interest in Salem witchcraft of James Russell Lowell, for instance, or of Professor Kit-tredge, proves to be merely preliminary to an attempt to exculpate their Puritan ancestors from the opprobrium of history.[11] Hawthorne, as we have seen, had the courage to recognize the cosmic irony of the situa-tion in which innocent, charitable Christians were tortured to death by the ministers and magistrates of God's chosen people. But it is not only his tragic sense of the family connection that makes witchcraft a master-ful metaphor in Hawthorne's tale. From his wide study of witchcraft and of the witchcraft trials came the materials he fused into the multiplex pattern of 'Young Goodman Brown': from the self-righteous accounts by zealots like Increase and Cotton Mather, the caustic attack upon them by Robert Calef, the records in the Essex County Courthouse, as well as from Hawthorne's awareness of oral traditions concerning witch-craft and of treatments of the subject in literature by Cervantes, Goethe, and Irving. The peculiar significances of this story are [158] rooted in the cultural significances of witchcraft itself. This we can see by ex-amining a schematic statement of the way his structural metaphor served Hawthorne. We can trace the elaboration in his tale of the several kinds

[10] For a survey of 'New England Witchcraft in Fiction' see G. H. Orians, *American Literature*, II (March, 1930), 54–71.

[11] Lowell, in his essay 'Witchcraft,' occasioned by the publication in 1867 of *Salem Witchcraft* by Charles W. Upham, echoes that historian in averring that 'The proceedings of the Salem trials are sometimes spoken of as though they were exceptionally cruel. But, in fact, if compared with others of the same kind, they were exceptionally humane . . . it is rather wonderful that no mode of torture other than mental was tried at Salem. . . . all died protesting their inno-cence. . . . though an acknowledgment of guilt would have saved the lives of all [sic]. This martyr proof of the efficacy of Puritanism in the character and conscience may be allowed to outweigh a great many sneers at Puritan fanat-icism.' Lowell cites the case of Goody Cary to prove that 'The accused . . . were not abandoned by their friends. In all the trials of this kind there is nothing so pathetic as the picture of [Nathaniel] Cary holding up the weary arms of his wife . . . and wiping away the sweat from her brow and the tears from her face.' Of Mr. Hathorne's retort he says nothing. *Among My Books* (Boston, 1882), pp. 146–7.
See G. L. Kittredge, *Witchcraft in Old and New England* (Cambridge, Mass., 1922), pp. 362–5.

of meaning associated by long tradition with witchcraft and the Witches' Sabbath.

Hawthorne's protagonist takes a journey, away from daylight, reality, piety, and Faith. Traveling through darkness he is guided by the Satanic image of his own father (and grandfather) toward an initiation into both forbidden knowledge and a secret cult. The ceremony of initiation is a ritual representing the spiritual inversion of Christianity (the rock 'altar,' the trees ablaze like both 'hell-kindled torches' and 'candles' at an evening meeting, and the 'mark of baptism' which the Devil is about to place on their foreheads). The forbidden knowledge in whose name the Devil-Father welcomes Brown and Faith 'to the communion of your race' is not only knowledge of man's evil nature generally, but knowledge specifically of original sin, represented by the welcoming spirit of Brown's father among the fiends as well as by the Devil's having assumed his father's form. It is also carnal knowledge, sexual sin. As we have seen, however, Faith is in the forest too; in one sense she *is* the forest, and Brown has qualified for admission to the witches' orgy by having carnal knowledge of her. (In another sense, however, which is ever equally valid in the tale, Faith transcends Brown's knowledge of evil with all-encompassing love.) In rejecting her love after his initiation, Brown is guilty of that Manichean prepossession with the dark side of man's nature which Hawthorne presents as the special sin of the Puritans. Each of these suggestions is a characteristic feature of the traditional attitudes toward witchcraft.

In the Salem trial records it is apparent that belief in witches was held on two different levels of conception by the seventeenth-century Puritans in New England.[12] [159]

On the one hand there is the belief of the Accusers. What, in fact, did such witnesses as those who testified against Goody Cory offer as evidence of her guilt? That she afflicted them, made them sick, caused them to itch or to vomit, afflicted their livestock, caused shipwrecks at sea, wrought havoc with their silverware, invisibly caused solid objects to move, had intercourse with devils, suckled her familiar at a hidden teat on her body. Such charges as these recur innumerably in the long

---

[12] An acquaintance with the British and Continental literature on the subject shows that these two types of belief were characteristic of Christian attitudes toward witchcraft since the Middle Ages. In no way was the experience of Salem uniquely a Colonial American phenomenon; indeed, much has been made by Kittredge and other writers of the comparative mildness of the American epidemic when seen in the context of English, Scottish, French, German, or Scandinavian experience.

annals of witchcraft. They led Professor Kittredge to regard as the basis of witchcraft the belief that human beings can with supernatural powers wreak harm and destruction on their enemies.

The second type of belief in witches is of a different sort. The Black Sabbath in 'Young Goodman Brown' may stand as representative of the more highly organized, conceptual regard for witchcraft as the involvement of the witches in religious cult which rivals Christianity. Indeed, it is a sect which threatens the Christian commonwealth with destruction. Consequently the witches are not content with the expression of personal malice; nor are they merely individuals who have made solitary compacts with the Devil. They are organized into covens, the Devil or one of his minions is their acknowledged priest and leader, they hold services which are horrible and blasphemous parodies of the Christian Mass, and the working of their will is one of the trials with which God in His Almighty Wisdom has decreed that the Faith of the Christian Commonwealth shall be tried on earth.

This sophisticated intellectual conception is in fact a development of medieval theology, which took for granted the identity of the sorcerers and necromancers mentioned in the Bible with the witches discovered in contemporary Christendom. The [160] prodigious learning of Increase and Cotton Mather, both of whose works on witchcraft Hawthorne studied, reflects their intimate familiarity with a large corpus of theological literature on witchcraft. The authoritative compendium of orthodox theological opinion on this subject is the *Malleus Maleficarum* of Henricus Institoris (1489). The arguments quoted above in favor of belief in witchcraft, offered exactly two centuries later by Cotton Mather and his four sponsors, are contained in the answer to the first Question in *Malleus*. Kittredge, whose *Witchcraft in Old and New England* lists the prolific theological discussion of the problem on both sides of the Atlantic, concludes that

the orgies of the Witches' Sabbath [were] systematized in the fourteenth and fifteenth centuries by the scholastic ingenuity of devout theologians and described in confessions innumerable wrung by torture from ignorant and superstitious defendants in response to leading questions framed by inquisitors who had the whole system in mind before the trial began.[13]

To support this theory Kittredge suggests that the Church, from its first concern with witchcraft, regarded the practice as heretical. Since the Church had had long experience with the perpetration of other heresies

[13] Op. cit., p. 243.

—Manichaean, Paulician, Catharian, Waldensian—in each instance of which there was a rival religious organization, when the medieval theologians turned their attention to witchcraft their speculation followed long-established dogmatic practice.[14]

In 'Young Goodman Brown' Hawthorne makes effective use [161] of both sets of beliefs. He employs the theological conceptualization of witchcraft as the cult of the Antichrist for the architecture of his tale, and he uses several folk beliefs (not necessarily dependent upon the foregoing) for verisimilitude of detail and for the evocation of wonder, awe, and terror. The compact with the Black Man, the Devil's shape-shifting and his serpentine staff, the transportation of witches by means of magical ointments and broomsticks, their existence as disembodied spirits, the withering of living things at the witches' or Devil's touch, are motifs of folk belief often encountered independently of the Witches' Sabbath. Yet the theological construct had by the late seventeenth century passed into popular tradition, since such notorious cases as the trials of the Lancashire witches in 1612 had been celebrated in unnumbered chapbooks, black-letter ballads, popular narratives, and literary works. Consequently some of the informants (like Abigail Williams) averred that they had witnessed Black Masses and the ceremonial partaking of the evil sacrament by the neighbors they accused.

Hawthorne thus is able to take advantage of the idea—by Puritan times both theological and popular—that witchcraft represents forbidden knowledge, and that its attainment takes the form of an initiatory ceremonial, a Witches' Sabbath. In folklore the two strains of witchcraft and demonology merged in this ceremony, where the witch sold his soul to the Devil. Hawthorne quotes almost verbatim from Cotton Mather's *Wonders of the Invisible World* when he tells us that Faith stepped forward to receive the Devil's baptism beside 'Martha Carrier, who had received the devil's promise to be queen of hell.' [15]

The theological level of 'Young Goodman Brown' is greatly strength-

[14] 'In the course of the fourteenth century the papal inquisitors discovered (so they thought) a new heretical sect—the sect of devil-worshipping witches. These, it logically followed, must hold meetings, and such meetings must resemble those of other heretics. . . . The idea of a Sabbath of Witches was neither ancient nor of popular origin. It was a mere transference. What was already established in the inquisitorial mind with regard to the Satanic Synagogue of the Cathari was shifted, as a matter of logical course, to the alleged assemblies of the new heretical sect, the devotees of witchcraft.' *Witchcraft in Old and New England*, p. 246.

[15] Burr, *Narratives*, p. 144.

ened by the youth's horrified recognition that the form of his father
seems to beckon him toward the unholy communion. This is itself a
dreamlike duplication of the first appearance of the Black Man in the
forest, for when Goodman walked [162] beside him 'they might have
been taken for father and son.' The paternal image is reduplicated yet
again when Goody Cloyse greets 'The devil! . . . Yes, truly it is, and
in the very image of my old gossip, Goodman Brown, the grandfather
of the silly fellow that now is.' She of course is using *gossip* in its
original sense of *God-sib*—'A person spiritually related to another
through being a sponsor at a baptism.' This is to say that Goodman
Brown's grandfather had taken Goody Cloyse to her first witch meeting.
The tripling of generations in Brown's family who have taken the
Devil's Mass reinforces the theological conception of witchcraft as one
of Satan's entrapments of the human soul. Our original sin makes us
vulnerable.

The inference is unmistakeable that Old Brown had had carnal knowledge of Goody Cloyse, and that it was through such carnal knowledge
that her initiation was completed. Young Goodman's bitter rejection
of Faith after his return to the 'real' world supports the inference that
it was through his knowledge of her that he made acquaintance with the
Black Man in the first place. He is reliving the Puritan allegory of the
Fall, in which woman, as Governor Endicott warned the May Lord, is
'that sex which requireth the stricter discipline.' But if woman is the
agent of the Fall, for Young Goodman Brown that Fall is anything but
fortunate, for it fails to prepare the way for his salvation.

The forbidden knowledge, then, is sexual knowledge and its attendant
guilt. Its possession forces Brown to recognize that all the antecedent
generations of his name have also sinned as he has sinned. If the procrea-
tive act is sinful, then all mankind is indeed knit together in the Devil's
skein: 'Evil is the nature of mankind. Evil must be your only happiness.'

The association of witchcraft itself with sexuality, debauchery, and
carnal abandon is an aspect of popular tradition of which Hawthorne
shows his empathetic understanding. The evidence of modern anthropological scholarship strongly suggests that witchcraft perpetuated the
same fertility cult religion which survived also in the folk rituals observing the seasonal festivals. 'The only [163] essential difference between
these two kinds of rites is that, while the popular fertility rites were
carried out publicly with the whole village participating, the witches'
sabbaths were carried out in secret, at night, and were participated in

only by witches and wizards who were initiated into the secret art.'[16] In the *Malleus Maleficarum* witches are said to copulate with devils, to impair the power of generation, and to deprive man of his virile member. Such ecclesiastical negation of their influence on fecundity argues that the witches themselves claimed exactly the contrary power.

Since the association of witchcraft with fertility is rooted in the rites performed to invoke increase, the connection is maintained most strongly where witches are thought of as members of a sect performing communal rituals. Contrarily, when popular belief regards the witch as merely an individual malefactor, the connection with sexual abundance withers in the popular mind. The latter is the stage in which New England tradition for the most part conceived of the witches. Although there is sporadic mention of witch meetings among travellers' accounts of the seventeenth century[17] and although some of the Salem Accusers spoke of witch meetings, the notion of the witch most generally held was that of the malicious woman who uses the limitless infernal powers bestowed on her by the Prince of Darkness—to [164] prevent the farmer's butter or annoy her neighbors' cows.[18] By the end of the eighteenth century the idea of the coven drops out of recorded beliefs; oral traditions, as Hawthorne heard them, would elaborate the simple motifs of transformation, malice, the magic weapon, and the afflicted crone which he knew from a poem he praised—'The Country Lovers' (1795) by his friend Thomas Green Fessenden:

> . . . a witch, in shape of owl,
> Did steal her neighbor's geese, sir,

[16] Runeberg, *Witches, Demons, and Fertility Magic*, p. 241. Runeberg suggests that witchcraft in its modern form emerged when the pagan magicians and the Catharian cultists were driven to join forces by inquisitorial persecution.

[17] For example, John Josselyn (1675) reported how Mr. Foxwell, sailing a shallop off Cape Ann at night, heard 'loud voices from the shore, calling Foxwell, Foxwell, come a shore . . . upon the Sands they saw a great fire, and Men and Women hand in hand dancing about it in a ring, after an hour or two they vanished . . .' Landing by daylight 'he found the footing of Men, Women and Children shod with shoes; and an infinite number of brand-ends thrown up by the water but neither *Indian* nor *English* could be met with on the shore, nor in the woods. . . . *There are many stranger things in the world, than are to be seen between London and Stanes.*' Quoted in Dorson, *Jonathan Draws the Long Bow* (Cambridge, 1946), pp. 26–7.

[18] Dorson gives some sixty instances of such witchcraft beliefs in nineteenth-century New England, *Jonathan Draws the Long Bow*, pp. 33–47. See also Clifton Johnson, *What They Say in New England* (Boston, 1896), pp. 235–60; John Greenleaf Whittier, *The Supernaturalism of New England* (London, 1847), pp. 49–55, 62–3.

And turkeys too, and other fowl,
When people did not please her.

And how a man, one dismal night,
Shot her with silver bullet,
And then she flew straight out of sight
As fast as she could pull it.

How Widow Wunks was sick next day,
The parson went to view her,
And saw the very place, they say,
Where forsaid ball went through her! [19]

Nonetheless in 'Young Goodman Brown' the projection of witch-craft as sexual knowledge is arrestingly clear. It is true that much of the traditional imagery of witchcraft is easily susceptible of carnal inter-pretation—the serpentine staff, flying, the leaping flames—but Hawthorne manages his descriptions so skillfully that the phallic and psychosexual associations are made [165] intrinsic to the thematic development of his story. The Puritan focus of the tale brings out with special clarity the inherent sexual character of Young Goodman's quest. Brown's whole experience is described as the penetration of a dark and lonely way through a branched forest—to the Puritans, the Devil's domain. At journey's end is the orgiastic communion amidst the leaping flames. Along the way, when Young Goodman abandons himself to the Devil, he 'grasp[ed] his staff and . . . seemed to fly along the forest path . . . rushing onward with the instinct that guides mortal man to evil.' Where, if in neither the Salem trial records nor in contemporary traditions of witch lore, did Hawthorne find the connection between witchcraft and sexuality that becomes one of the important cruces of his story?

The answer can only be in Hawthorne's reading of European writings which presented witchcraft in a different aspect from his American sources. We know that he was intimately familiar with Goethe's *Faust*,[20] and that he had read *El colloquio de los perros* of Cervantes in the Spanish. These works include two of the most important imaginative

[19] For folk provenience of the belief that only a silver bullet can kill a witch, see Whittier, *Supernaturalism of New England*, p. 49; Johnson, *What They Say in New England*, p. 240; Dorson, pp. 40–41; for the transference of the wound from the witch's animal to her human form, see Whittier, pp. 52, 63; Johnson, pp. 238, 239, 260; Dorson, pp. 35–6. These references span the entire nineteenth century.

[20] Hawthorne mentions Goethe in 'A Virtuoso's Collection.' His dependence on Goethe for the theme of the Devil's Compact is proposed by William Bysshe Stein, *Hawthorne's Faust* (Gainesville, Fla., 1953).

treatments of witchcraft. In *Faust*, Part I, after witnessing the disgusting orgies of Walpurgisnacht, Faust is given the witches' potion by Mephistopheles and immediately turns into a goatish lecher. In Cervantes he found a detailed enumeration of witch beliefs that extended the moral and theological implications of Goethe's treatment. The witch Canizares, mistaking one of the dogs for the son of another witch, pours out to him a long monologue revealing her own witchcraft. We know Hawthorne to have read this one of *Los novelas ejemplares*, for when, in 'Young Goodman Brown,' Goody Cloyse meets the Devil, they exchange a recipe for flying ointment: an application of 'juice of smallage, and cinquefoil, and wolf's bane—Mingled with fine wheat and the fat of a new-born babe' gives the witch the gift of flight. It has been observed [166] that Hawthorne used this identical recipe a year later (July 1836) in a magazine he edited, and here he added a comment which shows that he knew exactly what he was doing with his witches in 'Young Goodman Brown':

Cervantes, in one of his tales, seems of the opinion that the ointment cast them into a trance, during which they merely dreamt of holding intercourse with Satan. If so, witchcraft differs little from nightmare.[21]

But Cervantes provided Hawthorne with more than the recipe for flying salve and the equating of witchcraft with nightmare, important as these are in 'Young Goodman Brown.' The old witch in *El colloquio de los perros* tells the dog,

We go to meet [our lord and master] in a large field that is a long way from here. There we find a huge throng of people, made up of witches and wizards . . . we gorge ourselves with food, and other things happen which . . . I should not dare tell you as they are so filthy and loathesome that they would be an offense to your chaste ears . . . Vice becomes second nature and witchcraft is something that enters into our blood and bones. It is marked by a great ardor, and at the same time it lays such a chill upon the soul as to benumb its faith and cause it to forget its own

[21] 'Witch Ointment,' from *The American Magazine*, reprinted in Arlin Turner, *Hawthorne as Editor* (University, La., 1941), p. 253. See Fanny N. Cherry, 'The Sources of Hawthorne's "Young Goodman Brown,"' *American Literature*, V (Jan. 1934), 342–8. Another source of the formula was Bacon, *Sylva Sylvarum* X, 975. Hawthorne's recipe corresponds roughly to the first of three formulae in Margaret Murray, *The Witch Cult of Western Europe* (Oxford, 1921), with the addition of baby fat from the third. Miss Murray had these tested by A. J. Clark, an analytical chemist, who reported that aconite (wolf's bane) and hemlock (smallage) would in fact produce the illusion of flight (pp. 100–105, 279–80).

well-being, so that it no longer remembers the terrors with which God threatens it nor the glories of Heaven that he holds out to it.

In short, seeing that it is a sin that is concerned with carnal pleasure, it must of necessity deaden, stupefy, and absorb the senses . . . I see and understand everything, but carnal pleasure keeps my will enchained, and I always have been and always shall be evil.[22] [167]

Hawthorne, too, would send his Goodman Brown to a nightmare-meeting of carnal pleasure and universal sexual guilt. The youth's acceptance of fleshly ardor lays a chill upon his soul, benumbs his faith, and alienates him from the glories of Heaven. When the Devil welcomes Goodman and his bride to the communion of the damned, he endows them with the power to know the secret sins of 'all whom ye have reverenced from youth'; and these are sins of sexual passion—adultery, murder of mates, of babes born out of wedlock. To know such sins as these, the Devil tells them, is 'your nature and your destiny.'

The lore of witchcraft thus served Hawthorne well, connecting 'the communion of the race' superstitiously with the Devil's Compact, psychologically with sexual knowledge and guilt, theologically with evil and original sin, and culturally with acceptance of the past. Young Goodman's journey resembles Robin's search for his kinsman, but the fertility rites he celebrates are a bitter parody not only of the Christian sacraments but of the pagan paradise of 'The Maypole of Merry Mount.' His Fall from innocence is unredeemed, as we have seen, by his incapacity to return Faith's love. Like Aylmer in 'The Birthmark,' he had to have perfection—or nothing. In his sense of his own sin, then, Young Goodman is self-deceived. For it is not his implication in sexual sin which damns him, but his Puritan misanthropy, his unforgiving lovelessness, his lack of faith in Faith. She, as both his mortal wife and his *ange blanche*, had, like him, appeared before the Font of Evil. She is in fact the Devil's only antagonist in this tale, for are not all the Puritans—preachers, teachers, catechists and all—roaring about in the orgiastic coven? They have all taken the Black Man's black bread; Faith alone has such faith in man that she can transcend the revelation that he is fallen. But Young Goodman Brown, like his own fathers, like Goody Cloyse and all of Salem, like Hawthorne's distinguished ancestors too, really believed in witches, rather than in men. And so he joylessly became one.[168]

[22] Cervantes, *Three Exemplary Novels,* transl. by Samuel Putnam (New York, 1950), pp. 186, 189.

CLASSICAL HAWTHORNE CRITICISM

Nathaniel Hawthorne *

The reputation of the author of *Twice-Told Tales* has been confined, until very lately, to literary society; and I have not been wrong, perhaps, in citing him as *the* example, *par excellence*, in this country, of the privately-admired and publicly-unappreciated man of genius. Within the last year or two, it is true, an occasional critic has been urged, by honest indignation, into very warm approval. Mr. Webber, for instance (than whom no one [188] has a keener relish for that kind of writing which Mr. Hawthorne has best illustrated), gave us, in a late number of the *American Review*, a cordial and certainly a full tribute to his talents; and since the issue of the *Mosses from an Old Manse* criticisms of similar tone have been by no means infrequent in our more authoritative journals. I can call to mind few reviews of Hawthorne published *before* the *Mosses*. One I remember in *Arcturus* (edited by Mathews and Duyckinck) for May 1841; another in the *American Monthly* (edited by Hoffman and Herbert) for March 1838; a third in the ninety-sixth number of the *North American Review*. These criticisms, however, seemed to have little effect on the popular taste; at least, if we are to form any idea of the popular taste by reference to its expression in the newspapers, or by the sale of the author's book. It was never the fashion (until lately) to speak of him in any summary of our best authors.

The daily critics would say, on such occasions, "Is there not Irving, and Cooper, and Bryant, and Paulding, and—Smith?" or, "Have we not Halleck, and Dana, and Longfellow, and—Thompson?" or, "Can we not point triumphantly to our own Sprague, Willis, Channing, Bancroft, Prescott, and—Jenkins?" but these unanswerable queries were never wound up by the name of Hawthorne.

* Edgar Allan Poe, "Nathaniel Hawthorne," *The Works of Edgar Allan Poe*, with a memoir by R. W. Griswold and notices of his life and genius by N. Willis and J. R. Lowell (4 vols; Redfield, N.Y.: 1858), III, 188–202.

For this article Griswold took Poe's review of Hawthorne in *Godey's Lady's Book*, November, 1847, and combined it with another that Poe did for *Graham's Magazine* in May, 1842. This combination of articles has come to be known as Poe's opinion of Hawthorne.

Beyond doubt, this inappreciation of him on the part of the public arose chiefly from the two causes to which I have referred—from the facts that he is neither a man of wealth nor a quack; but these are insufficient to account for the whole effect. No small portion of it is attributable to the very marked idiosyncrasy of Mr. Hawthorne himself. In one sense, and in great measure, to be peculiar is to be original, and than the true originality there is no higher literary virtue. This true or commendable originality, however, implies not the uniform, but the continuous peculiarity—a peculiarity springing from ever-active vigor of fancy—better still if from ever-present force of imagination, giving its own hue, its own character, to everything it touches, and, especially, *self-impelled to touch everything.*

It is often said, inconsiderately, that very original [189] writers always fail in popularity, that such and such persons are too original to be comprehended by the mass. "Too peculiar," should be the phrase, "too idiosyncratic." It is, in fact, the excitable, undisciplined, and childlike popular mind which most keenly feels the original.

The criticism of the conservatives, of the hackneys, of the cultivated old clergymen of the *North American Review*, is precisely the criticism which condemns, and alone condemns it. "It becometh not a divine," saith Lord Coke, "to be of a fiery and salamandrine spirit." Their conscience allowing them to move nothing themselves, these dignitaries have a holy horror of being moved. "Give us *quietude*," they say. Opening their mouths with proper caution, they sigh forth the word *"Repose."* And this is, indeed, the one thing they should be permitted to enjoy, if only upon the Christian principle of give and take.

The fact is, that if Mr. Hawthorne were really original, he could not fail of making himself felt by the public. But the fact is, he is not original in any sense. Those who speak of him as original mean nothing more than that he differs in his manner or tone, and in his choice of subjects, from any author of their acquaintance—their acquaintance not extending to the German Tieck, whose manner, in *some* of his works, is absolutely identical with that *habitual* to Hawthorne. But it is clear that the element of the literary originality is novelty. The element of its appreciation by the reader is the reader's sense of the new. Whatever gives him a new, and, insomuch, a pleasurable emotion, he considers original; and whoever frequently gives him such emotion, he considers an original writer. In a word, it is by the sum total of these emotions that he decides upon the writer's claim to originality. I may observe here, however, that there is clearly a point at which even novelty itself would cease to produce the legitimate originality, if we judge this originality, as we should, by the effect designed; this point is that at which *novelty becomes nothing novel*, and here the artist, *to preserve his originality*, will subside into the commonplace. No one, I think, has noticed that, merely through inattention to this matter, Moore has comparatively failed in his *Lalla Rookh*. Few readers, and indeed few critics, have commended this poem for originality [190]—and, in fact, the effect, originality, is not produced by it; yet no work of equal size so abounds in the happiest originalities, individually considered. They are so excessive as, in the end, to deaden in the reader all capacity for their appreciation.

These points properly understood, it will be seen that the critic (unacquainted with Tieck) who reads a single tale or essay by Hawthorne, may be justified in thinking him original; but the tone, or manner, or choice of subject, which induces in this critic the sense of the new, will —if not in a second tale, at least in a third and all subsequent ones—not only fail of inducing it, but bring about an exactly antagonistic impression. In concluding a volume, and more especially in concluding all the volumes of the author, the critic will abandon his first design of calling him "original," and content himself with styling him "peculiar."

With the vague opinion that to be original is to be unpopular, I could, indeed, agree, were I to adopt an understanding of originality which, to my surprise, I have known adopted by many who have a right to be called critical. They have limited, in a love for mere words, the literary to the metaphysical originality. They regard as original in letters only such combinations of thought, of incident, and so forth, as are, in fact, absolutely novel. It is clear, however, not only that it is the novelty of *effect* alone which is worth consideration, but that this effect is *best* wrought, for the end of all fictitious composition, pleasure, by shunning rather than by seeking the absolute novelty of combination. Originality, thus understood, tasks and startles the intellect, and so brings into undue action the faculties to which, in the lighter literature, we least appeal. And thus understood, it cannot fail to prove unpopular with the masses, who, seeking in this literature amusement, are positively offended by instruction. But the true originality—true in respect of its purposes—is that which, in bringing out the half-formed, the reluctant, or the unexpressed fancies of mankind, or in exciting the more delicate pulses of the heart's passion, or in giving birth to some universal sentiment or instinct in embryo, thus combines with the pleasurable effect of *apparent* novelty a real egotistic delight. The reader, in the case first supposed (that of the absolute novelty), is excited, but embarrassed, disturbed, in some degree even pained, at his own want [191] of perception, at his own folly in not having himself hit upon the idea. In the second case, his pleasure is doubled. He is filled with an intrinsic and extrinsic delight. He feels and intensely enjoys the seeming novelty of the thought, enjoys it as really novel, as absolutely original with the writer—*and* himself. They two, he fancies, have, alone of all men, thought thus. They two have, together, created this thing. Henceforward there is a bond of sympathy between them—a sympathy which irradiates every subsequent page of the book.

There is a species of writing which, with some difficulty, may be admitted as a lower degree of what I have called the true original. In its perusal, we say to ourselves, not "how original this is!" nor "here is an idea which I and the author have alone entertained," but "here is a charmingly obvious fancy," or sometimes even, "here is a thought which I am not sure has ever occurred to myself, but which, of course, has occurred to all the rest of the world." This kind of composition (which still appertains to a high order) is usually designated as "the natural." It has little external resemblance, but strong internal affinity to the true original, if, indeed, as I have suggested, it is not of this latter an inferior degree. It is best exemplified, among English writers, in Addison, Irving, and *Hawthorne*. The "ease" which is so often spoken of as its distinguishing feature, it has been the fashion to regard as ease in appearance alone, as a point of really difficult attainment. This idea, however, must be received with some reservation. The natural style is difficult only to those who should never intermeddle with it—to the unnatural. It is but the result of writing with the understanding, or with the instinct, that the *tone*, in composition, should be that which, at any given point or upon any given topic, would be the tone of the great mass of humanity. The author who, after the manner of the "North Americans," is merely at *all* times *quiet*, is, of course, upon *most* occasions, merely silly or stupid, and has no more right to be thought "easy" or "natural" than has a cockney exquisite, or the sleeping beauty in the waxworks.

The "peculiarity," or sameness, or monotone of Hawthorne, would, in its mere character of "peculiarity," and without reference to what *is* the peculiarity, suffice to deprive him of all chance [192] of popular appreciation. But at his failure to be appreciated, we can, of course, no longer wonder, when we find him monotonous at decidedly the worst of all possible points—at that point which, having the least concern with Nature, is the farthest removed from the popular intellect, from the popular sentiment, and from the popular taste. I allude to the strain of allegory which completely overwhelms the greater number of his subjects, and which in some measure interferes with the direct conduct of absolutely all.

In defense of allegory (however or for whatever object employed) there is scarcely one respectable word to be said. Its best appeals are made to the fancy—that is to say, to our sense of adaptation, not of matters proper, but of matters improper for the purpose, of the real with the unreal; having never more of intelligible connection than has something with nothing, never half so much of effective affinity as has the substance for the shadow. The deepest emotion aroused within us by the happiest allegory, *as* allegory, is a very, very imperfectly satisfied sense of the writer's ingenuity in overcoming a difficulty we should have preferred his not having attempted to overcome. The fallacy of the idea that allegory, in any of its moods, can be made to enforce a truth, that metaphor, for example, may illustrate as well as embellish an argument, could be promptly demonstrated; the converse of the supposed fact might be shown, indeed, with very little trouble; but these are topics foreign to my present purpose. One thing is clear, that if allegory ever establishes a fact, it is by dint of overturning a fiction. Where the suggested meaning runs through the obvious one in a *very* profound undercurrent, so as never to interfere with the upper one without our own volition, so as never to show itself unless *called* to the surface, there only, for the proper uses of fictitious narrative, is it available at all. Under the best circumstances, it must always interfere with that unity of effect which, to the artist, is worth all the allegory in the world. Its vital injury, however, is rendered to the most vitally important point in fiction— that of earnestness or verisimilitude. That *The Pilgrim's Progress* is a ludicrously over-rated book, owing its seeming popularity to one or two of those accidents in critical literature which by the critical are sufficiently well understood, is a matter upon which no two thinking people [193] disagree; but the pleasure derivable from it, in any sense, will be found in the direct ratio of the reader's capacity to smother its true purpose, in the direct ratio of his ability to keep the allegory out of sight, or of his *in*ability to comprehend it. Of allegory properly handled, judiciously subdued, seen only as a shadow or by suggestive glimpses, and making its nearest approach to truth in a not obtrusive and therefore not unpleasant *appositeness*, the *Undine* of De La Motte Fouqué is the best, and undoubtedly a very remarkable specimen.

The obvious causes, however, which have prevented Mr. Hawthorne's *popularity* do not suffice to condemn him in the eyes of the few who belong properly to books, and to whom books, perhaps, do not quite so properly belong. These few estimate an author, not as do the public, altogether by what he does, but in great measure—indeed, even in the greatest measure—by what he evinces a capability of doing. In this view, Hawthorne stands among literary people in America much in the same light as did Coleridge in England. The few, also, through a certain warping of the taste, which long pondering upon books as books merely never fails to induce, are not in condition to view the errors of a scholar as errors altogether. At any time these gentlemen are prone to think the public not right rather than an educated author wrong. But the simple truth is that the writer who aims at impressing the people is *always* wrong when he fails in forcing that people to receive the impression. How far Mr. Hawthorne has addressed the people at all, is, of course, not a question for me to decide. His books afford strong internal evidence of having been written to himself and his particular friends alone.

There has long existed in literature a fatal and unfounded prejudice, which it will be the office of this age to overthrow, the idea that the mere bulk of a work must enter largely into our estimate of its merit. I do not suppose even the weakest of the *Quarterly* reviewers weak enough to maintain that in a book's size or mass, abstractly considered, there is anything which especially calls for our admiration. A mountain, simply through the sensation of physical magnitude which it conveys, does, indeed, affect us with a sense of the sublime, but we cannot admit any such influence in the contemplation even of *The Columbiad*. The [194] Quarterlies themselves will not admit it. And yet, what else are we to understand by their continual prating about "sustained effort"? Granted that this sustained effort has accomplished an epic—let us then admire the effort (if this be a thing admirable), but certainly not the epic on the effort's account. Common sense, in the time to come, may possibly insist upon measuring a work of art rather by the object it fulfills, by the impression it makes, than by the time it took to fulfill the object, or by the extent of "sustained effort" which became necessary to produce the impression. The fact is, that perseverance is one thing and genius quite another; nor can all the transcendentalists in Heathendom confound them.

The pieces in the volumes entitled *Twice-Told Tales* are now in their third republication, and, of course, are thrice-told. Moreover, they are by no means *all* tales, either in the ordinary or in the legitimate understanding of the term. Many of them are pure essays; for example, *Sights from a Steeple, Sunday at Home, Little Annie's Ramble, A Rill from the*

Town Pump, The Toll-Gatherer's Day. The Haunted Mind, The Sister Years, Snow Flakes, Night Sketches, and *Footprints on the Sea Shore.* I mention these matters chiefly on account of their discrepancy with that marked precision and finish by which the body of the work is distinguished.

Of the Essays just named, I must be content to speak in brief. They are each and all beautiful, without being characterized by the polish and adaptation so visible in the tales proper. A painter would at once note their leading or predominant feature, and style it *repose.* There is no attempt at effect. All is quiet, thoughtful, subdued. Yet this repose may exist simultaneously with high originality of thought; and Mr. Hawthorne has demonstrated the fact. At every turn we meet with novel combinations; yet these combinations never surpass the limits of the quiet. We are soothed as we read; and withal is a calm astonishment that ideas so apparently obvious have never occurred or been presented to us before. Herein our author differs materially from Lamb or Hunt or Hazlitt—who, with vivid originality of manner and expression, have less of the true novelty of thought than is generally [195] supposed, and whose originality, at best, has an uneasy and meretricious quaintness, replete with startling effects unfounded in nature, and inducing trains of reflection which lead to no satisfactory result. The essays of Hawthorne have much of the character of Irving, with more of originality, and less of finish; while, compared with *The Spectator,* they have a vast superiority at all points. *The Spectator,* Mr. Irving, and Hawthorne have in common that tranquil and subdued manner which I have chosen to denominate *repose;* but, in the case of the two former, this repose is attained rather by the absence of novel combination, or of originality, than otherwise, and consists chiefly in the calm, quiet, unostentatious expression of commonplace thoughts, in an unambitious, unadulterated Saxon. In them, by strong effort, we are made to conceive the absence of all. In the essays before me the absence of effort is too obvious to be mistaken, and a strong undercurrent of *suggestion* runs continuously beneath the upper stream of the tranquil thesis. In short, these effusions of Mr. Hawthorne are the product of a truly imaginative intellect, restrained, and in some measure repressed, by fastidiousness of taste, by constitutional melancholy, and by indolence.

But it is of his tales that I desire principally to speak. The tale proper, in my opinion, affords unquestionably the fairest field for the exercise of the loftiest talent, which can be afforded by the wide domains of mere prose. Were I bidden to say how the highest genius could be most advantageously employed for the best display of its own powers, I should answer, without hesitation—in the composition of a rhymed poem, not to exceed in length what might be perused in an hour. Within this limit alone can the highest order of true poetry exist. I need only here say, upon this topic, that, in almost all classes of composition, the unity of effect or impression is a point of the greatest importance. It is clear, moreover, that this unity cannot be thoroughly preserved in productions whose perusal cannot be completed at one sitting. We may continue the reading of a prose composition, from the very nature of prose itself, much longer than we can persevere, to any good purpose, in the perusal of a poem. This latter, if truly fulfilling the demands of the poetic sentiment, induces an exaltation of the soul which cannot be long sustained.[196] All high excitements are necessarily transient. Thus a long poem is a paradox. And, without unity of impression, the deepest effects cannot be brought about. Epics were the offspring of an imperfect sense of Art, and their reign is no more. A poem *too* brief may produce a vivid, but never an intense or enduring impression. Without a certain continuity of effort—without a certain duration or repetition of purpose —the soul is never deeply moved. There must be the dropping of the water upon the rock. De Béranger has wrought brilliant things, pungent and spirit-stirring; but, like all immassive bodies, they lack *momentum*, and thus fail to satisfy the Poetic Sentiment. They sparkle and excite, but, from want of continuity, fail deeply to impress. Extreme brevity will degenerate into epigrammatism; but the sin of extreme length is even more unpardonable. *In medio tutissimus ibis.*

Were I called upon, however, to designate that class of composition which, next to such a poem as I have suggested, should best fulfill the demands of high genius—should offer it the most advantageous field of exertion—I should unhesitatingly speak of the prose tale, as Mr. Hawthorne has here exemplified it. I allude to the short prose narrative, requiring from a half-hour to one or two hours in its perusal. The ordinary novel is objectionable, from its length, for reasons already stated in substance. As it cannot be read at one sitting, it deprives itself, of course, of the immense force derivable from *totality*. Worldly interests intervening during the pauses of perusal, modify, annul, or counteract, in a greater or less degree, the impressions of the book. But simple cessation in reading would, of itself, be sufficient to destroy the true unity. In the brief tale, however, the author is enabled to carry out the fullness of his intention, be it what it may. During the hour of perusal the soul of the reader is at the writer's control. There are no external or extrinsic influences—resulting from weariness or interruption.

A skillful literary artist has constructed a tale. If wise, he has not fashioned his thoughts to accommodate his incidents; but having conceived, with deliberate care, a certain unique or single *effect* to be wrought out, he then invents such incidents—he then combines such events as may best aid him in establishing this [197] preconceived effect. If his very initial sentence tend not to the outbringing of this effect, then he has failed in his first step. In the whole composition there should be no word written, of which the tendency, direct or indirect, is not to the one pre-established design. And by such means, with such care and skill, a picture is at length painted which leaves in the mind of him who contemplates it with a kindred art, a sense of the fullest satisfaction. The idea of the tale has been presented unblemished, because undisturbed; and this is an end unattainable by the novel. Undue brevity is just as exceptionable here as in the poem; but undue length is yet more to be avoided.

We have said that the tale has a point of superiority even over the poem. In fact, while the *rhythm* of this latter is an essential aid in the development of the poem's highest idea—the idea of the Beautiful—the artificialities of this rhythm are an inseparable bar to the development of all points of thought or expression which have their basis in *Truth*. But Truth is often, and in very great degree, the aim of the tale. Some of the finest tales are tales of ratiocination. Thus the field of this species of composition, if not in so elevated a region on the mountain of Mind, is a tableland of far vaster extent than the domain of the mere poem. Its products are never so rich, but infinitely more numerous, and more appreciable by the mass of mankind. The writer of the prose tale, in short, may bring to his theme a vast variety of modes or inflections of thought and expression (the ratiocinative, for example, the sarcastic, or the humorous)—which are not only antagonistical to the nature of the poem, but absolutely forbidden by one of its most peculiar and indispensable adjuncts; we allude, of course, to rhythm. It may be added, here, *par parenthèse*, that the author who aims at the purely beautiful in a prose tale is laboring at a great disadvantage. For Beauty can be better treated in the poem. Not so with terror, or passion, or horror, or a multitude of such other points. And here it will be seen how full of prejudice are the usual animadversions against those *tales of effect*, many fine examples of which were found in the earlier numbers of *Blackwood*.

The impressions produced were wrought in a legitimate sphere of action, and constituted a legitimate although sometimes an exaggerated interest. They were relished [198] by every man of genius: although there were found many men of genius who condemned them without just ground. The true critic will but demand that the design intended be accomplished, to the fullest extent, by the means most advantageously applicable.

We have very few American tales of real merit—we may say, indeed, none, with the exception of *The Tales of a Traveller* of Washington Irving, and these *Twice-Told Tales* of Mr. Hawthorne. Some of the pieces of Mr. John Neal abound in vigor and originality; but, in general, his compositions of this class are excessively diffuse, extravagant, and indicative of an imperfect sentiment of Art. Articles at random are, now and then, met with in our periodicals which might be advantageously compared with the best effusions of the British magazines; but, upon the whole, we are far behind our progenitors in this department of literature.

Of Mr. Hawthorne's *Tales* we would say, emphatically, that they belong to the highest region of Art—an Art subservient to genius of a very lofty order. We had supposed, with good reason for so supposing, that he had been thrust into his present position by one of the impudent cliques which beset our literature, and whose pretensions it is our full purpose to expose at the earliest opportunity; but we have been most agreeably mistaken. We know of few compositions which the critic can more honestly commend than these *Twice-Told Tales*. As Americans, we feel proud of the book.

Mr. Hawthorne's distinctive trait is invention, creation, imagination, originality—a trait which, in the literature of fiction, is positively worth all the rest. But the nature of the originality, so far as regards its manifestation in letters, is but imperfectly understood. The inventive or original mind as frequently displays itself in novelty of *tone* as in novelty of matter. Mr. Hawthorne is original in *all* points.

It would be a matter of some difficulty to designate the best of these tales; we repeat that, without exception, they are beautiful. *Wakefield* is remarkable for the skill with which an old idea—a well-known incident —is worked up or discussed. A man of whims conceives the purpose of quitting his wife and residing [199] *incognito*, for twenty years, in her immediate neighborhood. Something of this kind actually happened in London. The force of Mr. Hawthorne's tale lies in the analysis of the motives which must or might have impelled the husband to such folly, in the first instance, with the possible causes of his perseverance. Upon this thesis a sketch of singular power has been constructed. *The Wedding Knell* is full of the boldest imagination—an imagination fully controlled by taste. The most captious critic could find no flaw in this production. *The Minister's Black Veil* is a masterly composition of which the sole defect is that to the rabble its exquisite skill will be *caviare*. The obvious meaning of this article will be found to smother its insinuated one. The moral put into the mouth of the dying minister will be supposed to convey the true import of the narrative; and that a crime of dark dye (having reference to the "young lady") has been committed, is a point which only minds congenial with that of the author will perceive. *Mr. Higginbotham's Catastrophe* is vividly original and managed most dexterously. *Dr. Heidegger's Experiment* is exceedingly well imagined, and executed with surpassing ability. The artist breathes in every line of it. *The White Old Maid* is objectionable, even more than *The Minister's Black Veil*, on the score of its mysticism. Even with the thoughtful and analytic, there will be much trouble in penetrating its entire import.

The Hollow of the Three Hills we would quote in full, had we space; not as evincing higher talent than any of the other pieces, but as affording an excellent example of the author's peculiar ability. The subject is commonplace. A witch subjects the Distant and the Past to the view of a mourner. It has been the fashion to describe, in such cases, a mirror in which the images of the absent appear; or a cloud of smoke is made to arise, and thence the figures are gradually unfolded. Mr. Hawthorne has wonderfully heightened his effect by making the ear, in place of the eye, the medium by which the fantasy is conveyed. The head of the mourner is enveloped in the cloak of the witch, and within its magic folds there arise sounds which have an all-sufficient intelligence. Throughout this article also, the artist is conspicuous—not more in positive than in negative merits. Not only is all done that should be done, but (what perhaps is an end with more [200] difficulty attained) there is nothing done which should not be. Every word *tells*, and there is not a word which does *not* tell.

In *Howe's Masquerade* we observe something which resembles a plagiarism,—but which *may be* a very flattering coincidence of thought. We quote the passage in question.

With a dark flush of wrath upon his brow, they saw the General *draw his sword* and *advance to meet* the figure *in the cloak* before the latter had stepped one pace upon the floor. *"Villain, unmuffle yourself,"* cried he. "You pass no farther!" The figure, without blenching a hair's breadth from the sword which was pointed at his breast, made a solemn pause, and *lowered the cape of the cloak* from about his face, yet not sufficiently for the spectators to catch a glimpse of it. But Sir William Howe had evidently seen enough. The sternness of his countenance gave place to a look of wild amazement, if not horror, while he recoiled several steps from the figure, *and let fall his sword* upon the floor. ii. 20.

The idea here is, that the figure in the cloak is the phantom or reduplication of Sir William Howe; but in an article called *William Wilson*, one of the *Tales of the Grotesque and Arabesque*,* we have not only the same idea, but the same idea similarly presented in several respects. We quote two paragraphs, which our readers may compare with what has been already given. We have italicized, above, the immediate particulars of resemblance.

The brief moment in which I averted my eyes had been sufficient to produce, apparently, a material change in the arrangement at the upper or farther end of the room. A large mirror, it appeared to me, now stood where none had been perceptible before: and as I stepped up to it in extremity of terror, mine own image, but with features all pale and dabbled in blood, *advanced* with a feeble and tottering gait to meet me.

Thus it appeared, I say, but was not. It was Wilson, who then stood before me in the agonies of dissolution. Not a line in all the marked and singular lineaments of that face which was not even identically mine own. *His mask and cloak lay where he had thrown them, upon the floor.* ii. 57.

Here, it will be observed that, not only are the two general conceptions identical, but there are various *points* of similarity. In each case the figure seen is the wraith or duplication of the beholder. In each case the scene is a masquerade. In each case the figure is cloaked. In each there is a quarrel,—that is to say, angry words pass between the parties. In each the beholder is enraged. In each the cloak and sword fall upon the floor. The "villain, unmuffle yourself," of Mr. Hawthorne is precisely paralleled by a passage at page 56 of *William Wilson.*

I must hasten to conclude this paper with a summary of Mr. Hawthorne's merits and demerits.[201]

He is peculiar and not original—unless in those detailed fancies and detached thoughts which his want of general originality will deprive of the appreciation due to them, in preventing them from ever reaching the public eye. He is infinitely too fond of allegory, and can never hope for popularity so long as he persists in it. This he will not do, for allegory

* [Written by E. A. Poe.]

is at war with the whole tone of his nature, which disports itself never so well as when escaping from the mysticism of his *Goodman Browns* and *White Old Maids* into the hearty, genial, but still Indian-summer sunshine of his *Wakefields* and *Little Annie's Rambles*. Indeed, his spirit of "metaphor run mad" is clearly imbibed from the phalanx and phalanstery atmosphere in which he has been so long struggling for breath. He has not half the material for the exclusiveness of authorship that he possesses for its universality. He has the purest style, the finest taste, the most available scholarship, the most delicate humor, the most touching pathos, the most radiant imagination, the most consummate ingenuity; and with these varied good qualities he has done *well* as a mystic. But is there any one of these qualities which should prevent his doing doubly as well in a career of honest, upright, sensible, prehensible, and comprehensible things? Let him mend his pen, get a bottle of visible ink, come out from the Old Manse, cut Mr. Alcott, hang (if possible) the editor of the *Dial,* and throw out of the window to the pigs all his odd numbers of the *North American Review.*[202]

Hawthorne and His Mosses *

By a Virginian Spending July in Vermont†

A papered chamber in a fine old farmhouse, a mile from any other dwelling, and dipped to the eaves in foliage—surrounded by mountains, old woods, and Indian pools,—this, surely, is the place to write of Hawthorne. Some charm is in this northern air, for love and duty seem both impelling to the task. A man of a deep and noble nature has seized me in this seclusion. His wild witch voice rings through me; or, in softer cadences, I seem to hear it in the songs of the hillside birds that sing in the larch trees at my window.

Would that all excellent books were foundlings, without father or mother, that so it might be we could glorify them, without including their ostensible authors! Nor would any true man take exception to this; least of all, he who writes, "When the Artist rises high enough to

* Herman Melville, "Hawthorne and His *Mosses*," *The Literary World,* VII (August 17, 1850; August 24, 1850), 125-27, 145-47.
† [Melville was the alleged "Virginian."]

achieve the Beautiful, the symbol by which he makes it perceptible to mortal senses becomes of little value in his eyes, while his spirit possesses itself in the enjoyment of the reality."

But more than this. I know not what would be the right name to put on the title page of an excellent book; but this I feel, that the names of all fine authors are fictitious ones, far more so than that of Junius; simply standing, as they do, for the mystical, ever-eluding spirit of all beauty, which ubiquitously possesses men of genius. Purely imaginative as this fancy may appear, it nevertheless seems to receive some warranty from the fact that on a personal interview no great author has ever come up to the idea of his reader. But that dust of which our bodies are composed, how can it fitly express the nobler intelligences among us? With reverence be it spoken, that not even in the case of one deemed more than man, not even in our Savior, did his visible frame betoken anything of the augustness of the nature within. Else, how could those Jewish eye-witnesses fail to see heaven in his glance!

It is curious how a man may travel along a country road, and yet miss the grandest or sweetest of prospects by reason of an intervening hedge, so like all other hedges, as in no way to hint of the wide landscape beyond. So has it been with me concerning the enchanting landscape in the soul of this Hawthorne, this most excellent Man of Mosses. His *Old Manse* has been written now four years, but I never read it till a day or two since. I had seen it in the bookstores—heard of it often—even had it recommended to me by a tasteful friend, as a rare, quiet book, perhaps too deserving of popularity to be popular. But there are so many books called "excellent," and so much unpopular merit, that amid the thick stir of other things, the hint of my tasteful friend was disregarded, and for four years the *Mosses on the Old Manse* never refreshed me with their perennial green. It may be, however, that all this while the book, likewise, was only improving in flavor and body. At any rate, it so chanced that this long procrastination eventuated in a happy result. At breakfast the other day, a mountain girl, a cousin of mine, who for the last two weeks has every morning helped me to strawberries and raspberries, which, like the roses and pearls in the fairy tale, seemed to fall into the saucer from those strawberry beds, her cheeks—this delightful creature, this charming Cherry says to me—"I see you spend your mornings in the haymow; and yesterday I found there 'Dwight's Travels in New England.' Now I have something far better than that, something more congenial to our summer on these hills. Take these raspberries, and then I will give you some moss."

"Moss!" said I. "Yes, and you must take it to the barn with you, and good-by to 'Dwight.' "

With that she left me, and soon returned with a volume, verdantly bound, and garnished with a curious frontispiece in green; nothing less than a fragment of real moss, cunningly pressed to a fly-leaf. "Why, this," said I, spilling my raspberries, "this is the *Mosses from an Old Manse*." "Yes," said Cousin Cherry, "Yes, it is that flowery Hawthorne." "Hawthorne and Mosses," said I, "no more it is morning: it is July in the country: and I am off for the barn."

Stretched on that new-mown clover, the hillside breeze blowing over me through the wide barn door, and soothed by the hum of the bees in the meadows around, how magically stole over me this Mossy Man! and how amply, how bountifully, did he redeem that delicious promise to his guests in the Old Manse, of whom it is written: "Others could give them pleasure, or amusement, or instruction—these could be picked up anywhere; but it was for me to give them rest—rest, in a life of trouble! What better could be done for those weary and world-worn spirits? . . . what better could be done for anybody who came within our magic circle than to throw the spell of a tranquil spirit over him?" So all that day, half buried in the new clover, I watched this Hawthorne's "Assyrian dawn, and Paphian sunset and moonrise from the summit of our eastern hill."

The soft ravishments of the man spun me round about in a web of dreams, and when the book was closed, when the spell was over, this wizard "dismissed me with but misty reminiscences, as if I had been dreaming of him."

What a wild moonlight of contemplative humor bathes that Old Manse!—the rich and rare distilment of a spicy and slowly-oozing heart. No rollicking rudeness, no gross fun fed on fat dinners, and bred in the lees of wine,—but a humor so spiritually gentle, so high, so deep, and yet so richly relishable, that it were hardly inappropriate in an angel. It is the very religion of mirth; for nothing so human but it may be advanced to that. The orchard of the Old Manse seems the visible type of the fine mind that has described it—those twisted and contorted old trees, "they stretch out their crooked branches, and take such hold of the imagination that we remember them as humorists and odd-fellows." And then, as surrounded by these grotesque forms, and hushed in the noonday repose of this Hawthorne's spell, how aptly might the still fall of his ruddy thoughts into your soul be symbolized by: "In the stillest afternoon, if I listened, the thump of a great apple was audible, falling without a breath of wind, from the mere necessity of perfect ripeness." For no less ripe than ruddy are the apples of the thoughts and fancies in this sweet Man of Mosses.

"BUDS AND BIRD VOICES"

What a delicious thing is that! "Will the world ever be so decayed, that spring may not renew its greenness?" And the *Fire Worship*. Was ever the hearth so glorified into an altar before? The mere title of that piece is better than any common work in fifty folio volumes. How exquisite is this: "Nor did it lessen the charm of his soft, familiar courtesy and helpfulness that the mighty spirit, were opportunity offered him, would run riot through the peaceful house, wrap its inmates in his terrible embrace, and leave nothing of them save their whitened bones. This possibility of mad destruction only made his domestic kindness the more beautiful and touching. It was so sweet of him, being endowed with such power, to dwell day after day, and one long lonesome night after another, on the dusky hearth, only now and then betraying his wild nature by thrusting his red tongue out of the chimney top! True, he had done much mischief in the world, and was pretty certain to do more, but his warm heart atoned for all; He was kindly to the race of man."

But he has still other apples, not quite so ruddy, though full as ripe: apples that have been left to wither on the tree, after the pleasant autumn gathering is past. The sketch of *The Old Apple Dealer* is conceived in the subtlest spirit of sadness; he whose "subdued and nerveless boyhood prefigured his abortive prime, which likewise contained within itself the prophecy and image of his lean and torpid age." Such touches as are in this piece cannot proceed from any common heart. They argue such a depth of tenderness, such a boundless sympathy with all forms of being, such an omnipresent love, that we must needs say that this Hawthorne is here almost alone in his generation—at least, in the artistic manifestation of these things. Still more. Such touches as these—and many, very many similar ones, all through his chapters—furnish clues whereby we enter a little way into the intricate, profound heart where they originated. And we see that suffering, sometime or other, and in some shape or other—this only can enable any man to depict it in others. All over him, Hawthorne's [125] melancholy rests like an Indian-summer, which, though bathing a whole country in one softness, still reveals the distinctive hue of every towering hill and each far-winding vale.

But it is the least part of genius that attracts admiration. Where Hawthorne is known, he seems to be deemed a pleasant writer, with a pleasant style,—a sequestered, harmless man, from whom any deep and weighty thing would hardly be anticipated—a man who means no meanings. But there is no man in whom humor and love, like mountain peaks, soar to such a rapt height as to receive the irradiations of the upper skies; there is no man in whom humor and love are developed in that high form called genius; no such man can exist without also possessing, as the indispensable complement of these, a great, deep intellect, which drops down into the universe like a plummet. Or, love and humor are only the eyes through which such an intellect views this world. The great beauty in such a mind is but the product of its strength. What, to all readers, can be more charming than the piece entitled *Monsieur du Miroir;* and to a reader at all capable of fully fathoming it, what, at the same time, can possess more mystical depth of meaning?—yes, there he sits and looks at me—this "shape of mystery," this "identical MONSIEUR DU MIROIR!" "Methinks I should tremble now were his wizard power of gliding through all impediments in search of me to place him suddenly before my eyes."

How profound, nay, appalling, is the moral evolved by the *Earth's Holocaust;* where—beginning with the hollow follies and affectations of the world—all vanities and empty theories and forms are, one after another, and by an admirably graduated, growing comprehensiveness, thrown into the allegorical fire, till, at length, nothing is left but the all-engendering heart of man; which remaining still unconsumed, the great conflagration is naught.

Of a piece with this is the *Intelligence Office,* a wondrous symbolizing of the secret workings in men's souls. There are other sketches still more charged with ponderous import.

The Christmas Banquet and *The Bosom Serpent* would be fine subjects for a curious and elaborate analysis, touching the conjectural parts of the mind that produced them. For spite of all the Indian-summer sunlight on the hither side of Hawthorne's soul, the other side—like the dark half of the physical sphere—is shrouded in a blackness, ten times black. But this darkness but gives more effect to the ever-moving dawn, that forever advances through it, and circumnavigates his world. Whether Hawthorne has simply availed himself of this mystical blackness as a means to the wondrous effects he makes it to produce in his lights and shades; or whether there really lurks in him, perhaps unknown to himself, a touch of Puritanic gloom,—this, I cannot altogether tell. Certain it is, however, that this great power of blackness in him derives its force from its appeals to that Calvinistic sense of Innate Depravity and Original

Sin, from whose visitations, in some shape or other, no deeply thinking mind is always and wholly free. For, in certain moods, no man can weigh this world without throwing in something, somehow like Original Sin, to strike the uneven balance. At all events, perhaps no writer has ever wielded this terrific thought with greater terror than this same harmless Hawthorne. Still more: this black conceit pervades him through and through. You may be witched by his sunlight—transported by the bright gildings in the skies he builds over you; but there is the blackness of darkness beyond; and even his bright gildings but fringe and play upon the edges of thunder-clouds. In one word, the world is mistaken in this Nathaniel Hawthorne. He himself must often have smiled at its absurd misconception of him. He is immeasurably deeper than the plummet of the mere critic. For it is not the brain that can test such a man; it is only the heart. You cannot come to know greatness by inspecting it; there is no glimpse to be caught of it, except by intuition; you need not ring it, you but touch it, and you find it is gold.

Now, it is that blackness in Hawthorne, of which I have spoken, that so fixes and fascinates me. It may be, nevertheless, that it is too largely developed in him. Perhaps he does not give us a ray of light for every shade of his dark. But however this may be, this blackness it is that furnishes the infinite obscure of his background—that background against which Shakespeare plays his grandest conceits, the things that have made for Shakespeare his loftiest but most circumscribed renown, as the profoundest of thinkers. For by philosophers Shakespeare is not adored, as the great man of tragedy and comedy: "Off with his head; so much for Buckingham!" This sort of rant, interlined by another hand, brings down the house—those mistaken souls, who dream of Shakespeare as a mere man of Richard-the-Third humps and Macbeth daggers. But it is those deep, far-away things in him; those occasional flashings-forth of the intuitive Truth in him; those short, quick probings at the very axis of reality,—these are the things that make Shakespeare, Shakespeare. Through the mouths of the dark characters of Hamlet, Timon, Lear, and Iago, he craftily says, or sometimes insinuates the things which we feel to be so terrifically true that it were all but madness for any good man, in his own proper character, to utter, or even hint of them. Tormented into desperation, Lear, the frantic king, tears off the mask, and speaks the same madness of vital truth. But, as I before said, it is the least part of genius that attracts admiration. And so, much of the blind, unbridled admiration that has been heaped upon Shakespeare has been lavished upon the least part of him. And few of his endless commentators and critics seem to have remembered, or even perceived, that the immediate products of a great mind are not so great as that undeveloped and sometimes undevelopable yet dimly-discernible greatness to which those immediate products are but the infallible indices. In Shakespeare's tomb lies infinitely more than Shakespeare ever wrote. And if I magnify Shakespeare, it is not so much for what he did do as for what he did not do, or refrained from doing. For in this world of lies, Truth is forced to fly like a sacred white doe in the woodlands; and only by cunning glimpses will she reveal herself, as in Shakespeare and other masters of the great Art of Telling the Truth, even though it be covertly and by snatches.

But if this view of the all-popular Shakespeare be seldom taken by his readers, and if very few who extol him have ever read him deeply, or, perhaps, only have seen him on the tricky stage (which alone made, and is still making him, his mere mob renown)—if few men have time, or patience, or palate, for the spiritual truth as it is in that great genius—it is then no matter of surprise that in a contemporaneous age Nathaniel Hawthorne is a man as yet almost utterly mistaken among men. Here and there, in some quiet armchair in the noisy town, or some deep nook among the noiseless mountains, he may be appreciated for something of what he is. But unlike Shakespeare, who was forced to the contrary course by circumstances, Hawthorne (either from simple disinclination, or else from inaptitude) refrains from all the popularizing noise and show of broad farce and blood-besmeared tragedy; content with the still, rich utterance of a great intellect in repose, and which sends few thoughts into circulation, except they be arterialized at his large warm lungs, and expanded in his honest heart.

Nor need you fix upon that blackness in him, if it suit you not. Nor, indeed, will all readers discern it; for it is, mostly, insinuated to those who may best understand it, and account for it; it is not obtruded upon everyone alike.

Some may start to read of Shakespeare and Hawthorne on the same page. They may say that if an illustration were needed, a lesser light might have sufficed to elucidate this Hawthorne, this small man of yesterday. But I am not willingly one of those who, as touching Shakespeare at least, exemplify the maxim of Rochefoucauld, that "we exalt the reputation of some, in order to depress that of others"—who, to teach all noble-souled aspirants that there is no hope for them, pronounce Shakespeare absolutely unapproachable. But Shakespeare has been approached. There are minds that have gone as far as Shakespeare into the universe.

And hardly a mortal man, who, at some time or other, has not felt as great thoughts in him as any you will find in Hamlet. We must not inferentially malign mankind for the sake of any one man, whoever he may be. This is too cheap a purchase of contentment for conscious mediocrity to make. Besides, this absolute and unconditional adoration of Shakespeare has grown to be a part of our Anglo-Saxon superstitions. The Thirty-Nine Articles are now Forty. Intolerance has come to exist in this matter. You must believe in Shakespeare's unapproachability, or quit the country. But what sort of a belief is this for an American, a man who is bound to carry republican progressiveness into Literature as well as into Life? Believe me, my friends, that men not very much inferior to Shakespeare are this day being born on the banks of the Ohio. And the day will come when you shall say, Who reads a book by an Englishman that is a modern? The great mistake seems to be, that even with those Americans who look forward to the coming of a great literary genius among us, they somehow fancy he will come in the costume of Queen Elizabeth's day; be a writer of dramas founded upon old English history or the tales of Boccaccio. Whereas, great geniuses are parts of the times, they themselves are the times, and possess a corresponding coloring. It is of a piece with the Jews, who, while their Shiloh was meekly walking in their streets, were still praying for his magnificent coming; looking for him in a chariot, who was already among them on an ass. Nor must we forget that, in his own lifetime, Shakespeare was not Shakespeare, but only Master William Shakespeare of the shrewd, thriving business firm of Condell, Shakespeare & Co., proprietors of the Globe Theater in London; and by a courtly author, of the name of Chettle, was looked at as an "upstart crow," beautified "with other birds' feathers." For, mark it well, imitation is often the first charge brought against originality. Why this is so, there is not space [126] to set forth here. You must have plenty of sea-room to tell the Truth in; especially when it seems to have an aspect of newness, as America did in 1492, though it was then just as old, and perhaps older than Asia, only those sagacious philosophers, the common sailors, had never seen it before, swearing it was all water and moonshine there.[127]

Now I do not say that Nathaniel of Salem is a greater man than William of Avon, or as great. But the difference between the two men is by no means immeasurable. Not a very great deal more, and Nathaniel were verily William.

This, too, I mean: that if Shakespeare has not been equaled, give the world time, and he is sure to be surpassed in one hemisphere or the other. Nor will it at all do to say that the world is getting gray and grizzled now, and has lost that fresh charm which she wore of old, and by virtue of which the great poets of past times made themselves what we esteem them to be. Not so. The world is as young today as when it was created; and this Vermont morning dew is as wet to my feet as Eden's dew to Adam's. Nor has nature been all over ransacked by our progenitors, so that no new charms and mysteries remain for this latter generation to find. Far from it. The trillionth part has not yet been said; and all that has been said but multiplies the avenues to what remains to be said. It is not so much paucity as superabundance of material that seems to incapacitate modern authors.

Let America, then, prize and cherish her writers; yea, let her glorify them. They are not so many in number as to exhaust her goodwill. And while she has good kith and kin of her own to take to her bosom, let her not lavish her embraces upon the household of an alien. For believe it or not, England, after all, is in many things an alien to us. China has more bonds of real love for us than she. But even were there no strong literary individualities among us, as there are some dozens at least, nevertheless, let America first praise mediocrity even, in her children, before she praises (for everywhere, merit demands acknowledgment from everyone) the best excellence in the children of any other land. Let her own authors, I say, have the priority of appreciation. I was much pleased with a hot-headed Carolina cousin of mine, who once said, "If there were no other American to stand by, in literature, why, then, I would stand by Pop Emmons and his *Fredoniad*, and till a better epic came along, swear it was not very far behind the *Iliad*." Take away the words, and in spirit he was sound.

Not that American genius needs patronage in order to expand. For that explosive sort of stuff will expand though screwed up in a vise, and burst it, though it were triple steel. It is for the nation's sake, and not for her authors' sake, that I would have America be heedful of the increasing greatness among her [145] writers. For how great the shame, if other nations should be before her, in crowning her heroes of the pen! But this is almost the case now. American authors have received more just and discriminating praise (however loftily and ridiculously given, in certain cases) even from some Englishmen, than from their own countrymen. There are hardly five critics in America; and several of them are asleep. As for patronage, it is the American author who now patronizes his country, and not his country him. And if at times some among them appeal to the people for more recognition, it is not always with selfish motives, but patriotic ones.

It is true that but few of them as yet have evinced that decided originality which merits great praise. But that graceful writer who perhaps of all Americans has received the most plaudits from his own country for his productions—that very popular and amiable writer, however good and self-reliant in many things, perhaps owes his chief reputation to the self-acknowledged imitation of a foreign model, and to the studied avoidance of all topics but smooth ones.* But it is better to fail in originality than to succeed in imitation. He who has never failed somewhere, that man cannot be great. Failure is the true test of greatness. And if it be said that continual success is a proof that a man wisely knows his powers, it is only to be added that, in that case, he knows them to be small. Let us believe it, then, once for all, that there is no hope for us in these smooth, pleasing writers that know their powers. Without malice, but to speak the plain fact, they but furnish an appendix to Goldsmith and other English authors. And we want no American Goldsmiths, nay, we want no American Miltons. It were the vilest thing you could say of a true American author that he were an American Tompkins. Call him an American and have done, for you cannot say a nobler thing of him. But it is not meant that all American writers should studiously cleave to nationality in their writings; only this, no American writer should write like an Englishman or a Frenchman; let him write like a man, for then he will be sure to write like an American. Let us away with this leaven of literary flunkeyism toward England. If either must play the flunkey in this thing, let England do it, not us. While we are rapidly preparing for that political supremacy among the nations which prophetically awaits us at the close of the present century, in a literary point of view, we are deplorably unprepared for it; and we seem studious to remain so. Hitherto, reasons might have existed why this should be; but no good reason exists now. And all that is requisite to amendment in this matter is simply this: that while fully acknowledging all excellence everywhere, we should refrain from unduly lauding foreign writers, and, at the same time, duly recognize the meritorious writers that are our own; those writers who breathe that unshackled, democratic spirit of Christianity in all things, which now takes the practical lead in this world, though at the same time led by ourselves—us Americans. Let us boldly condemn all imitation, though it comes to us graceful and fragrant as the morning;

* [Melville is alluding to Washington Irving.]

and foster all originality, though at first it be crabbed and ugly as our own pine knots. And if any of our authors fail, or seem to fail, then, in the words of my Carolina cousin, let us clap him on the shoulder and back him against all Europe for his second round. The truth is, that in one point of view this matter of a national literature has come to such a pass with us, that in some sense we must turn bullies, else the day is lost, or superiority so far beyond us, that we can hardly say it will ever be ours.

And now, my countrymen, as an excellent author of your own flesh and blood—an unimitating, and, perhaps, in his way, an inimitable man —whom better can I commend to you, in the first place, than Nathaniel Hawthorne? He is one of the new, and far better generation of your writers. The smell of young beeches and hemlocks is upon him; your own broad prairies are in his soul; and if you travel away inland into his deep and noble nature, you will hear the far roar of his Niagara. Give not over to future generations the glad duty of acknowledging him for what he is. Take that joy to yourself, in your own generation; and so shall he feel those grateful impulses on him, that may possibly prompt him to the full flower of some still greater achievement in your eyes. And by confessing him you thereby confess others; you brace the whole brotherhood. For genius, all over the world, stands hand in hand, and one shock of recognition runs the whole circle round.

In treating of Hawthorne, or rather of Hawthorne in his writings (for I never saw the man; and in the chances of a quiet plantation life, remote from his haunts, perhaps never shall); in treating of his works, I say, I have thus far omitted all mention of his *Twice-Told Tales* and *Scarlet Letter*. Both are excellent, but full of such manifold, strange, and diffusive beauties, that time would all but fail me to point the half of them out. But there are things in those two books which, had they been written in England a century ago, Nathaniel Hawthorne had utterly displaced many of the bright names we now revere on authority. But I am content to leave Hawthorne to himself, and to the infallible finding of posterity; and however great may be the praise I have bestowed upon him, I feel that in so doing I have served and honored myself, rather than him. For, at bottom, great excellence is praise enough to itself; but the feeling of a sincere and appreciative love and admiration toward it, this is relieved by utterance, and warm, honest praise ever leaves a pleasant flavor in the mouth; and it is an honorable thing to confess to what is honorable in others.

But I cannot leave my subject yet. No man can read a fine author, and relish him to his very bones while he reads, without subsequently fancying to himself some ideal image of the man and his mind. And if you rightly look for it, you will almost always find that the author himself has somewhere furnished you with his own picture. For poets (whether in prose or verse), being painters by nature, are like their brethren of the pencil, the true portrait-painters, who, in the multitude of likenesses to be sketched, do not invariably omit their own; and in all high instances, they paint them without any vanity, though at times with a lurking something that would take several pages to properly define.

I submit it, then, to those best acquainted with the man personally, whether the following is not Nathaniel Hawthorne; and to himself, whether something involved in it does not express the temper of his mind—that lasting temper of all true, candid men—a seeker, not a finder yet:

A man now entered, in neglected attire, with the aspect of a thinker, but somewhat too roughhewn and brawny for a scholar. His face was full of sturdy vigor, with some finer and keener attribute beneath; though harsh at first, it was tempered with the glow of a large, warm heart, which had force enough to heat his powerful intellect through and through. He advanced to the Intelligencer, and looked at him with a glance of such stern sincerity, that perhaps few secrets were beyond its scope. "I seek for Truth," said he.

Twenty-four hours have elapsed since writing the foregoing. I have just returned from the haymow, charged more and more with love and admiration of Hawthorne. For I have just been gleaning through the *Mosses*, picking up many things here and there that had previously escaped me. And I found that but to glean after this man is better than to be in at the harvest of others. To be frank (though, perhaps, rather foolish), notwithstanding what I wrote yesterday of these *Mosses*, I had not then culled them all; but had, nevertheless, been sufficiently sensible of the subtle essence in them as to write as I did. To what infinite height of loving wonder and admiration I may yet be borne, when by repeatedly banqueting on these *Mosses* I shall have thoroughly incorporated their whole stuff into my being—that, I cannot tell. But already I feel that this Hawthorne has dropped germinous seeds into my soul. He expands and deepens down, the more I contemplate him; and further and further, shoots his strong New England roots into the hot soil in my Southern soul.

By careful reference to the "Table of Contents," I now find that I have gone through all the sketches; but that when I yesterday wrote, I had not at all read two particular pieces, to which I now desire to call special attention—*A Select Party* and *Young Goodman Brown*. Here, be it said to all those whom this poor fugitive scrawl of mine may tempt to the perusal of the *Mosses*, that they must on no account suffer themselves to be trifled with, disappointed, or deceived by the triviality of many of the titles to these sketches. For in more than one instance the title utterly belies the piece. It is as if rustic demijohns containing the very best and costliest of Falernian and Tokay were labeled "Cider," "Perry," and "Elder-berry wine." The truth seems to be, that like many other geniuses, this Man of Mosses takes great delight in hoodwinking the world—at least, with respect to himself. Personally, I doubt not that he rather prefers to be generally esteemed but a so-so sort of author; being willing to reserve the thorough and acute appreciation of what he is, to that party most qualified to judge—that is, to himself. Besides, at the bottom of their natures, men like Hawthorne, in many things, deem the plaudits of the public such strong presumptive evidence of mediocrity in the object of them, that it would in some degree render them doubtful of their own powers did they hear much and vociferous braying concerning them in the public pastures. True, I have been braying myself (if you please to be witty enough to have it so), but then I claim to be the first that has so brayed in this particular matter; and, therefore, while pleading guilty to the charge, still claim all the merit due to originality.

But with whatever motive, playful or profound, Nathaniel Hawthorne has chosen to entitle his pieces in the manner he has, it is certain that some of them are directly calculated to deceive—egregiously deceive, the superficial skimmer of pages. To be downright and candid once more, let me cheerfully say that two of these titles did dolefully dupe no less an eager-eyed reader than myself; and that, too, after I had been impressed with a sense of the great depth and breadth of this American [146] man. "Who in the name of thunder" (as the country people say in this neighborhood), "who in the name of thunder would anticipate any marvel in a piece entitled *Young Goodman Brown?*" You would, of course, suppose that it was a simple little tale, intended as a supplement to *Goody Two Shoes*. Whereas, it is deep as Dante; nor can you finish it without addressing the author in his own words—"It shall be yours to penetrate, in every bosom, the deep mystery of sin." . . . And with Young Goodman, too, in allegorical pursuit of his Puritan wife, you cry out in your anguish:

"Faith!" shouted Goodman Brown, in a voice of agony and desperation; and the echoes of the forest mocked him, crying, "Faith! Faith!" as if bewildered wretches were seeking her all through the wilderness.

Now this same piece entitled *Young Goodman Brown* is one of the two that I had not all read yesterday; and I allude to it now, because it is, in itself, such a strong, positive illustration of the blackness in Hawthorne which I had assumed from the mere occasional shadows of it, as revealed in several of the other sketches. But had I previously perused *Young Goodman Brown*, I should have been at no pains to draw the conclusion, which I came to at a time when I was ignorant that the book contained one such direct and unqualified manifestation of it.

The other piece of the two referred to is entitled *A Select Party*, which, in my first simplicity upon originally taking hold of the book, I fancied must treat of some pumpkin-pie party in old Salem; or some chowder party on Cape Cod. Whereas, by all the gods of Peedee, it is the sweetest and sublimest thing that has been written since Spenser wrote. Nay, there is nothing in Spenser that surpasses it, perhaps nothing that equals it. And the test is this. Read any canto in *The Faerie Queene* and then read *A Select Party*, and decide which pleases you most, that is, if you are qualified to judge. Do not be frightened at this; for when Spenser was alive, he was thought of very much as Hawthorne is now—was generally accounted just such a "gentle," harmless man. It may be that to common eyes the sublimity of Hawthorne seems lost in his sweetness,—as perhaps in that same *Select Party* of his; for whom he has builded so august a dome of sunset clouds, and served them on richer plate than Belshazzar when he banqueted his lords in Babylon.

But my chief business now is to point out a particular page in this piece, having reference to an honored guest, who under the name of "The Master Genius" but in the guise "of a young man of poor attire, with no insignia of rank or acknowledged eminence," is introduced to the Man of Fancy, who is the giver of the feast. Now, the page having reference to this "Master Genius" so happily expresses much of what I yesterday wrote, touching the coming of the literary Shiloh of America, that I cannot but be charmed by the coincidence; especially when it shows such a parity of ideas, at least in this one point, between a man like Hawthorne and a man like me.

And here let me throw out another conceit of mine touching this American Shiloh, or "Master Genius," as Hawthorne calls him. May it not be that this commanding mind has not been, is not, and never will be, individually developed in any one man? And would it, indeed, appear so unreasonable to suppose that this great fullness and overflowing may be, or may be destined to be, shared by a plurality of men of genius? Surely, to take the very greatest example on record, Shakespeare cannot be regarded as in himself the concretion of all the genius of his time; nor as so immeasurably beyond Marlowe, Webster, Ford, Beaumont, Jonson, that these great men can be said to share none of his power? For one, I conceive that there were dramatists in Elizabeth's day, between whom and Shakespeare the distance was by no means great. Let anyone, hitherto little acquainted with those neglected old authors, for the first time read them thoroughly, or even read Charles Lamb's *Specimens* of them, and he will be amazed at the wondrous ability of those Anaks of men, and shocked at this renewed example of the fact that Fortune has more to do with fame than merit,—though without merit, lasting fame there can be none.

Nevertheless, it would argue too ill of my country were this maxim to hold good concerning Nathaniel Hawthorne, a man who already in some few minds has shed "such a light as never illuminates the earth save when a great heart burns as the household fire of a grand intellect."

The words are his—in the *Select Party;* and they are a magnificent setting to a coincident sentiment of my own, but ramblingly expressed yesterday, in reference to himself. Gainsay it who will, as I now write, I am Posterity speaking by proxy—and after-times will make it more than good, when I declare that the American who up to the present day has evinced, in literature, the largest brain with the largest heart, that man is Nathaniel Hawthorne. Moreover, that whatever Nathaniel Hawthorne may hereafter write, *Mosses from an Old Manse* will be ultimately accounted his masterpiece. For there is a sure, though secret sign in some works which proves the culmination of the powers (only the developable ones, however) that produced them. But I am by no means desirous of the glory of a prophet. I pray Heaven that Hawthorne may *yet* prove me an impostor in this prediction. Especially, as I somehow cling to the strange fancy that, in all men, hiddenly reside certain wondrous, occult properties—as in some plants and minerals—which by some happy but very rare accident (as bronze was discovered by the melting of the iron and brass at the burning of Corinth) may chance to be called forth here on earth; not entirely waiting for their better discovery in the more congenial, blessed atmosphere of heaven.

Once more—for it is hard to be finite upon an infinite subject, and all subjects are infinite. By some people this entire scrawl of mine may be esteemed altogether unnecessary, inasmuch "as years ago" (they may say) "we found out the rich and rare stuff in this Hawthorne, whom you now parade forth, as if only you *yourself* were the discoverer of this Portuguese diamond in your literature." But even granting all this—and adding to it the assumption that the books of Hawthorne have sold by the five thousand—what does that signify? They should be sold by the hundred thousand; and read by the million; and admired by every one who is capable of admiration.[147]

Hawthorne *

I. EARLY YEARS

It will be necessary, for several reasons, to give this short sketch the form rather of a critical essay than of a biography. The data for a life of Nathaniel Hawthorne are the reverse of copious, and even if they were abundant they would serve but in a limited measure the purpose of the biographer. Hawthorne's career was probably as tranquil and uneventful a one as ever fell to the lot of a man of letters; it was almost strikingly deficient in incident, in what may be called the dramatic quality. Few men of equal genius and of equal eminence can have led on the whole a simpler life. His six volumes of *Note-Books* illustrate this simplicity; they are a sort of monument to an unagitated fortune. Hawthorne's career had few vicissitudes or variations; it was passed for the most part in a small and homogeneous society, in a provincial, rural community; it had few perceptible points of contact with what is called the world, with public events, with the manners of his [1] time, even with the life of his neighbors. Its literary incidents are not numerous. He produced, in quantity, but little. His works consist of four novels and the fragment of another, five volumes of short tales, a collection of sketches, and a couple of storybooks for children. And yet some account of the man and the writer is well worth giving. Whatever may have been Hawthorne's private lot, he has the importance of being the most beautiful and most eminent representative of a literature. The importance of the literature may be questioned, but at any rate, in the field of letters, Hawthorne is the most valuable example of the American genius.

* From Henry James, *Hawthorne* (London: Macmillan, 1879), pp. 1–5, 45–47, 56–68, 101–103, 117–20, 183.

That genius has not, as a whole, been literary; but Hawthorne was on his limited scale a master of expression. He is the writer to whom his countrymen most confidently point when they wish to make a claim to have enriched the mother tongue, and, judging from present appearances, he will long occupy this honorable position. If there is something very fortunate for him in the way that he borrows an added relief from the absence of competitors in his own line and from the general flatness of the literary field that surrounds him, there is also, to a spectator, something almost touching in his situation. He was so modest and delicate a genius that we may fancy him appealing from the lonely honor of a representative attitude—perceiving a painful incongruity between his imponderable literary baggage and the large conditions of American life. Hawthorne on the one side is so subtle and slender and unpretending, and the American world on the other is so vast and various and substantial, that it might seem to the author of *The Scarlet Letter* and the *Mosses from an Old Manse* that we render him a [2] poor service in contrasting his proportions with those of a great civilization. But our author must accept the awkward as well as the graceful side of his fame; for he has the advantage of pointing a valuable moral. This moral is that the flower of art blooms only where the soil is deep, that it takes a great deal of history to produce a little literature, that it needs a complex social machinery to set a writer in motion. American civilization has hitherto had other things to do than to produce flowers, and before giving birth to writers it has wisely occupied itself with providing something for them to write about. Three or four beautiful talents of trans-Atlantic growth are the sum of what the world usually recognizes, and in this modest nosegay the genius of Hawthorne is admitted to have the rarest and sweetest fragrance.

His very simplicity has been in his favor; it has helped him to appear complete and homogeneous. To talk of his being national would be to force the note and make a mistake of proportion; but he is, in spite of the absence of the realistic quality, intensely and vividly local. Out of the soil of New England he sprang—in a crevice of that immitigable granite he sprouted and bloomed. Half of the interest that he possesses for an American reader with any turn for analysis must reside in his latent New England savor; and I think it no more than just to say that whatever entertainment he may yield to those who know him at a distance, it is an almost indispensable condition of properly appreciating him to have received a personal impression of the manners, the morals, indeed of the very climate, of the great region of which the remarkable city of Boston is the metropolis. The cold, bright [3] air of New England seems to blow through his pages, and these, in the opinion of many people, are the medium in which it is most agreeable to make the acquaintance of that tonic atmosphere. As to whether it is worth while to seek to know something of New England in order to extract a more intimate quality from *The House of the Seven Gables* and *The Blithedale Romance*, I need not pronounce; but it is certain that a considerable observation of the society to which these productions were more directly addressed is a capital preparation for enjoying them. I have alluded to the absence in Hawthorne of that quality of realism which is now so much in fashion, an absence in regard to which there will of course be more to say; and yet I think I am not fanciful in saying that he testifies to the sentiments of the society in which he flourished almost as pertinently (proportions observed) as Balzac and some of his descendants— MM. Flaubert and Zola—testify to the manners and morals of the French people. He was not a man with a literary theory; he was guiltless of a system, and I am not sure that he had ever heard of Realism, this remarkable compound having (although it was invented sometime earlier) come into general use only since his death. He had certainly not proposed to himself to give an account of the social idiosyncrasies of his fellow citizens, for his touch on such points is always light and vague, he has none of the apparatus of an historian, and his shadowy style of portraiture never suggests a rigid standard of accuracy. Nevertheless, he virtually offers the most vivid reflection of New England life that has found its way into literature. His value in this respect is not diminished by the fact that he has not attempted [4] to portray the usual Yankee of comedy, and that he has been almost culpably indifferent to his opportunities for commemorating the variations of colloquial English that may be observed in the New World. His characters do not express themselves in the dialect of the *Biglow Papers*—their language indeed is apt to be too elegant, too delicate. They are not portraits of actual types, and in their phraseology there is nothing imitative. But nonetheless, Hawthorne's work savors thoroughly of the local soil—it is redolent of the social system in which he had his being.[5]

· · · · ·

II. EARLY MANHOOD

· · · · ·

Everything in the Notes [*American Notebooks*] indicates a simple, democratic, thinly-composed society; there is no evidence of the writer finding himself in any variety or intimacy of relations with anyone or with anything. We find a good deal of warrant for believing that if we add that statement of Mr. Lathrop's about his meals being left at the door of his room, to rural rambles of which an impression of the temporary phases of the local apple-crop were the usual, and an encounter with an organ-grinder, or an eccentric dog, the rarer, outcome, we construct a rough image of our author's daily life during the several years that preceded his marriage. He appears to have read a good deal, and that he must have been familiar with the sources of good English we see from his charming, expressive, slightly self-conscious, cultivated, but not too cultivated, style. Yet neither in these early volumes of his *Note-Books* nor in the later is there any mention of his reading. There are no literary judgments or impressions—there is almost no allusion to works or to authors. The allusions to individuals of any kind are indeed much less numerous than one might have expected; there is little psychology,[45] little description of manners. We are told by Mr. Lathrop that there existed at Salem during the early part of Hawthorne's life "a strong circle of wealthy families," which "maintained rigorously the distinctions of class," and whose "entertainments were splendid, their manners magnificent." This is a rather pictorial way of saying that there were a number of people in the place—the commercial and professional aristocracy, as it were—who lived in high comfort and respectability, and who, in their small provincial way, doubtless had pretensions to be exclusive. Into this delectable company Mr. Lathrop intimates that his hero was free to penetrate. It is easy to believe it, and it would be difficult to perceive why the privilege should have been denied to a young man of genius and culture, who was very good-looking (Hawthorne must have been in these days, judging by his appearance later in life, a strikingly handsome fellow), and whose American pedigree was virtually as long as the longest they could show. But in fact Hawthorne appears to have ignored the good society of his native place almost completely; no echo of its conversation is to be found in his tales or his journals. Such an echo would possibly not have been especially melodious, and if we regret the shyness and stiffness, the reserve, the timidity, the suspicion, or whatever it was, that kept him from knowing what there was to be known, it is not because we have any very definite assurance that his gains would have been great. Still, since a beautiful writer was growing up in Salem, it is a pity that he should not have given himself a chance to commemorate some of the types that flourished in the richest soil of the place. Like almost all people who possess in a strong degree the story-telling [46] faculty, Hawthorne had a democratic strain in his composition and a relish for the commoner stuff of human nature. Thoroughly American in all ways, he was in none more so than in the vagueness of his sense of social distinctions and his readiness to forget them if a moral or intellectual sensation were to be gained by it. He liked to fraternize with plain people, to take them on their own terms, and put himself if possible into their shoes. His *Note-Books*, and even his tales, are full of evidence of this easy and natural feeling about all his unconventional fellow mortals—this imaginative interest and contemplative curiosity—and it sometimes takes the most charming and graceful forms. Commingled as it is with his own subtlety and delicacy, his complete exemption from vulgarity, it is one of the points in his character which his reader comes most to appreciate—that reader I mean for whom he is not, as for some few, a dusky and malarious genius.[47]

. . . . .

III. EARLY WRITINGS

. . . . .

Among these shorter things (it is better to speak of the whole collection, including the *Snow Image*, and the *Mosses from an Old Manse* at once) there are three sorts of tales, each one of which has an original stamp. There are, to begin with, the stories of fantasy and allegory— those among which the three I have just mentioned would be numbered, and which, on the whole, are the most original. This is the group to which such little masterpieces as *Malvin's Burial*, *Rappaccini's Daughter*, and *Young Goodman Brown* also belong—these two last perhaps representing the highest point that Hawthorne reached in this direction. Then there are the little tales of New England history, which are scarcely less admirable, and of which *The Grey Champion*, *The Maypole of Merry Mount*, and the four beautiful *Legends of the Province House*, as [56] they are called, are the most successful specimens. Lastly come the slender sketches of actual scenes and of the objects and manners about him, by means of which, more particularly, he endeavored "to open an intercourse with the world," and which, in spite of their slenderness, have an infinite grace and charm. Among these things *A Rill from the Town Pump*, *The Village Uncle*, *The Toll-Gatherer's Day*, the *Chippings with a Chisel*, may most naturally be mentioned. As we turn over these volumes we feel that the pieces that spring most directly from his fancy, constitute, as I have said (putting his four novels aside), his most substantial claim to our attention. It would be a mistake to insist too much upon them; Hawthorne was himself the first to recognize that. "These fitful sketches," he says in the preface to the *Mosses from an Old Manse*, "with so little of external life about them, yet claiming no profundity of purpose—so reserved even while they sometimes seem so frank—often but half in earnest, and never, even when most so, expressing satisfactorily the thoughts which they profess to image—such trifles, I truly feel, afford no solid basis for a literary reputation." This is very becomingly uttered; but it may be said, partly in answer to it, and partly in confirmation, that the valuable element in these things was not what Hawthorne put into them consciously, but what passed into them without his being able to measure it—the element of simple genius, the quality of imagination. This is the real charm of Hawthorne's writing—this purity and spontaneity and naturalness of fancy. For the rest, it is interesting to see how it borrowed a particular color from the other faculties that lay near it—how the imagination, in this capital son of the old [57] Puritans, reflected the hue of the more purely moral part, of the dusky, overshadowed conscience. The conscience, by no fault of its own, in every genuine offshoot of that somber lineage, lay under the shadow of the sense of *sin*. This darkening cloud was no essential part of the nature of the individual; it stood fixed in the general moral heaven under which he grew up and looked at life. It projected from above, from outside, a black patch over his spirit, and it was for him to do what he could with the black patch. There were all sorts of possible ways of dealing with it; they depended upon the personal temperament. Some natures would let it lie as it fell, and contrive to be tolerably comfortable beneath it. Others would groan and sweat and suffer; but the dusky blight would remain, and their lives would be lives of misery. Here and there an individual, irritated beyond endurance, would throw it off in anger, plunging probably into what would be deemed deeper abysses of depravity. Hawthorne's way was the best, for he contrived, by an exquisite process, best known to himself, to transmute this heavy moral burden into the very substance of the imagination, to make it evaporate in the light and charming fumes of artistic production. But Hawthorne, of course, was exceptionally fortunate; he had his genius to help him. Nothing is more curious and interesting than this almost exclusively *imported* character of the sense of sin in Hawthorne's mind; it seems to exist there merely for an artistic or literary purpose. He had ample cognizance of the Puritan conscience; it was his natural heritage; it was reproduced in him; looking into his soul, he found it there. But his relation to it was only, as one may say, intellectual; it was not moral and [58] theological. He played with it and used it as a pigment; he treated it, as the metaphysicians say, objectively. He was not discomposed, disturbed, haunted by it, in the manner of its usual and regular victims, who had not the little postern door of fancy to slip through, to the other side of the wall. It was, indeed, to his imaginative vision, the great fact of man's nature; the light element that had been mingled with his own composition always clung to this rugged prominence of moral responsibility, like the mist that hovers about the mountain. It was a necessary condition for a man of Hawthorne's stock that if his imagination should take license to amuse itself, it should at least select this grim precinct of the Puritan morality for its playground. He speaks of the dark disapproval with which his old ancestors, in the case of their coming to life, would see him trifling himself away as a story-teller. But how far more darkly would they have frowned could they have understood that he had converted the very principle of their own being into one of his toys!

It will be seen that I am far from being struck with the justice of that view of the author of the *Twice-Told Tales*, which is so happily expressed by the French critic to whom I alluded at an earlier stage of this essay. To speak of Hawthorne, as M. Emile Montégut does, as a *romancier pessimiste*, seems to me very much beside the mark. He is no more a pessimist than an optimist, though he is certainly not much of either. He does not pretend to conclude, or to have a philosophy of human nature; indeed, I should even say that at bottom he does not take human nature as hard as he may seem to do. "His bitterness," says M. Montégut, "is [59] without abatement, and his bad opinion of man is without compensation. . . . His little tales have the air of confessions which the soul makes to itself; they are so many little slaps which the author applies to our face." This, it seems to me, is to exaggerate almost immeasurably the reach of Hawthorne's relish of gloomy subjects. What pleased him in such subjects was their picturesqueness, their rich duskiness of color, their chiaroscuro; but they were not the expression of a hopeless, or even of a predominantly melancholy, feeling about the human soul. Such at least is my own impression. He is to a considerable degree ironical —this is part of his charm—part even, one may say, of his brightness; but he is neither bitter nor cynical—he is rarely even what I should call tragical. There have certainly been story-tellers of a gayer and lighter spirit; there have been observers more humorous, more hilarious—though on the whole Hawthorne's observation has a smile in it oftener than may at first appear; but there has rarely been an observer more serene, less agitated by what he sees, and less disposed to call things deeply into question. As I have already intimated, his *Note-Books* are full of this simple and almost childlike serenity. That dusky preoccupation with the misery of human life and the wickedness of the human heart which such a critic as M. Emile Montégut talks about, is totally absent from them; and if we may suppose a person to have read these diaries before looking into the tales, we may be sure that such a reader would be greatly surprised to hear the author described as a disappointed, disdainful genius. "This marked love of cases of conscience," says M. Montégut, "this taciturn, scornful cast of mind, this habit of seeing sin everywhere and hell [60] always gaping open, this dusky gaze bent always upon a damned world and a nature draped in mourning, these lonely conversations of the imagination with the conscience, this pitiless analysis resulting from a perpetual examination of one's self, and from the tortures of a heart closed before men and open to God—all these elements of the Puritan character have passed into Mr. Hawthorne, or to speak more justly, have *filtered* into him, through a long succession of generations." This is a very pretty and very vivid account of Hawthorne, superficially considered; and it is just such a view of the case as would commend itself most easily and most naturally to a hasty critic. It is all true indeed, with a difference; Hawthorne was all that M. Montégut says, *minus* the conviction. The old Puritan moral sense, the consciousness of sin and hell, of the fearful nature of our responsibilities and the savage character of our Taskmaster —these things had been lodged in the mind of a man of Fancy, whose fancy had straightway begun to take liberties and play tricks with them— to judge them (Heaven forgive him!) from the poetic and aesthetic point of view, the point of view of entertainment and irony. This absence of conviction makes the difference; but the difference is great. Hawthorne was a man of fancy, and I suppose that in speaking of him it is inevitable that we should feel ourselves confronted with the familiar problem of the difference between the fancy and the imagination. Of the larger and more potent faculty he certainly possessed a liberal share; no one can read *The House of the Seven Gables* without feeling it to be a deeply imaginative work. But I am often struck, especially in the shorter tales, of which I am now chiefly speaking, with [61] a kind of small ingenuity, a taste for conceits and analogies, which bears more particularly what is called the fanciful stamp. The finer of the shorter tales are redolent of a rich imagination.

Had Goodman Brown fallen asleep in the forest and only dreamed a wild dream of witch-meeting? Be it so, if you will; but, alas, it was a dream of evil omen for young Goodman Brown! a stern, a sad, a darkly meditative, a distrustful, if not a desperate, man, did he become from the night of that fearful dream. On the Sabbath day, when the congregation were singing a holy psalm, he could not listen, because an anthem of sin rushed loudly upon his ear and drowned all the blessed strain. When the minister spoke from the pulpit, with power and fervid eloquence, and with his hand on the open Bible of the sacred truth of our religion, and of saintlike lives and triumphant deaths, and of future bliss or misery unutterable, then did Goodman Brown grow pale, dreading lest the roof should thunder down upon the gray blasphemer and his hearers. Often, awaking suddenly at midnight, he shrank from the bosom of Faith; and at morning or eventide, when the family knelt down at prayer, he scowled and muttered to himself, and gazed sternly at his wife, and turned away. And when he had lived long, and was borne to his grave a hoary corpse, followed by Faith, an aged woman, and children, and grandchildren, a goodly procession, besides neighbors not a few, they carved no hopeful verse upon his tombstone, for his dying hour was gloom.

There is imagination in that, and in many another passage that I might quote; but as a general thing I should characterize the more metaphysical of our author's short stories as graceful and felicitous conceits. They seem to me to be qualified in this manner by the very fact that they belong to the province of allegory. Hawthorne, in his metaphysical moods, is nothing if not allegorical, and allegory, to my sense, is quite one of the [62] lighter exercises of the imagination. Many excellent judges, I know, have a great stomach for it; they delight in symbols and correspondences, in seeing a story told as if it were another and a very different story. I frankly confess that I have as a general thing but little enjoyment of it and that it has never seemed to me to be, as it were, a first-rate literary form. It has produced assuredly some first-rate works; and Hawthorne in his younger years had been a great reader and devotee of Bunyan and Spenser, the great masters of allegory. But it is apt to spoil two good things—a story and a moral, a meaning and a form; and the taste for it is responsible for a large part of the forcible-feeble writing that has been inflicted upon the world. The only case in which it is endurable is when it is extremely spontaneous, when the analogy presents itself with eager promptitude. When it shows signs of having been groped and fumbled for, the needful illusion is of course absent and the failure complete. Then the machinery alone is visible, and the end to which it operates becomes a matter of indifference. There was but little literary criticism in the United States at the time Hawthorne's earlier works were published; but among the reviewers Edgar Poe perhaps held the scales the highest.

He at any rate rattled them loudest, and pretended, more than anyone else, to conduct the weighing process on scientific principles. Very remarkable was this process of Edgar Poe's, and very extraordinary were his principles; but he had the advantage of being a man of genius, and his intelligence was frequently great. His collection of critical sketches of the American writers flourishing in what M. Taine would call his *milieu* and *moment* is very curious and [63] interesting reading, and it has one quality which ought to keep it from ever being completely forgotten. It is probably the most complete and exquisite specimen of *provincialism* ever prepared for the edification of men. Poe's judgments are pretentious, spiteful, vulgar; but they contain a great deal of sense and discrimination as well, and here and there, sometimes at frequent intervals, we find a phrase of happy insight imbedded in a patch of the most fatuous pedantry. He wrote a chapter upon Hawthorne, and spoke of him on the whole very kindly; and his estimate is of sufficient value to make it noticeable that he should express lively disapproval of the large part allotted to allegory in his tales—in defense of which, he says, "however, or for whatever object employed, there is scarcely one respectable word to be said. . . . The deepest emotion," he goes on, "aroused within us by the happiest allegory *as* allegory, is a very, *very* imperfectly satisfied sense of the writer's ingenuity in overcoming a difficulty we should have preferred his not having attempted to overcome. . . . One thing is clear, that if allegory ever establishes a fact, it is by dint of overturning a fiction"; and Poe has furthermore the courage to remark that the *Pilgrim's Progress* is a "ludicrously overrated book." Certainly, as a general thing, we are struck with the ingenuity and felicity of Hawthorne's analogies and correspondences; the idea appears to have made itself at home in them easily. Nothing could be better in this respect than the *Snow-Image* (a little masterpiece), or *The Great Carbuncle*, or *Doctor Heidegger's Experiment*, or *Rappaccini's Daughter*. But in such things as *The Birth-Mark* and *The Bosom-Serpent* we are struck with something stiff and mechanical, slightly [64] incongruous, as if the kernel had not assimilated its envelope. But these are matters of light impression, and there would be a want of tact in pretending to discriminate too closely among things which all, in one way or another, have a charm. The charm—the great charm—is that they are glimpses of a great field, of the whole deep mystery of man's soul and conscience. They are moral, and their interest is moral; they deal with something more than the mere accidents and conventionalities, the surface occurrences of life. The fine thing in Hawthorne is that he cared for the deeper psychology, and that, in his way, he tried to become familiar with it. This natural, yet fanciful familiarity with it, this air, on the author's part, of being a confirmed *habitué* of a region of mysteries and subtleties, constitutes the originality of his tales. And then they have the further merit of seeming, for what they are, to spring up so freely and lightly. The author has all the ease, indeed, of a regular dweller in the moral, psychological realm; he goes to and fro in it, as a man who knows his way. His tread is a light and modest one, but he keeps the key in his pocket.

His little historical stories all seem to me admirable; they are so good that you may reread them many times. They are not numerous, and they are very short; but they are full of a vivid and delightful sense of the New England past; they have, moreover, the distinction, little tales of a dozen and fifteen pages as they are, of being the only successful attempts at historical fiction that have been made in the United States. Hawthorne was at home in the early New England history; he had thumbed its records and he had breathed its air, in whatever odd receptacles this somewhat pungent compound [65] still lurked. He was fond of it, and he was proud of it, as any New Englander must be, measuring the part of that handful of half-starved fanatics who formed his earliest precursors, in laying the foundations of a mighty empire. Hungry for the picturesque as he always was, and not finding any very copious provision of it around him, he turned back into the two preceding centuries, with the earnest determination that the primitive annals of Massachusetts should at least *appear* picturesque. His fancy, which was always alive, played a little with the somewhat meager and angular facts of the colonial period and forthwith converted a great many of them into impressive legends and pictures. There is a little infusion of color, a little vagueness about certain details, but it is very gracefully and discreetly done, and realities are kept in view sufficiently to make us feel that if we are reading romance, it is romance that rather supplements than contradicts history. The early annals of New England were not fertile in legend, but Hawthorne laid his hands upon everything that would serve his purpose, and in two or three cases his version of the story has a great deal of beauty. *The Grey Champion* is a sketch of less than eight pages, but the little figures stand up in the tale as stoutly, at the least, as if they were propped up on half-a-dozen chapters by a dryer annalist, and the whole thing has the merit of those cabinet pictures in which the artist has been able to make his persons look the size of life. Hawthorne, to say it again, was not in the least a realist—he was not to my mind enough of one; but there is no genuine lover of the good city of Boston but will feel grateful to him for

his courage in attempting to recount the "traditions" of Washington
Street, the main thoroughfare of the Puritan capital.[66] The four *Legends of the Province House* are certain shadowy stories which he professes to have gathered in an ancient tavern lurking behind the modern
shop-fronts of this part of the city. The Province House disappeared some
years ago, but while it stood it was pointed to as the residence of the
Royal Governors of Massachusetts before the Revolution. I have no recollection of it, but it cannot have been, even from Hawthorne's account
of it, which is as pictorial as he ventures to make it, a very imposing
piece of antiquity. The writer's charming touch, however, throws a rich
brown tone over its rather shallow venerableness; and we are beguiled
into believing, for instance, at the close of *Howe's Masquerade* (a story
of a strange occurrence at an entertainment given by Sir William Howe,
the last of the Royal Governors, during the siege of Boston by Washington), that "superstition, among other legends of this mansion, repeats
the wondrous tale that on the anniversary night of Britain's discomfiture the ghosts of the ancient governors of Massachusetts still glide
through the Province House. And last of all comes a figure shrouded in a
military cloak, tossing his clenched hands into the air and stamping his
iron-shod boots upon the freestone steps, with a semblance of feverish
despair, but without the sound of a foot-tramp." Hawthorne had, as
regards the two earlier centuries of New England life, that faculty which
is called nowadays the historic consciousness. He never sought to exhibit
it on a large scale; he exhibited it indeed on a scale so minute that we
must not linger too much upon it. His vision of the past was filled with
definite images—images nonetheless definite, that they were concerned
with events as shadowy as this dramatic passing away of the last of [67]
King George's representatives in his long loyal but finally alienated
colony.[68]

. . . . .

IV. BROOK FARM VERSUS CONCORD

. . . . .

Our writer's imagination, as has been abundantly conceded, was a
gloomy one; the old Puritan sense of sin, of penalties to be paid, of the
darkness and wickedness of life, had, as I have already suggested, passed
into it. It had not passed into the parts of Hawthorne's nature corresponding to those occupied by the same horrible vision of things in his [101]
ancestors; but it had still been determined to claim this later comer as its
own, and since his heart and his happiness were to escape, it insisted on

setting its mark upon his genius—upon his most beautiful organ, his admirable fancy. It may be said that when his fancy was strongest and keenest, when it was most itself, then the dark Puritan tinge showed in it most richly; and there cannot be a better proof that he was not the man of a somber *parti-pris* whom M. Montégut describes, than the fact that these duskiest flowers of his invention sprang straight from the soil of his happiest days. This surely indicates that there was but little direct connection between the products of his fancy and the state of his affections. When he was lightest at heart, he was most creative, and when he was most creative, the moral picturesqueness of the old secret of mankind in general and of the Puritans in particular most appealed to him—the secret that we are really not by any means so good as a well-regulated society requires us to appear. It is not too much to say, even, that the very condition of production of some of these unamiable tales would be that they should be superficial, and, as it were, insincere. The magnificent little romance of *Young Goodman Brown*, for instance, evidently means nothing as regards Hawthorne's own state of mind, his conviction of human depravity and his consequent melancholy; for the simple reason that if it meant anything, it would mean too much. Mr. Lathrop speaks of it as a "terrible and lurid parable"; but this, it seems to me, is just what it is not. It is not a parable, but a picture, which is a very different thing. What does M. Montégut make, one would ask, from the point [102] of view of Hawthorne's pessimism, of the singularly objective and unpreoccupied tone of the Introduction to the *Old Manse*, in which the author speaks from himself, and in which the cry of metaphysical despair is not even faintly sounded? [103]

. . . . .

V. THE THREE AMERICAN NOVELS

. . . . .

In *The Scarlet Letter* there is a great deal of symbolism, there is, I think, too much. It is overdone at times, and becomes mechanical; it ceases to be impressive, and grazes triviality. The idea of the mystic *A* which the young minister finds imprinted upon his breast and eating into his flesh, in sympathy with the embroidered badge that Hester is condemned to wear, appears to me to be a case in point. This suggestion should, I think, have been just made and dropped; to insist upon it and return to it is to exaggerate the weak side of the subject. Hawthorne returns to it constantly, plays with it, and seems charmed by it; until at last the reader feels tempted to declare that his enjoyment of it is puerile. In the admirable scene, so superbly conceived and beautifully executed, in which Mr. Dimmesdale, in the stillness of the night, in the middle of the sleeping town, feels impelled to go and stand upon the scaffold where his mistress had formerly enacted her dreadful penance, and then, seeing Hester pass along the street, from watching at a sick-bed, with little Pearl at her side, calls them both to come and stand there beside him— in this masterly episode the effect is almost spoiled by the introduction of one of these superficial conceits. What leads up to it is very fine—so fine that I cannot do better than quote it [117] as a specimen of one of the striking pages of the book.

But before Mr. Dimmesdale had done speaking, a light gleamed far and wide over all the muffled sky. It was doubtless caused by one of those meteors which the night watcher may so often observe burning out to waste in the vacant regions of the atmosphere. So powerful was its radiance that it thoroughly illuminated the dense medium of cloud, betwixt the sky and earth. The great vault brightened, like the dome of an immense lamp. It showed the familiar scene of the street with the distinctness of midday, but also with the awfulness that is always imparted to familiar objects by an unaccustomed light. The wooden houses, with their jutting stories and quaint gable-peaks; the doorsteps and thresholds, with the early grass springing up about them; the garden-plots, black with freshly-turned earth; the wheel track, little worn, and, even in the market place, margined with green on either side,—all were visible, but with a singularity of aspect that seemed to give another moral interpretation to the things of this world than they had ever borne before. And there stood the minister, with his hand over his heart; and Hester Prynne, with the embroidered letter glimmering on her bosom; and little Pearl, herself a symbol, and the connecting-link between these two. They stood in the noon of that strange and solemn splendor, as if it were the light that is to reveal all secrets, and the daybreak that shall unite all that belong to one another.

That is imaginative, impressive, poetic; but when, almost immediately afterwards, the author goes on to say that "the minister looking upward to the zenith, beheld there the appearance of an immense letter—the letter *A*—marked out in lines of dull red light," we feel that he goes too far and is in danger of crossing the line that separates the sublime from its intimate neighbor. We are tempted to say that this is not [118] moral tragedy, but physical comedy. In the same way, too much is made of the intimation that Hester's badge had a scorching property, and that if one touched it one would immediately withdraw one's hand. Hawthorne is perpetually looking for images which shall place themselves in picturesque correspondence with the spiritual facts with which he is concerned, and of course the search is of the very essence of poetry. But in such a process discretion is everything, and when the image becomes importunate it is in danger of seeming to stand for nothing more serious than itself. When Hester meets the minister by appointment in the forest, and sits talking with him while little Pearl wanders away and plays by the edge of the brook, the child is represented as at last making her way over to the other side of the woodland stream, and disporting herself there in a manner which makes her mother feel herself, "in some indistinct and tantalizing manner, estranged from Pearl; as if the child, in her lonely ramble through the forest, had strayed out of the sphere in which she and her mother dwelt together, and was now vainly seeking to return to it." And Hawthorne devotes a chapter to this idea of the child's having, by putting the brook between Hester and herself, established a kind of spiritual gulf, on the verge of which her little fantastic person innocently mocks at her mother's sense of bereavement. This conception belongs, one would say, quite to the lighter order of a story-teller's devices, and the reader hardly goes with Hawthorne in the large development he gives to it. He hardly goes with him either, I think, in his extreme predilection for a small number of vague ideas which are represented by such terms as "sphere" and "sympathies." [119] Hawthorne makes too liberal a use of these two substantives; it is the solitary defect of his style, and it counts as a defect partly because the words in question are a sort of specialty with certain writers immeasurably inferior to himself.

I had not meant, however, to expatiate upon his defects, which are of the slenderest and most venial kind. *The Scarlet Letter* has the beauty and harmony of all original and complete conceptions, and its weaker spots, whatever they are, are not of its essence; they are mere light flaws and inequalities of surface. One can often return to it; it supports familiarity and has the inexhaustible charm and mystery of great works of art. It is admirably written.
. . . . . [120]

VII. LAST YEARS

. . . . .

He was a beautiful, natural, original genius, and his life had been singularly exempt from worldly preoccupations and vulgar efforts. It had been as pure, as simple, as unsophisticated, as his work. He had lived primarily in his domestic affections, which were of the tenderest kind;

and then—without eagerness, without pretension, but with a great deal of quiet devotion—in his charming art. His work will remain; it is too original and exquisite to pass away; among the men of imagination he will always have his niche. No one has had just that vision of life, and no one has had a literary form that more successfully expressed his vision. He was not a moralist, and he was not simply a poet. The moralists are weightier, denser, richer, in a sense; the poets are more purely inconclusive and irresponsible. He combined in a singular degree the spontaneity of the imagination with a haunting care for moral problems. Man's conscience was his theme, but he saw it in the light of a creative fancy which added, out of its own substance, an interest, and, I may almost say, an importance.[183]

Nathaniel Hawthorne and "The Scarlet Letter" *

Nathaniel Hawthorne writes romance.

And what's romance? Usually, a nice little tale where you have everything As You Like It, where rain never wets your jacket and gnats never bite your nose and its always daisy-time. *As You Like It* and *Forest Lovers*, etc. *Morte D'Arthur*.

Hawthorne obviously isn't this kind of romanticist: though nobody has muddy boots in the *Scarlet Letter*, either.

But there is more to it. *The Scarlet Letter* isn't a pleasant, pretty romance. It is a sort of parable, an earthly story with a hellish meaning.

All the time there is this split in the American art and art-consciousness. On the top it is as nice as pie, goody-goody [92] and lovey-dovey. Like Hawthorne being such a blue-eyed darling, in life, and Longfellow and the rest such sucking doves. Hawthorne's wife said she "never saw him in time," which doesn't mean she saw him too late. But always in the "frail effulgence of eternity."

Serpents they were. Look at the inner meaning of their art and see what demons they were.

* From *Studies in Classic American Literature* by D. H. Lawrence. Copyright 1923 by Thomas Seltzer, Inc., 1951 by Frieda Lawrence. Reprinted by permission of The Viking Press, Inc. The page numbers in brackets refer to the Doubleday Anchor edition, 1953.

You *must* look through the surface of American art, and see the inner diabolism of the symbolic meaning. Otherwise it is all mere childishness.

That blue-eyed darling Nathaniel knew disagreeable things in his inner soul. He was careful to send them out in disguise.

Always the same. The deliberate consciousness of Americans so fair and smooth-spoken, and the under-consciousness so devilish. *Destroy! destroy! destroy!* hums the under-consciousness. *Love and produce! Love and produce!* cackles the upper consciousness. And the world hears only the Love-and-produce cackle. Refuses to hear the hum of destruction underneath. Until such time as it will *have* to hear.

The American has got to destroy. It is his destiny. It is his destiny to destroy the whole corpus of the white psyche, the white consciousness. And he's got to do it secretly. As the growing of a dragon-fly inside a chrysalis or cocoon destroys the larva grub, secretly.

Though many a dragon-fly never gets out of the chrysalis case: dies inside. As America might.

So the secret chrysalis of *The Scarlet Letter*, diabolically destroying the old psyche inside.

Be good! Be good! warbles Nathaniel. *Be good, and never sin! Be sure your sins will find you out.*

So convincingly that his wife never saw him "as in time."

Then listen to the diabolic undertone of *The Scarlet Letter*.

Man ate of the tree of knowledge, and became ashamed of himself.

Do you imagine Adam had never lived with Eve before [93] that apple episode? Yes, he had. As a wild animal with his mate.

It didn't become "sin" till the knowledge-poison entered. That apple of Sodom.

We are divided in ourselves, against ourselves. And that is the meaning of the cross symbol.

In the first place, Adam knew Eve as a wild animal knows its mate, momentaneously, but vitally, in blood-knowledge. Blood-knowledge, not mind-knowledge. Blood-knowledge, that seems utterly to forget, but doesn't. Blood-knowledge, instinct, intuition, all the vast vital flux of knowing that goes on in the dark, antecedent to the mind.

Then came that beastly apple, and the other sort of knowledge started.

Adam began to look at himself. "My hat!" he said. "What's this? My Lord! What the deuce!—And Eve! I wonder about Eve."

Thus starts KNOWING. Which shortly runs to UNDERSTANDING, when the devil gets his own.

When Adam went and took Eve, *after* the apple, he didn't do any more than he had done many a time before, in act. But in consciousness he did something very different. So did Eve. Each of them kept an eye on what they were doing, they watched what was happening to them. They wanted to KNOW. And that was the birth of sin. Not *doing* it, but KNOWING about it. Before the apple, they had shut their eyes and their minds had gone dark. Now, they peeped and pried and imagined. They watched themselves. And they felt uncomfortable after. They felt self-conscious. So they said, "The *act* is sin. Let's hide. We've sinned."

No wonder the Lord kicked them out of the Garden. Dirty hypocrites.

The sin was the self-watching, self-consciousness. The sin, and the doom. Dirty understanding.

Nowadays men do hate the idea of dualism. It's no good, dual we are. The Cross. If we accept the symbol, then,[94] virtually, we accept the fact. We are divided against ourselves.

For instance, the blood *hates* being KNOWN by the mind. It feels itself destroyed when it is KNOWN. Hence the profound instinct of privacy.

And on the other hand, the mind and the spiritual consciousness of man simply *hates* the dark potency of blood-acts: hates the genuine dark sensual orgasms, which do, for the time being, actually obliterate the mind and the spiritual consciousness, plunge them in a suffocating flood of darkness.

You can't get away from this.

Blood-consciousness overwhelms, obliterates, and annuls mind-consciousness.

Mind-consciousness extinguishes blood-consciousness, and consumes the blood.

We are all of us conscious in both ways. And the two ways are antagonistic in us.

They will always remain so.

That is our cross.

. . . . .   [95]

. . . . .

There is a basic hostility in all of us between the physical and the mental, the blood and the spirit. The mind is "ashamed" of the blood. And the blood is destroyed by the mind, actually. Hence pale-faces.

At present the mind-consciousness and the so-called spirit triumphs. In America supremely. In America, nobody does anything from the blood. Always from the nerves, if not from the mind. The blood is chemically reduced by the nerves, in American activity.

When an Italian labourer labours, his mind and nerves sleep, his blood acts ponderously.

Americans, when they are *doing* things, never seem really to be doing them. They are "busy about" it. They are always busy "about" something. But truly *immersed* in *doing* something, with the deep blood-consciousness active, that they never are.

They *admire* the blood-conscious spontaneity. And they want to get it in their heads. "Live from the body," they shriek. It is their last mental shriek. *Co-ordinate.*

It is a further attempt still to rationalize the body and blood. "Think about such and such a muscle," they say, "and relax there."

And every time you "conquer" the body with the mind (you can say "heal" it, if you like) you cause a deeper, more dangerous complex or tension somewhere else.

Ghastly Americans, with their blood no longer blood. A yellow spiritual fluid.

The Fall.

There have been lots of Falls.

We *fell* into *knowledge* when Eve bit the apple. Self-conscious knowledge. for the first time the mind put up a fight against the blood. Wanting to UNDERSTAND. That is to intellectualize the blood.

The blood must be *shed*, says Jesus.

Shed on the cross of our own divided psyche.

Shed the blood, and you become mind-conscious. Eat the body and drink the blood, self-cannibalizing, and you [96] become extremely conscious, like Americans and some Hindus. Devour yourself, and God knows what a lot you'll know, what a lot you'll be conscious of.

Mind you don't choke yourself.

For a long time men *believed* that they could be perfected through the mind, through the spirit. They believed, passionately. They had their ecstasy in pure consciousness. They *believed* in purity, chastity, and the wings of the spirit.

America soon plucked the bird of the spirit. America soon killed the *belief* in the spirit. But not the practice. The practice continued with a sarcastic vehemence. America, with a perfect inner contempt for the spirit and the consciousness of man, practises the same spirituality and universal love and KNOWING all the time, incessantly, like a drug habit. And inwardly gives not a fig for it. Only for the *sensation*. The pretty-pretty *sensation* of love, loving all the world. And the nice fluttering aeroplane *sensation* of knowing, knowing, knowing. Then the prettiest of all sensations, the sensation of UNDERSTANDING. Oh, what a lot they understand, the darlings! So good at the trick, they are. Just a trick of self-conceit.

The Scarlet Letter gives the show away.

You have your pure-pure young parson Dimmesdale.

You have the beautiful Puritan Hester at his feet.

And the first thing she does is to seduce him.

And the first thing he does is to be seduced.

And the second thing they do is to hug their sin in secret, and gloat over it, and try to understand.

Which is the myth of New England.

Deerslayer refused to be seduced by Judith Hutter. At least the Sodom apple of sin didn't fetch him.

But Dimmesdale was seduced gloatingly. Oh, luscious Sin!

He was such a pure young man.

That he had to make a fool of purity.

The American psyche.[97]

Of course the best part of the game lay in keeping up pure appearances.

The greatest triumph a woman can have, especially an American woman, is the triumph of seducing a man: especially if he is pure.

And he gets the greatest thrill of all, in falling.—"Seduce me, Mrs. Hercules."

And the pair of them share the subtlest delight in keeping up pure appearances, when everybody knows all the while. But the power of pure appearances is something to exult in. All America gives in to it. *Look* pure!

To seduce a man. To have everybody know. To keep up appearances of purity. Pure!

This is the great triumph of woman.

A. The Scarlet Letter. Adulteress! The great Alpha. Alpha! Adulteress! The new Adam and Adama! American!

A. Adulteress! Stitched with gold thread, glittering upon the bosom. The proudest insignia.

Put her upon the scaffold and worship her there. Worship her there. The Woman, the Magna Mater. *A.* Adulteress! Abel!

Abel! Abel! Abel! Admirable!

It becomes a farce.

The fiery heart. *A.* Mary of the Bleeding Heart. Mater Adolorata! *A.* Capital *A.* Adulteress. Glittering with gold thread. Abel! Adultery. Admirable!

It is, perhaps, the most colossal satire ever penned. *The Scarlet Letter.* And by a blue-eyed darling of a Nathaniel.

Not Bumppo, however.

The human spirit, fixed in a lie, adhering to a lie, giving itself perpetually the lie.

All begins with *A*.

Adulteress. Alpha. Abel, Adam. A. America.

The Scarlet Letter.

.   .   .   .   .   [98]

.   .   .   .   .

Dimmesdale has a "coup" in the very end. He gives the whole show away by confessing publicly on the scaffold, and dodging into death, leaving Hester dished, and Roger as it were, doubly cuckolded. It is a neat last revenge.

Down comes the curtain, as in Ligeia's poem.

But the child Pearl will be on in the next act, with her Italian Count and a new brood of vipers. And Hester greyly Abelling, in the shadows, after her rebelling.

It is a marvellous allegory. It is to me one of the greatest allegories in all literature, *The Scarlet Letter*. Its marvellous under-meaning! And its perfect duplicity.

The absolute duplicity of that blue-eyed *Wunderkind* of a Nathaniel. The American wonder-child, with his magical allegorical insight.

But even wonder-children have to grow up in a generation or two. And even SIN becomes stale.[110]

Maule's Curse: Or Hawthorne
and the Problem of Allegory *

"At the moment of execution—with the halter about his neck and while Colonel Pyncheon sat on horseback, grimly gazing at the scene—Maule had addressed him from the scaffold, and uttered a prophecy, of which history as well as fireside tradition, has preserved the very words. 'God,' said the dying man, pointing his finger, with a ghastly look, at the undismayed countenance of his enemy, 'God will give him blood to drink!' "—*The House of the Seven Gables*

* Reprinted from *In Defense of Reason* by Yvor Winters by permission of the publisher, Alan Swallow. Copyright 1947 by Yvor Winters.

Of Hawthorne's three most important long works—*The Scarlet Letter*, *The House of the Seven Gables*, and *The Marble Faun*—the first is pure allegory, and the other two are impure novels, or novels with unassimilated allegorical elements. The first is faultless, in scheme and in detail; it is one of the chief masterpieces of English prose. The second and third are interesting, the third in particular, but both are failures, and neither would suffice to give the author a very high place in the history of prose fiction. Hawthorne's sketches and short stories, at best, are slight performances; either they lack meaning, as in the case of *Mr. Higginbotham's Catastrophe*, or they lack reality of embodiment, as in the case of *The Birthmark*, or, having a measure of both, as does *The Minister's Black Veil*, they yet seem incapable of justifying the intensity of the method, their very brevity and attendant simplification, perhaps, working against them; the best of them, probably, is *Young Goodman Brown*. In his later romances, *Septimius Felton*, *Dr. Grimshaw's Secret*, *The Ancestral Footstep*, and *The Dolliver Romance*, and in much of *The Blithedale Romance* as well, Hawthorne struggles unsuccessfully with the problem of allegory, but he is still obsessed with it.

Hawthorne is, then, essentially an allegorist; had he followed [157] the advice of Poe and other well-wishers, contemporary with himself and posthumous, and thrown his allegorizing out the window, it is certain that nothing essential to his genius would have remained. He appears to have had none of the personal qualifications of a novelist, for one thing: the sombre youth who lived in solitude and in contemplation in Salem, for a dozen years or more, before succumbing to the charms and propinquity of Miss Sophia Peabody and making the spasmodic and only moderately successful efforts to accustom himself to daylight which were to vex the remainder of his life, was one far more likely to concern himself with the theory of mankind than with the chaos, trivial, brutal, and exhausting, of the actuality. Furthermore, as we shall see more fully, the Puritan view of life was allegorical, and the allegorical vision seems to have been strongly impressed upon the New England literary mind. It is fairly obvious in much of the poetry of Emerson, Emily Dickinson, Bryant, Holmes, and even Very—Whittier, a Quaker and a peasant, alone of the more interesting poets escaping; Melville, relatively an outsider, shows the impact of New England upon his own genius as much through his use of allegory as through his use of New England character; and the only important novelist purely a New Englander, aside from Hawthorne, that is, O. W. Holmes, was primarily concerned with the Puritan tendency to allegory, as its one considerable satirist, yet was himself more or less addicted to it.

These matters are speculative. That New England predisposed Hawthorne to allegory cannot be shown; yet the disposition in both is obvious. And it can easily be shown that New England provided the perfect material for one great allegory, and that, in all likelihood, she was largely to blame for the later failures.

The Puritan theology rested primarily upon the doctrine of predestination and the inefficaciousness of good works; it separated men sharply and certainly into two groups, the saved and the damned, and, technically, at least, was not concerned with any subtler shadings. This in itself represents a long step toward the allegorization of experience, for a very broad abstraction is substituted for the patient study of the minutiae of moral behavior long encouraged by Catholic tradition. Another step was [158] necessary, however, and this step was taken in Massachusetts almost at the beginning of the settlement, and in the expulsion of Anne Hutchinson became the basis of governmental action: whereas the wholly Calvinistic Puritan denied the value of the evidence of character and behavior as signs of salvation, and so precluded the possibility of their becoming allegorical symbols—for the orthodox Calvinist, such as Mrs. Hutchinson would appear to have been, trusted to no witness save that of the Inner Light—it became customary in Massachusetts to regard as evidence of salvation the decision of the individual to enter the Church and lead a moral life. "The Puritans," says Parkes, "were plain blunt men with little taste for mysticism and no talent for speculation. A new conception was formulated by English theologians, of whom William Ames was the most influential. The sign of election was not an inner assurance; it was a sober decision to trust in Christ and obey God's law. Those who made this sober decision might feel reasonably confident that they had received God's grace; but the surest proof of it was its fruit in conduct; complete assurance was impossible. It was assumed that all was the work of grace; it was God, without human coöperation, who caused the sober decision to be made. But in actual practice this doctrine had the effect of unduly magnifying man's ability to save himself, as much as Calvin's conception had unduly minimized it; conversion was merely a choice to obey a certain code of rules, and did not imply any emotional change, any love for God, or for holiness, or any genuine religious experience; religion in other words was reduced to mere morality." [1] Objective evidence thus took the place of inner assurance, and the behavior of the individual took

[1] *The Puritan Heresy*, by H. B. Parkes, The Hound and Horn V-2, Jan.-March 1932, pages 173-4. See also *The Pragmatic Test* by H. B. Parkes, The Colt Press, San Francisco.

on symbolic value. That is, any sin was evidence of damnation; or, in other words, any sin represented all sin. When Hester Prynne committed adultery, she committed an act as purely representative of complete corruption as the act of Faustus in signing a contract with Satan. This view of the matter is certainly not Catholic and is little short of appalling; it derives [159] from the fact, that although, as Parkes states in the passage just quoted, there occurred an exaggeration of the will in the matter of practical existence, this same will was still denied in the matter of doctrine, for according to doctrine that which man willed had been previously willed by God.

The belief that the judgment of a man is predestined by God, and the corollary that the judgment of a good man, since all men are either good or bad, purely and simply, is the judgment of God, may lead in the natural course of events to extraordinary drama; and this the more readily if the actors in the drama are isolated from the rest of the world and believe that the drama in which they take part is of cosmic importance and central in human destiny. Andrews writes: "The belief that God had selected New England as the chosen land was profoundly held by the Puritans who went there. Winthrop himself in 1640 wrote to Lord Saye and Sele of 'this good land which God hath found and given to his people,' adding that 'God had chosen this country to plant his people in.' Cotton in his sermon, *God's Promise to His Plantation* (London, 1634), devotes much space to the same idea—'This place is appointed me of God.'" [2] And Schneider writes on the same subject: "No one can live long in a Holy Commonwealth without becoming sensitive, irritable, losing his sense of values and ultimately his balance. All acts are acts either of God or of the devil; all issues are matters of religious faith; and all conflicts are holy wars. No matter how trivial an opinion might appear from a secular point of view, it became vital when promulgated as a theological dogma; no matter how harmless a fool might be, he was intolerable if he did not fit into the Covenant of Grace; no matter how slight an offense might be, it was a sin against Almighty God and hence infinite. Differences of opinion became differences of faith. Critics became blasphemers, and innovators, heretics." [3] And again: ". . . the mind of the Puritan was singularly unified and his imagination thoroughly moralized. The clergy were, of course, the professional [160] moral scientists, but the laymen were no less dominated by such mental habits. The

[2] *The Colonial Period of American History*, by Charles M. Andrews; Yale University Press, 1934. Vol. I, page 386, note 2.
[3] *The Puritan Mind*, by H. W. Schneider; Henry Holt, 1930, pages 51-2.

common man and illiterate shared with the expert this interest in divining God's purposes in the course of events. No event was merely natural; it was an act of God and was hence charged with that 'numinous' quality which gives birth to both prophetic insight and mystic illumination." [4] And again: "Nature was instructive to them only in so far as it suggested the hidden mysterious operations of designing agents. God and devil were both active, scheming, hidden powers, each pursuing his own ends by various ministrations, and natural events were therefore to be understood only in so far as they showed evidence of some divine or diabolical plot." [5]

Now according to the doctrine of predestination, if we interpret it reasonably, Hester merely gave evidence, in committing adultery, that she had always been one of the damned. This point of view, if really understood, could never have led to the chain of events which Hawthorne described in *The Scarlet Letter;* neither could it have led to the events of the actual history of New England. It is at this point that we must consider that fluid element, history, in connection with dogma, for Hester, like the witches who so occupied the Mathers, was treated as if she had wilfully abandoned the ways of God for the ways of Satan. This final illogicality introduces the element of drama into the allegory of *The Scarlet Letter* and into the allegorical morality of the Puritans.

The English Puritans who settled Massachusetts were socially the product of centuries of the type of ethical discipline fostered by the Catholic and Anglo-Catholic Churches. They may have denied the freedom of the will and the efficaciousness of good works by lip, but by habit, and without really grasping the fact, they believed in them and acted upon them. Edwards exhorts sinners to repent while preaching the doctrine of the inability to repent; the Mathers wrestled with demons physically and in broad daylight, and quite obviously felt virtuous for having done so; in fact, to such a pass did Puritanism come, that Melville's Ahab, who wilfully embarks upon the Sea of Unpredictability [161] in order to overtake and slay the Spirit of Evil—an effort in which he is predestined and at the end of which he is predestined to destruction— appears to us merely the heroic projection of a common Puritan type. The Puritan may be said to have conceived the Manicheistic struggle between Absolute Good and Absolute Evil, which he derived through the processes of simplification and misunderstanding which have already been enumerated, as a kind of preordained or mechanical, yet also holy combat, in which his own part was a part at once intense and holy and yet immutably regulated.

[4] Ibid., page 48.   [5] Ibid., pages 42-3.

There were at least two motives in the new environment which tended to intensify the effect of habit in this connection: one was the inevitable impulse given to the will by the exaltation attendant upon a new religious movement; the other was the impulse given by the supremely difficult physical surroundings in which the new colonies found themselves. Foster writes on these points: "The first Puritans, sure in their own hearts that they were the elect of God, found the doctrine necessary to sustain them in the tremendous struggle through which they passed. . . . Hence the doctrine nerved to greater activity; and it produced a similar effect during the first period of the promulgation of Calvinism, among every nation which accepted the system." [6] The force of the will was strengthened at the beginning, then, at the same time that its existence was denied and that reliance upon its manner of functioning (that is, upon good works) was, from a doctrinal standpoint, regarded as sin. The will, highly stimulated, but no longer studied and guided by the flexible and sensitive ethical scholarship of the Roman tradition, might easily result in dangerous action.

Andrews speaks of this subject as follows: "The dynamic agency . . . the driving force which overrode all opposition, legal and otherwise, was the profound conviction of the Puritan leaders that they were doing the Lord's work. They looked upon themselves as instruments in the divine hand for the carrying out of a great religious mission, the object of which was the rebuilding [162] of God's church in a land—the undefiled land of America—divinely set apart as the scene of a holy experiment that should renovate the church at large, everywhere corrupt and falling into ruins. This new and purified community was to be the home of a saving remnant delivered from the wrath to come and was to serve as an example to the mother church of a regenerated form of faith and worship. It was also to become a proselyting center for the conversion of the heathen and the extension of the true gospel among those who knew it not. In the fulfillment of this mission the Puritans counted obstacles, moral and physical, of no momen* Theirs was a religious duty to frustrate their enemies, to eradicate all inimical opinions, religious and political, and to extend the field of their influence as widely as possible. Once they had determined on their rules of polity and conduct, as laid down in the Bible and interpreted by the clergy, they had no doubts of the justness and rightness of their course. The means employed might savor of harshness and inequity, but at all costs and under all circumstances, error, sin, and idolatry, in whatever form appearing and as determined by them-

[6] *A Genetic History of the New England Theology*, by Frank Hugh Foster; University of Chicago Press, 1907; page 29.

selves, must be destroyed. In the process, as events were to prove, a great many very human motives played an important part in interpreting the law of God, and personal likes and dislikes, hypocrisy, prejudice, and passion got badly mixed with the higher and more spiritual impulses that were actively at work purging the church of its errors." [7]

Over a long period, however, the doctrine of predestination would naturally lead to religious apathy, for it offered no explicit motive to action; and this is precisely that to which it led, for after the Great Awakening of the middle of the eighteenth century, itself a reaction to previous decay in the Church, the Church lost power rapidly, and by the opening of the nineteenth century was succumbing on every hand to Unitarianism, a mildly moralistic creed, in which the element of supernaturalism was minimized, and which, in turn, yielded rapidly among the relatively intellectual classes to Romantic ethical theory, especially as propounded by the Transcendentalists. "It has never been a good [163] way to induce men to repent," says Foster, "to tell them that they cannot." [8] Or at least the method has never been highly successful except when employed by a rhetorician of the power of Edwards, or by an orator of the effectiveness of Whitefield; and the effect can scarcely be expected long to outlive the immediate presence of the speaker. The Unitarians, in depriving the ethical life of the more impressive aspects of its supernatural sanction, and in offering nothing to take the place of that sanction, all but extinguished intensity of moral conviction, although their own conviction—we may see it portrayed, for example, in *The Europeans*, by Henry James, and exemplified in the lucid and classical prose of W. E. Channing—was a conviction, at least for a period, of the greatest firmness and dignity. Emerson eliminated the need of moral conviction and of moral understanding alike, by promulgating the allied doctrines of equivalence and of inevitable virtue. In an Emersonian universe there is equally no need and no possibility of judgment; it is a universe of amiable but of perfectly unconscious imbeciles; it is likewise a universe in which the art of the fictionist—or for that matter, any other art—can scarcely be expected to flourish. A fictionist who has been in any considerable measure affected by Emersonian or allied concepts, or even who is the product of the historical sequence which gave rise to Emerson, is likely to find himself gravely confused and may even find himself paralyzed; and we have only to read such a document, to cite a single example, as *The New Adam and Eve*, to realize that Hawthorne's own moral ideas, in spite of

[7] Charles M. Andrews, op. cit., Vol. I, pages 430–1.
[8] Frank Hugh Foster, op. cit., page 29.

his intense but conflicting moral sentiments, and in spite of his professed dislike for Emerson's philosophy, were much closer to the ideas of Emerson than to those of Edwards.

Now in examining Hawthorne, we are concerned with two historical centers: that of the first generation of Puritans in New England, in which occurs the action of *The Scarlet Letter;* and that of the post-Unitarian and Romantic intellectuals, in which was passed the life of Hawthorne.

Hawthorne, by nature an allegorist, and a man with a strong moral instinct, regardless of the condition of his ideas, found in [164] the early history of his own people and region the perfect material for a master-piece. By selecting sexual sin as the type of all sin, he was true alike to the exigencies of drama and of history. In the setting which he chose, allegory was realism, the idea was life itself; and his prose, always remarkable for its polish and flexibility, and stripped, for once, of all superfluity, was reduced to the living idea, it intensified pure exposition to a quality comparable in its way to that of great poetry.

. . . . . [165]

. . . . .

In *The Scarlet Letter* . . . Hawthorne composed a great allegory; or, if we look first at the allegorical view of life upon which early Puritan society was based, we might almost say that he composed a great historical novel. History, which by placing him in an anti-intellectual age had cut him off from the ideas which might have enabled him to deal with his own period, in part made up for the injustice by facilitating his entrance, for a brief time, into an age more congenial to his nature. Had he possessed the capacity for criticizing and organizing conceptions as well as for dramatizing them, he might have risen superior to his disadvantages, but like many other men of major genius he lacked this capacity. In turning his back upon the excessively simplified conceptions of his Puritan ancestors, he abandoned the only orderly concepts, whatever their limitations, to which he had access, and in his last work he is restless and dissatisfied. The four last romances are unfinished, and in each successive one he sought to incorporate and perfect elements from those preceding; the last, *The Dolliver Romance*, which he had sought to make the best, had he lived, is a mere fragment, but on the face of it is the most preposterous of all. His dilemma, the choice between abstractions inadequate or irrelevant to experience on the one hand, and experience on the other as far as practicable unilluminated by understanding, is tragically characteristic of the history of this country and of its literature; only a few scattered individuals, at the cost of inordinate labor, and often impermanently, have achieved the permeation of human [174] experience by a consistent moral understanding which results in wisdom and in great art. If art is to be measured by the greatness of the difficulties overcome—and the measure is not wholly unreasonable, for there can scarcely be virtue without a comprehension of sin, and the wider and more careful the comprehension the richer the virtue—then these few writers are very great indeed. Hawthorne, when he reversed his formula of alternative possibilities, and sought to grope his way blindly to significance, made the choice of the later Romantics; and his groping was met wherever he moved by the smooth and impassive surface of the intense inane.[175]

Hawthorne's Psychology:
The Acceptance of Good and Evil*

That there are aspects of art which can hardly be reached by the scalpels of economic and social analysis was maintained by Yeats' belief that poetry is not 'a criticism of life' but 'a revelation of a hidden life.' This belief would unquestionably have been accepted by Hawthorne, who declared in one of his processional sketches—in another sentence marked by Melville—that human nature can be more truly represented in the wishes of its heart than in its actions, since such a portrayal has 'more of good and more of evil in it; more redeeming points of the bad and more errors of the virtuous; higher upsoarings, and baser degradations of the soul; in short, a more perplexing amalgamation of vice and virtue than we witness in the outward world.'

Why Hawthorne held this has been explained in part by such circumstances of his biography as we have dwelt on; and those circumstances were conditioned in turn by the centrifugal movement of American society. In like fashion, his conception of good and evil, which drove him to take the tragic view of life, might also be accounted for by his background, by his relation to a particular phase of the decay of the Puritan

* From F. O. Matthiessen, "Hawthorne's Psychology: The Acceptance of Good and Evil," *American Renaissance: Art and Expression in the Age of Emerson and Whitman,* by F. O. Matthiessen, pp. 337–47, 349–51. Copyright 1941 by Oxford University Press, Inc., and reprinted by permission.

tradition. But unless the explaining of such things be considered an explaining away, unless all religious belief is held to be merely deluded
fantasy to be dealt with only by the psychoanalyst, the value of Hawthorne's portrayal of spiritual conflict still remains to be reckoned with.
This reckoning can be made only if we start from inside, so to speak—
only if, instead of discounting his views as part of a world gone by, we
try to experience to the full what he thought and felt about human
destiny. For only then will we be in a position to test his interpretation
against others, and against what we ourselves may believe to be primary
forces in the universe.

Everywhere he looked he was struck by what, he conjectured,
even [337] confused Clifford might have seen, 'in the mirror of his deeper
consciousness': how 'he was an example and representative of that great
class of people whom an inexplicable Providence is continually putting
at cross-purposes with the world: breaking what seems its own promise
in their nature; withholding their proper food, and setting poison before
them for a banquet: and thus—when it might so easily, as one would
think, have been adjusted otherwise—making their existence a strangeness, a solitude, and torment.' It is no wonder that Holgrave went still
farther in his conclusions about the perverse labyrinth of circumstances.
Observing, as the ultimate reach of Pyncheon domineering, a timid spin-
ster and a degraded and shattered gentleman, and thinking too of how
his own poor family had been kept out of its only inheritance, he could
see all the life that had passed within the house reduced to the reiterated
pattern of 'perpetual remorse of conscience, a constantly defeated hope,
strife amongst kindred, various misery, a strange form of death, dark
suspicion, unspeakable disgrace.'

Such an accumulation of oppressive evil upon the roof of one family
hardly falls short of the terrible imagination of Aeschylus. Speaking
from the great range of his reading, More held (1904) that *The Seven
Gables* was the one companion in modern literature 'to the Orestean
conception of satiety begetting insolence, and insolence calling down
upon a family the inherited curse of Ate.' This kinship in theme also
throws into relief Hawthorne's difference from the Greeks in conceiving the operation of a curse: not in sudden violent disasters so much as
in the prolonged 'disease of inner solitude.' More recognized this as a
consequence of Hawthorne's particular Christian tradition: 'Not with
impunity had the human race for ages dwelt on the eternal welfare of
the soul; for from such meditation the sense of personal importance had
become exacerbated to an extraordinary degree. What could result from

such teaching as that of Jonathan Edwards but an extravagant sense of individual existence, as if the moral governance of the world revolved about the action of each mortal soul?' Continuing this development to Hawthorne's day, More held that with the loss of Edwards' intensity, with the partial waning of the old faith attendant on the introspection, there could only be left a great residue of anguish and bereavement, a loneliness of the individual of 'a poignancy altogether unexampled.' Thus the most compact examination of theological history brings us to the very point that we have already reached in noting the effect of American social forces on an [338] individual like Hawthorne, who was not content with Emerson's new freedom of solitude.[339]

. . . . .

Hawthorne's tragic vision is hardly attested by his adoption of a few of the devices of drama, but rather by his ability to endow such a pathetic character as Hepzibah with a measure of heroic dignity. He presents her absurd confusion of feelings as she stands behind her counter: her desire to be treated like a lady, and her recoil from expressions of sympathy; her inability to suppress a sense of superiority to her customers, and her bitter virulence against 'the idle aristocracy,' to which she had so recently been proud to belong. She had lived so long alone in the house that its dry-rot had begun to eat into her mind. 'She needed'—and we know how much Hawthorne implied in such a remark—'a walk along the noonday street to keep her sane.'

He was aware of the problem with which he had confronted himself by choosing for one of his protagonists not 'even the stately remains of beauty, storm-shattered by affliction—but a gaunt, sallow, rusty-jointed maiden, in a long-waisted silk gown, and with the strange horror of a turban on her head.' Her insignificance was not even redeemed by real ugliness, and her great life-trial 'seems to be, that, after sixty years of idleness, she finds it convenient to earn comfortable bread.' Yet Hawthorne held that if a writer looked 'through all the heroic fortunes of mankind,' he would find this same mixture of the mean and ludicrous in 'the purest pathos which life anywhere supplies to him.' This was particularly the case for anyone who wanted to represent human nature as it was in a democracy, a truth that Melville was to proclaim later in this very year, in his eloquent statement of the 'august dignity' to be found in his *dramatis personae*, the miscellaneous crew of a whaler. Hawthorne's lead to a similar discovery lay in his final remark in the chapter wherein Hepzibah opened her shop: 'What is called poetic insight is the gift of discerning, in this sphere of strangely mingled elements, the beauty and majesty which are compelled to assume a garb so sordid.' Again this discovery [340] is significantly close to Eliot's that 'the essential advantage for a poet is not, to have a beautiful world with which to deal: it is to be able to see beneath both beauty and ugliness; to see the boredom, and the horror, and the glory.' Hawthorne's belief in the dramatic reality of the issues of conscience can also be phrased most concisely in Eliot's statement, in *After Strange Gods,* that in moments of intense 'moral and spiritual struggle . . . men and women come nearest to being real.' In no conviction are the novelist and the poet more akin.

What Hawthorne could see in Hepzibah, and what Melville checked, was 'the moral force of a deeply grounded antipathy,' the strength of conscience that enabled her to stand up against the Judge and confront him with what he really was beneath the oily layers of respectability. Yet Hawthorne's somewhat wavering effort to create the scene that builds up to Hepzibah's moment is an exact instance of Whipple's observation that he was more interested in the conflict of ideas and passions than in the individuals who embodied them, that his characters were introduced 'not as thinking, but as the illustration of thought,' that he used them in order to express 'the last results of patient moral perception.'

Yet it was primarily by virtue of that perception that he broke through the individualism of his day to a reassertion not of man's idiosyncrasies, but of his elemental traits. It is no exaggeration to say that his recognition of the general bond of sin brought him closest to universality. He believed that 'man must not disclaim his brotherhood, even with the guiltiest, since, though his hand be clean, his heart has surely been polluted by the flitting phantoms of iniquity.' That bare, somewhat conventional statement of innate depravity is from one of his early sketches, but it formulates the conviction from which he never swerved. He possessed it, not as a result of any mere observation of mankind against the background of Puritan thought, but more especially in consequence of the sense of personal guilt that sprang from his dread that such a detached observer as himself was failing to participate adequately in life. Yet even such an explanation is oversimplified, and we may better describe his essential state of mind by saying that he felt in himself the presence of both Pyncheons and Maules.

When Eliot said once that you cannot understand James' quality of horror without knowing Hawthorne, he extended both background and foreground by remarking that both Judge John Hathorne and his own

first American ancestor, Andrew Eliot, had been among the witch hang-
ers.[341] Hawthorne's imagination had not been able to rest content with
its atonement, in 'The Gentle Boy,' for his first ancestor, Major William
Hathorne's cruelty to the Quakers. He also remembered that in the
next generation Judge Hathorne's peculiar severity towards a woman
in the witch trials had called out from her husband the prophecy that
God would take revenge upon such persecutors. This clearly gave Hawthorne the hint for the curse pronounced by Maule, whose name, incidentally, he had found in Felt's *Annals of Salem*, where one Thomas
Maule appears as a sympathizer with the Quakers and as the author of a
tract called *Truth Held Forth*, whose career involved being flogged
for saying that the Reverend Mr. Higginson 'preached lies.'

One aspect of Maule's curse in operation was the mysterious disap-
apearance of the title to a vast estate in Waldo County, in the vain dream
of recovering which many Pyncheons had wasted their lives. Such a
refraction of the American dream had been intertwined with his own
family's waning fortunes, in the tradition that his mother's kin had
been deprived of many acres in Raymond, Maine, through the loss of a
deed. This tradition may not seem to have much to do with Hawthorne's
sense of sin, yet it entered into his separation from the dominant Salem
world to which his ancestors had belonged. In this way he became partly
identified with the dispossessed Maules, whom he describes as having
been marked off from other men—'not strikingly,' but 'by an hereditary
characteristic of reserve.' Moreover, as Holgrave recognizes his share in
other traits of the Maules, some of them are likewise those which Hawthorne felt dangerous in himself. His cool habit of scrutinizing the characters of others, which is symbolized by his daguerreotype portraits,
causes the young man to say to Phoebe that this tendency, taken together
with his faculty of mesmerism, might have brought him to Gallows Hill
in the old days. As far as Holgrave's own career is concerned, the novelist
makes clear that his unscrupulous power of analysis, his seeming lack of
reverence for anyone else, inculcated in him by his feeling that the
world's hand is against him, is saved from hardening into fatal arrogance
by the birth of his love for Phoebe—which was also one of Hawthorne's
names for his bird-like Sophia.

Seen thus, the common denominator between Holgrave and Judge
Pyncheon and even Hepzibah, as well as between Hollingsworth and
Ethan Brand and a dozen others, consists in pride, the worst sin in Dante's
theology as well as in Milton's and Edwards'. In his stress on this sin
Hawthorne's [342] sense of innate depravity and his sense of social isola-

tion are united. Not sin, but its consequence for human lives is Hawthorne's major theme. Newton Arvin, whose study of him (1929) contains some of the most incisive social criticism to have been stimulated by
the earlier work of Van Wyck Brooks, was the first to make the linkage
between this theme and the major problem of American society, its continual dissidence and dispersion. In the most eloquent passage of his book,
a declaration of our newer mutual dependence, Arvin summed up the
significance of our historical drift:

What have been our grand national types of personality? The explorer,
with his face turned toward the unknown; the adventurous colonist; the
Protestant sectarian, determined to worship his own God even in the wilderness; the Baptist, the Quaker, the Methodist; the freebooter and the
smuggler; the colonial revolutionary; the pioneer, wih his chronic defec-
tions; the sectional patriot and the secessionist; the come-outer, the claim-
jumper, the Mormon, the founder of communities; the Transcendentalist,
preaching the gospel of self-reliance; the philosophic anarchist in his hut
in the woods; the economic individualist and the captain of industry; the
go-getter, the tax-dodger, the bootlegger. The best and the worst of humanity, not to be confounded in one gesture of repudiation, but united
after all in their common distrust of centrality, their noble or their ignoble
lawlessness, their domination by spiritual pride. United in their refusal to
work together on any but a false basis. United, finally, in paying the penalty for disunion—in becoming partial and lopsided personalities, men
and women of one dimension, august or vulgar cranks. How can we forget the Dimmesdales and Hollingsworths and Pyncheons who have divided our life among them?

That Arvin's words can rise to such a pitch of feeling is evidence of
another function that has been fulfilled by Hawthorne's art. In recording the tragic implications for humane living of a whole phase of American development, the novelist has helped free us from our reckless
individualism in pointing to the need for a new ethical and cultural community. By understanding him, the goals of our own society become
more clear. Yet what Arvin has seemingly overlooked is that it was not
primarily Hawthorne's social observation, but his initial religious conception of man's nature which gave coherence to his interpretation of life.

As Melville said in his essay, existence became real for Hawthorne
only through suffering. He would have agreed with the statement of his
younger contemporary Dostoevsky, in *Letters from the Underworld* [343]
(1861): 'I am sure that man will never renounce the genuine suffering
that comes of ruin and chaos. Why, suffering is the one and only source

of knowledge.' Although Hawthorne had had no personal experience of the terrible godless freedom that became the Russian's most obsessive theme, he shared the belief that only those who can suffer intensely are fully alive, since, as he said, there are 'spiritual depths which no other spell can open.' Contemplating Donatello's transformation from innocence to experience, he came closer to Dostoevsky's words by saying that the faun had 'had glimpses of strange and subtle matters in those dark caverns, into which all men must descend, if they would know anything beneath the surface and illusive pleasures of existence.'

Hawthorne reached the same insights in all his books. Scrutinizing the sham that Dimmesdale had become by hiding his relationship with Hester from the world, he concluded that 'the only truth' that continued to give the minister 'a real existence on this earth was the anguish in his inmost soul.' What made Hollingsworth's notions of sin so entirely unreal in his philanthropic scheme for reforming criminals by an appeal to their 'higher instincts' was the incapacity of his stone-blind egotism to see any imperfections in himself. Hawthorne's own perceptions were at the farthest extreme from those of the self-confident reformer. He grew so absorbed with the lasting weight of misery in *The Seven Gables* that he even questioned whether good was as real as evil. With a penetration no less deep than Dostoevsky's into the discipline of suffering, he had none of the mystical fervor. He repeatedly described society as a tangled wilderness of cross-purposes, overwhelmed by which a man like Clifford became 'a ruin, a failure, as almost everybody is.'

That would seem to imply that Hawthorne was incapable of sustaining the balance of great tragedy, that he could portray the horror of existence but not its moments of transfigured glory. That would mean also that his imagination was stirred only by the subordination of his helpless characters to an iron necessity, and not by the courage of their awakened and resolute wills, or by the possibility of their regeneration. In that case his books would have to be placed in the literature of moral despair. Yet Melville's immediate response was not only to Hawthorne's blackness, but also to his 'depth of tenderness,' his 'boundless sympathy with all forms of being,' his 'omnipresent love,' to what he called Hawthorne's balance between mind and heart. Hawthorne had himself used similar terms when he stated that the Master Genius of the Age, that unknown [344] whom the country was looking for so anxiously, must be such a one 'as never illuminates the earth save when a great heart burns as the household fire of a grand intellect.'

These terms are fundamental in the psychology with which both Hawthorne and Melville worked, but their conception of the relation between the two was less simplified than that of the head-and-heart conflict that was dramatized by the followers of Rousseau—the frustrated romantic conflict between irony and pity. For Hawthorne, and Melville after him, were primarily concerned with envisaging the kind of harmony that might be established between thought and emotion, or, as the seventeenth century would have said, between reason and passion. Both believed disequilibrium between the two to be the chief source of tragedy, so it is necessary to pin down further Hawthorne's use of the terms. We remember that at the time of his one great emotional experience, giving himself in love to Sophia Peabody, he was already in his middle thirties, and therefore felt with exceptional acuteness the release from the prison of himself. That was what caused him to declare, with a fervency so rare for him, 'We are not endowed with real life . . . till the heart is touched. That touch creates us,—then we begin to be.' The experience was no mere interlude of romantic passion: he had glimpsed the same truth long before, and had already elucidated some of its implications in 'The Maypole of Merrymount' (1829). There the Lord and Lady of the May, their hearts opening for each other, feel suddenly something vague and insubstantial in the surrounding gaiety. When the heart is touched, one is born into life, which, even at that moment of ecstasy, is sensed by the lovers as something deeper than jubilation, as the shared burden of joy and sorrow and inevitable change.

The polar opposite from such full sharing was represented in 'Ethan Brand,' Hawthorne's most intense working out of the consequences of yielding to pride, which struck Melville by its fearful revelation of what happens when 'the cultivation of the brain eats out the heart.' That was its root idea, so integral to Hawthorne's reading of human nature that he had formulated it in his journal some years before writing the story: 'The Unpardonable Sin might consist in a want of love and reverence for the Human Soul; in consequence of which, the investigator pried into its dark depths, not with a hope or purpose of making it better, but from a cold philosophical curiosity,—content that it should be wicked in whatever kind or degree, and only desiring to study it out. Would not this,[345] in other words, be the separation of the intellect from the heart?' Such investigation was pursued by Roger Chillingworth as well as by Ethan Brand, who finally declared in a frenzy of tortured pride that he had found within himself 'the sin of an intellect that triumphed over the sense of brotherhood with man and reverence for God, and sacrificed everything to its own mighty claims! The only sin that deserves a recompense of immortal agony!'

But in determining Hawthorne's conception of the heart, it must not be supposed, though he often dramatized the tragedy of the man of adamant in whom this organ had withered, that he put any unqualified sentimental trust in its natural virtue. His most frequent way of symbolizing it was as a dark cavern. At the same period at the Manse when he articulated his view of the Unpardonable Sin, he developed this condensed allegory of the heart, an allegory which gave expression to his then prevailing vision of life:

At the entrance there is sunshine, and flowers growing about it. You step within, but a short distance, and begin to find yourself surrounded with a terrible gloom, and monsters of divers kinds; it seems like Hell itself. You are bewildered, and wander long without hope. At last a light strikes upon you. You peep towards it, and find yourself in a region that seems, in some sort, to reproduce the flowers and sunny beauty of the entrance, but all perfect. These are the depths of the heart, or of human nature, bright and peaceful; the gloom and terror may lie deep; but deeper still is the eternal beauty.

But though he felt himself irradiated by that beauty, especially during the first years of his marriage, he seldom neglected to point out how difficult it was for imperfect man to sustain this vision. His chief subject-matter remained the labyrinths in which man's desires became distorted; and he often wrote as though he had set himself to answer Lear's question, 'Is there any cause in nature that makes these hard hearts?' At the close of 'Earth's Holocaust' (1843), written when the activity of the Millerites had caused him to ponder how reforming zeal might bring to destruction all the age-old abuses and encumbrances of the world, he observed that 'there's one thing that these wiseacres have forgotten to throw into the fire,' without which all their efforts for perfectibility would still remain futile: 'What but the human heart itself? . . . And, unless they hit upon some method of purifying that foul cavern, forth from it will reissue all the shapes of wrong and misery—the same old [346] shapes or worse ones . . . The heart, the heart,—there was the little yet boundless sphere wherein existed the original wrong of which the crime and misery of this outward world were merely types.' Then he added a concluding sentence in which he revealed his understanding that the act of regeneration must involve the whole man, and in what manner his conception of the heart included also the will: 'Purify that inward sphere, and the many shapes of evil that haunt the outward, and which now seem almost our only realities, will turn to shadowy phantoms and vanish of their own accord; but if we go no deeper than the intellect, and strive, with merely that feeble instrument, to discern and rectify what is wrong, our whole accomplishment will be a dream.'

Hawthorne seldom portrayed his characters in a state of grace, since he was too thoroughly aware of how the heart as well as the head could go perversely astray. Yet with his thorough skepticism of all improvement except inner purification, and with only a limited hope of that, he habitually stopped short of what the next age in New England conceived as tragedy, short of Robinson's quiet curbing of despair as the last glimmerings of transcendentalism died away from the isolated 'man against the sky.' Hawthorne was grounded in a more coherent social order than Robinson could be, in his era of decay. Still Hawthorne could seize his saving truth only at the core of a paradox. He sometimes went as far as Holgrave in a hatred of the dead oppression of the past. Exhausted by the British Museum, he could wish that even the Elgin Marbles 'were all burnt into lime,' since 'we have not time, in our earthly existence, to appreciate what is warm with life, and immediately around us . . . I do not see how future ages are to stagger onward under all this dead weight, with the additions that will be continually made to it.' Nevertheless, picturing his home in the Manse, he had prayed for a long endurance for 'the institutions that had grown out of the heart of mankind.' It continued to be one of his fundamental tenets that if men were all intellect, as the transcendental reformers struck him as being, 'they would be continually changing, so that one age would be entirely unlike another. The great conservative is the heart.' In other passages he came near to saying that the heart is the great democrat.

. . . . .   [347]

. . . . .

Hawthorne's way of conceiving a rounded character thus demonstrates his own kind of response to the belief in the common man. It demonstrates likewise that the one-sided and broken figures who throng his most typical pages are seen against a human norm, that he was not so immersed in presenting distortion and defeat as to be incapable of imagining harmony. But his stature as a writer of tragedy cannot be attested even by this perception of the double nature of life, of the fact that there is no such thing as good unless there is also evil, or of evil

unless there is good. For tragic power springs not from the mind's recog-
nitions, but from the depth to which the writer's emotions have been
stirred by what he has recognized, from the degree to which he has
really been able to comprehend and accept what Edgar meant by saying,

> Men must endure
> Their going hence even as their coming hither:
> Ripeness is all.

The briefest description of the tragic attitude is the one Keats gave when
he called it 'the love of good and ill'; and by virtue of his courageous
acceptance of their inevitable mixture he also gave promise of possessing more of the Shakespearean type of imagination than any other poet
of the romantic movement.

The testing of an author's possession of that attitude depends on your
experience of one of his whole compositions. Its presence can be briefly
scrutinized, however, in his ability to hold an undismayed control between the pressure of conflicting forces. The kind of poise that is
demanded is what enabled Hawthorne to say in the opening scene of
The Scarlet Letter that if there had been a Papist among these Puritans
he might have been reminded by his first glimpse of this beautiful woman,
with her baby at her breast, 'of that sacred image of sinless motherhood,
whose infant was to redeem the world.' Yet he would have been quickly
disabused, for here, in bitterest contrast, was 'the taint of deepest sin in
the most sacred quality of human life, working such effect, that the
world was only the darker for this woman's beauty, and the more lost
for the infant she had borne.' Nevertheless, throughout the book Hawthorne [349] emphasizes the self-righteousness of the Puritan leaders who
pursue her with such relentless rigor. Her punishment and suffering are
treated as inevitable; but you are never allowed to forget the loss involved
in their sacrifice of her generosity and tenderness, by the lack of which
their own lives are starved.

The purgative effect of such acceptance of tragic fate was reinforced
in Greek drama by what Aristotle called the recognition scene, wherein
the protagonist became aware of the inexorable course of the action and
of his implication in it. Such is the scene where Iphigenia, a priestess at
last in a foreign country, accepts a victim for sacrifice, and then beholds
him to be her brother Orestes; such, even more terrifying, is that where
Oedipus finally sees in his unwitting self the criminal who has brought
destruction upon the state. These crises strike us now as affecting in

proportion to their not merely being discoveries of the necessity of external events, but involving also Oedipus' kind of inner, moral recognition. And this latter strain was developed to the full by Hawthorne. For his protagonists finally face their evil and know it deserving of the sternest justice, and thus participate in the purgatorial movement, the movement towards regeneration.[1] These last phrases may seem an unwarranted transfer of the tragic catharsis from the audience to the protagonist, but though I would not presume that such a formula would fit all tragedies, what I mean by purgatorial movement can be observed most fully in Shakespeare in Lear's purification through suffering; it also forms the basis for the rising inner action of Milton's Samson. Such too is the slow, heroic course by which Hester arrives at a state of penitence; such is the crisis that at last brings the wavering minister to confess his guilt and beg for mercy; such even is the desperate recognition by Chillingworth that he, 'a mortal man, with a once human heart,' has become a fiend for Dimmesdale's 'especial torment'—though by then his will has become so depraved, so remote from divine grace that he can only feel a revulsion of horror from the 'dark necessity' that he cannot escape.

Moral recognition is equally central to the remorse of Miriam and [350] Donatello, which we have observed to be so closely analogous to that of the protagonists in *Paradise Lost*. Another of Hawthorne's most affecting scenes is that which follows Hollingsworth's icy rejection of Zenobia, when she declares with passion to Coverdale, 'The whole universe, her own sex and yours, and Providence, or Destiny, to boot, make common cause against the woman who swerves one hair's-breadth, out of the beaten track. Yes; and add (for I may as well own it, now) that, with that one hair's-breadth, she goes all astray, and never sees the world in its true aspect afterwards.' Hawthorne does not slur over the fact that many evils are irreparable, that Clifford and Hepzibah are too warped by their experience ever to merge again with the stream of outer life, that there is no release for Zenobia save in death. Yet in such a figure, as well as in Hester and Miriam, since he was able also to convey their

---

[1] I have received some hints for this formulation from Maxwell Anderson's essay, 'The Essence of Tragedy' (1939). Meditation on the *Poetics* had taught him a primary rule for modern dramatic construction: 'A play should lead up to and away from a central crisis, and this crisis should consist in a discovery by the leading character which has an indelible effect on his thought and emotion and completely alters his course of action. The leading character, let me say again, must make the discovery; it must affect him emotionally; and it must alter his direction in the play.'

sexual fascination, Hawthorne was most able to affirm the warmth and strength of the heart, and so to create a sense not merely of life's inexorability and sordidness, but of its possibilities of beauty and grandeur.[351]

*Hawthorne as Poet**

I

For an English person to offer an opinion on Hawthorne, much more an evaluation of his *oeuvre*, must be felt in America to be an impertinence. But the excuse that would justify writing on Hawthorne in an English context—that he is, except as author of one "Puritanical" novel, unread and unrecognized, will, it seems to me, serve here too if somewhat modified. To me, a tremendous admirer of long standing of much of Hawthorne's work, it appears that the essential nature of his achievement has not been isolated and established critically, in spite of the immense amount that has been published on Hawthorne the man, Hawthorne as material for the psychologist, the Hawthorne period and all the rest. I should like to present my own reading of his work, if only to get endorsement from others. In England one can never assume an intelligent knowledge of Hawthorne in the professional world of letters —witness the complacently stupid whole-page article in our august *Times Literary Supplement* two years ago when Mr. Randall Stewart's book came up for review. And in the English academic world Hawthorne's existence as a considerable [179] writer is not even acknowledged. But what is one to conclude when faced with the account of Hawthorne in that admirable American work *The American People* (1949) by Professor H. B. Parkes? Here Hawthorne is characterized as

a man of low emotional pressure who adopted throughout his life the role of an observer. Remaining always aloof from the world around him, he was able to record what he felt with a remarkable balance and detachment. . . . But since he lacked the compulsive drive of the writer who is

* From Q. D. Leavis, "Hawthorne as Poet," *The Sewanee Review*, LIX (Spring and Summer, 1951), Part I: 179–85, 198–205; Part II: 456–58. Copyright © The University of the South, 1951. Reprinted by permission. Footnotes have been renumbered for this reprinting.

himself the victim of conflict and must find a way of salvation, his work lacked force and energy. Carefully and delicately constructed, it was devoid of color and drama and almost passionless. Hawthorne's obsessing personal problem was his sense of isolation. He came to regard isolation as almost the root of all evil, and made it the theme of many of his stories. But Hawthorne's treatment of the subject was always too conscious and deliberate; he expressed it allegorically and not in symbols; and consequently he was unable to say anything about it that enlarges our understanding either of human nature or of the society in which Hawthorne lived.

This is in effect the account of Hawthorne that has always been in currency—stated for instance with more authority and more persuasively by Mr. Yvor Winters in the interesting essay "Maule's Curse, or Hawthorne and the Problem of Allegory," where, though he claims that *The Scarlet Letter* is "faultless, in scheme and detail; it is one of the chief masterpieces of English prose," yet he classifies it as "pure allegory," and dismisses all "Hawthorne's sketches and short stories [as] at best slight performances." Even Henry James, whose monograph on Hawthorne is felt, and was clearly intended, to be the tribute of an artist to the predecessor from whom he inherits, even James demurs at what he calls "allegory, quite one of the lighter exercises of the imagination." But it is clear that James [180] is deploring Hawthorne's merely fanciful pieces; he exempts the works "redolent of a rich imagination." The standard account relegates Hawthorne along with Bunyan to an inferior class of writer who depends for his effects on "allegory," something mechanical and inferior, as Dr. Johnson implied when he wrote "allegory is perhaps one of the most pleasing vehicles of instruction." But when James wrote "Hawthorne is perpetually looking for images which shall place themselves in picturesque correspondence with the spiritual facts with which he is concerned, and of course the search is of the very essence of poetry," he admits, however inadequately, that Hawthorne's intention is a poetic one, nothing less. Similarly, in general acceptance Hawthorne is a "delicate" writer, but when he is praised for his "delicacy" it is intended to stamp his art as something minor. I should prefer to have the purity of his writing noted instead. Nor is the epithet "charming," selected by Henry James, appropriate.

The account, as endorsed by Mr. Parkes, contrives to be unjust to Hawthorne's object and to ignore the very nature of his art. Hawthorne's less interesting work bulks large, no doubt, but it is easily cut free from what is his essential contribution to American literature. The essential

Hawthorne—and he seems to me a great genius, the creator of a literary tradition as well as a wonderfully original and accomplished artist—is the author of *Young Goodman Brown, The Maypole of Merry Mount, My Kinsman Major Molineux, The Snow-Image, The Blithedale Romance, The Scarlet Letter*, and of a number of sketches and less pregnant stories associated with these works such as *The Gray Champion, Main Street, Old News, Endicott of the Red Cross, The Artist of the Beautiful*. This work is not comparable with the productions of the eighteenth-century "allegorical" essayists nor is it in the manner of Spenser, Milton, or Bunyan—whom of course it can be seen he has not merely studied but assimilated. The first batch of works I specified is [181] essentially dramatic, its use of language is poetic, and it is symbolic, and richly so, as is the dramatic poet's. In fact I should suggest that Hawthorne can have gone to school with no one but Shakespeare for his inspiration and model.[1] Mr. Wilson Knight's approach to Shakespeare's tragedies—each play an expanded metaphor—is a cue for the method of rightly apprehending these works of Hawthorne's, where the "symbol" is the thing itself, with no separable paraphrasable meaning as in an allegory: the language is directly evocative. Rereading this work, one is certainly not conscious of a limited and devitalized talent employing a simple-minded pedestrian technique; one is constantly struck by fresh subtleties of organization, of intention, expression and feeling, of original psychological insight and a new minting of terms to convey it, as well as of a predominantly dramatic construction. Yet of the above-mentioned works, apart from *The Scarlet Letter* which has had a good deal of inadequate attention, I can't find any serious *literary* criticism, even in *The American Renaissance* where Hawthorne is evidently intended in some way to be a focus and key-figure. Mr. Quentin Anderson at the end of his article "Henry James and the New Jerusalem" (*Kenyon Review*, Autumn, 1946) offers a metaphysical account of both *The Snow-Image* and *Major Molineux*—but these seem to me subjective interpretations (the second misses Hawthorne's meaning entirely) and not literary criticism rooted in the texts. The recent spate of Hawthorne books has not yet reached England but I am told—though I should be glad to hear that I have been told wrongly—that they add nothing.

The aspect of Hawthorne that I want to stress as the important one, decisive for American literature, and to be found most convincingly

---

[1] I find support for this in "Our Old Home": "Shakespeare has surface beneath surface, to an immeasurable depth. . . . There is no exhausting the various interpretation of his symbols."

in the works I specified, is this: that he was the critic and interpreter of American cultural history and thereby [182] the finder and creator of a literary tradition from which sprang Henry James on the one hand and Melville on the other. I find it impossible to follow Mr. Parkes's argument [2] that "what is lacking in [Hawthorne's] framework of experience is any sense of society as a kind of organic whole to which the individual belongs and in which he has his appointed place. And lacking the notion of social continuity and tradition, [he] lacks also the corresponding metaphysical conception of the natural universe as an ordered unity which harmonizes with human ideals." [3] It is precisely those problems, the relation of the individual to society, the way in which a distinctively American society developed and how it came to have a tradition of its own, the relation of the creative writer to the earlier nineteenth-century American community, and his function and how he could contrive to exercise it—the exploration of these questions and the communication in literary art of his findings—that are his claim to importance. It is true that he is most successful in treating pre-Revolutionary America, but that, after all, is, as he saw it, the decisive period, and *The Blithedale Romance* is the finest test of his dictum in *Old News* that "All philosophy that would abstract mankind from the present is no more than words." As I see it, Hawthorne's sense of being part of the contemporary America could be expressed only in concern for its evolution—he needed to see how it had come about, and by discovering what America had, culturally speaking, started from and with, to find what choices had faced his countrymen and what they had had to sacrifice in order to create that distinctive "organic whole." He was very conscious of the nature of his [183] work; he asserted that to be the function of every great writer, as when in *The Old Manse* he wrote: "A work of genius is but the newspaper of a century, or perchance of a hundred centuries." (Indeed, in some sketches, such as *Old News*, we can see the half-way stage between the newspapers and the work of genius; these sketches have a function like that of the *Letters* of Jane Austen in the evolution of her novels.) And he prepared himself for the task by study, though

[2] "Poe, Hawthorne, Melville: an Essay in Sociological Criticism," *Partisan Review*, Feb., 1949.
[3] This naïve demand should be measured against this passage from *Hawthorne's Last Phase* (E. H. Davidson, 1949): "The rare springtime beauty of the English scene struck him more forcibly than it could the ordinary tourist, for it represented to him the perfect balance between man and nature. This balance was conspicuously absent in the untamed forests of the U. S., where man was busily engaged in subduing nature and dominating a continent. 'It is only an American who can feel it,' Hawthorne wrote."

Providence had furnished him with an eminently usable private Past, in the history of his own family, which epitomized the earlier phases of New England history; this vividly stylized the social history of Colonial America, provided him with a personal mythology, and gave him an emotional stake in the past, a private key to tradition. We know that his first pieces which he later burnt in despair of getting published were called *Seven Tales of My Native Land*. Though he was the very opposite of a Dreiser (whom Mr. Parkes backs in contrast) yet I should choose to describe Hawthorne as a sociological novelist in effect, employing a poetic technique which communicates instead of stating his findings. The just comparison with *The Scarlet Letter* is not *The Pilgrim's Progress* but *Anna Karenina*, which in theme and technique it seems to me astonishingly to resemble. This brings up again the objection cited above that "Remaining always aloof from the world around him, he was able to record what he felt with a remarkable balance and detachment, but lacked the compulsive drive of the writer who is himself the victim of conflict and must find a way of salvation." There is disguised here a romantic assumption about the Artist. We surely recognize, equally in the Shakespeare of the great tragedies and *Measure for Measure*, in Henry James in his novels and *nouvelles*, and in the Tolstoy of *Anna* (as opposed to the Tolstoy of *Resurrection*) that "remarkable balance and detachment" which is indispensable to the greatest achievement of literary art. Like these artists Hawthorne in his best work is offering in dramatic [184] form an analysis of a complex situation in which he sides with no one party but is imaginatively present in each, having created each to represent a facet of the total experience he is concerned to communicate. The analysis and the synthesis help us to find our own "way of salvation" (not a form of words I should have chosen). Tolstoy *was* in many respects Levin, as we know, but *Anna Karenina* the novel is not presented through Levin's eyes, and could not have been written by Levin. To analyze the way in which Hawthorne actually works as a writer is the only safe way to come at the nature of his creation, to make sure we are taking what he has written and neither overlooking it nor fathering on the author some misreading of our own or of inert traditional acceptance. Until there is an established reading of the texts it is impossible to evaluate an author at all, and it is this, the very first business of the critic, that seems never to have been done for Hawthorne.

. . . . . [185]

. . . . .

In his introduction to a volume of tales brought out in 1851 but mostly written much earlier Hawthorne, then in his prime as an artist, with *The Scarlet Letter* a year behind him, confessed that he was "disposed to quarrel with the earlier sketches," most of all "because they come so nearly up to the standard of the best that I can achieve now." As one of the earlier sketches in his collection was *My Kinsman Major Molineux* (1831), he might justly have felt that he was never to achieve anything better.[198]

Ideally it should be preceded by a reading of the three studies collected under the title *Old News*, which give the historical background and are clearly the fruit of work preparatory for *Major Molineux*. This remarkable tale might have been less commonly overlooked or misunderstood if it had had a sub-title, such as Hawthorne often provided by way of a hint. It could do with some such explanatory sub-title as "America Comes of Age." But though if a naturalistic story is looked for the reader would be left merely puzzled, the tale lends itself readily to comprehension as a poetic parable in dramatic form, and the opening paragraph as usual clearly explains the situation and furnishes the required clue. We are in the age which was preparing the colonies for the War of Independence and we are made to take part in a dramatic precipitation of, or prophetic forecast of, the rejection of England that was to occur in fact much later.

The actual tale begins by describing a country-bred youth coming to town, starting with the significant sentence: "It was near nine o'clock of a moonlight evening, when a boat crossed the ferry with a single passenger." The sturdy pious youth Robin, the son of the typical farmer-clergyman, represents the young America; he has *left his home* in the village in the woods and crossing by the *ferry, alone, at nightfall*, reaches the little metropolis of a New England port—that is, the contemporary scene where the historic future will be decided. He arrives poor but hopeful, confidently anticipating help in making his fortune from "my kinsman Major Molineux," the reiteration of the phrase being an important contribution to the total effect. The kinsman is Hawthorne's and ours (if we are Americans) as well as Robin's, and his name suggests both his military and aristocratic status. Robin explains much later in the tale that his father and the Major are brother's sons—that is, one brother had stayed in England and the other left to colonize New England. Their children, the next generation, represented by [199] Robin's father and the Major, had kept on friendly terms and the rich Major, representative in New England of the British civil and military rule and keeping "great pomp," was in a position to patronize his poor country cousin. We do not get this straightforward account in the tale, of course, we have to unravel it for ourselves, for the presentation of the theme is entirely dramatic and we have to identify our consciousness with the protagonist Robin. The essential information is revealed only when we have ourselves experienced for some time the same bewilderment as poor Robin, who cannot understand why his request to be directed to the house of his kinsman is met by the various types of citizen with suspicion, with contempt, with anger, with disgust, with sneers, or with laughter. In fact, Robin has arrived at a critical moment in his kinsman's history. The colonists—with considerable skill and economy Hawthorne represents all ranks and classes of the states in this dream-town—have secretly planned to throw off British rule, or at any rate to rid themselves of Major Molineux, a symbolic action, which, performed in the street outside the church at midnight and before the innocent eyes of the mystified youth, takes the form of something between a pageant and a ritual drama, disguised in the emotional logic of a dream. As a dream it has a far greater emotional pull than actuality could have. Hawthorne never anywhere surpassed this tale (written when he was not more than twenty-seven) in dramatic power, in control of tone, pace, and tension, and in something more wonderful, the creation of a suspension between the fullest consciousness of meaning and the emotional incoherence of dreaming. How this is achieved and for what purpose can be seen only by a careful examination of the last half of the tale, but I will quote as sparingly as possible.

Until this point, precisely the middle of the work, no departure from the everyday normal has been necessary, though we [200] have been wrought to a state of exasperation which is ready for working on. And Hawthorne now introduces another note:

He now roamed desperately, and at random, through the town, almost ready to believe that a spell was on him, like that by which a wizard of his country had once kept three pursuers wandering, a whole winter night, within twenty paces of the cottage which they sought. The streets lay before him, strange and desolate, and the lights were extinguished in almost every house. Twice, however, little parties of men, among whom Robin distinguished individuals in outlandish attire, came hurrying along; but though on both occasions they paused to address him, such intercourse did not at all enlighten his perplexity. They did but utter a few words in some language of which Robin knew nothing, and perceiving his inability to answer, bestowed a curse upon him in plain English, and hastened away. Finally, the lad determined to knock at the door of every mansion, trusting that perseverance would overcome the fatality that had hitherto thwarted him. Firm in this resolve, he was passing beneath the walls of a church, which formed the corner of two streets, when, as he turned into the shade of its steeple, he encountered a bulky stranger, muffled in a cloak. The man was proceeding with the speed of earnest business, but Robin planted himself full before him, holding the oak cudgel with both hands across his body, as a bar to further passage.

"Halt, honest man, and answer me a question," said he, very resolutely. "Tell me, this instant, whereabouts is the dwelling of my kinsman, Major Molineux!"

. . . The stranger, instead of attempting to force his passage, stepped back into the moonlight, unmuffled his face, and stared full into that of Robin.

"Watch here an hour, and Major Molineux will pass by," said he.

Robin gazed with dismay and astonishment on the unprecedented physiognomy of the speaker. The forehead with its double prominence, the broad hooked nose, the shaggy eyebrow, and fiery eyes, were those which he had [201] noticed at the inn, but the man's complexion had undergone a singular, or, more properly, a two-fold change. One side of the face blazed an intense red, while the other was black as midnight, the division line being in the broad bridge of the nose; and a mouth which seemed to extend from ear to ear was black or red, in contrast to the color of the cheek. The effect was as if two individual devils, a fiend of fire and a fiend of darkness, had united themselves to form this infernal visage. The stranger grinned in Robin's face, muffled his parti-colored features, and was out of sight in a moment.

The stranger, whose unearthly appearance we were prepared for by the "individuals in outlandish attire" speaking in a code—for as we realize later they were obviously conspirators demanding from Robin a password he could not furnish, but they help to increase the nightmare atmosphere—is shown by his face to be something more than a man in disguise. The tension is being screwed up to the pitch needed for the approaching climax of the drama: this is not a man like the others but a Janus-like fiend of fire and darkness, that is, we presently learn, "war personified" in its dual aspects of Death and Destruction. But it is not just a personification, it is a symbol with emotional repercussions which passes through a series of suggestive forms. The account of its features at first: "The forehead with its double prominence, the broad hooked nose" etc. suggests Punch and so also the grotesque associations of puppet-show farce. The division of the face into black and red implies the conventional get-up of the jester, and indeed he "grinned in Robin's face" before he "muffled his parti-colored features." At this point Robin, carrying the reader with him, having "consumed a few moments in philosophical speculation upon the species of man who had just left him," is able to "settle this point shrewdly, rationally and satisfactorily." He and we are of course deceived in our complacency. He falls into a drowse by sending his [202] thoughts "to imagine how that evening of ambiguity and weariness had been spent in his father's household." This actually completes his bewilderment—"Am I here or there?" he cries, "But still his mind kept vibrating between fancy and reality."

Now, so prepared, we hear the murmur that becomes a confused medley of voices and shouts as it approaches, turning into "frequent bursts from many instruments of discord, and a wild and confused laughter filled up the intervals." "The antipodes of music" heralds "a mighty stream of people" led by a single horseman whom Robin recognizes as the eerie stranger in a fresh avatar. With the "rough music" that in Old England was traditionally used to drive undesirable characters out of the community, by the red glare of torches and with "War personified" as their leader, the citizens of America, with Indians in their train and cheered on by their women, are symbolically if proleptically casting out the English ruler. The nightmare impression reaches its climax: "In his train were wild figures in the Indian dress, and many fantastic shapes without a model, giving the whole march a visionary air, as if a dream had broken forth from some feverish brain, and were sweeping visibly through the midnight streets. . . . 'The double-faced fellow has his eye upon me' muttered Robin, with an indefinite but uncomfortable idea that he was himself to bear a part in the pageantry."

It seems indeed that the pageant has been brought to this place for Robin's benefit.

A moment more, and the leader thundered a command to halt: the trumpets vomited a horrid breath, and then held their peace; the shouts and laughter of the people died away, and there remained only a universal hum, allied to silence. Right before Robin's eyes was an uncovered cart. There the torches blazed the brightest, there the moon shone out like day, and there, in tar-and-feathery dignity, sat his kinsman Major Molineux! [203]

He was an elderly man, of large and majestic person, and strong, square features, betokening a steady soul; but steady as it was, his enemies had found means to shake it. His face was pale as death, and far more ghastly; the broad forehead was contracted in his agony, so that his eyebrows formed one grizzled line; his eyes were red and wild, and the foam hung white upon his quivering lip. His whole frame was agitated by a quick and continual tremor, which his pride strove to quell, even in those circumstances of overwhelming humiliation. But perhaps the bitterest pang of all was when his eyes met those of Robin; for he evidently knew him on the instant, as the youth stood witnessing the foul disgrace of a head grown gray in honor. They stared at each other in silence, and Robin's knees shook, and his hair bristled, with a mixture of pity and terror.

The pageant is thus seen to represent a tragedy and is felt by us as such; it arouses in Robin the appropriate blend of emotions—the classical "pity and terror." But Hawthorne has by some inspiration—for how could he have known except intuitively of the origins of tragedy in ritual drama?—gone back to the type of action that fathered Tragedy. Just as the "War personified" suggests an idol or a human representative of the god, so does the other terrible figure "in tar-and-feathery dignity" in the cart. We seem to be spectators at that most primitive of all dramatic representations, the conquest of the old king by the new.

If the story had ended here, on this note, it would have been remarkable enough, but Hawthorne has an almost incredible consummation to follow. I mean incredible in being so subtly achieved with such mastery of tone. From being a spectator at a tragedy, Robin has to fulfill his premonitions of having "to bear a part in the pageantry" himself. He is drawn into the emotional vortex and comes to share the reactions of the participants. He has felt intimately the dreadful degradation of [204] his English kinsman, but now he is seized with the excitement of the victors, his fellow-countrymen, and sees their triumph as his own—"a perception of tremendous ridicule in the whole scene affected him with a sort of mental inebriety." Drunk with success the whole town roars in a frenzy of laughter, and Robin's shout joins theirs and is the loudest. Then in a sudden calm that follows this orgy "the procession resumed its march. On they went, like fiends that throng in mockery around some dead potentate, mighty no more, but majestic still in his agony." We are left in the silent street, brought back into the world of problems in which the tale opened. Robin still has to settle with reality and decide his future, the future of his generation. He asks to be shown the way back to the ferry: "I begin to grow weary of a town life" he says to the townsman who has stayed behind to note his reactions. But his new friend replies: "Some few days hence, if you wish it, I will speed you on your journey. Or, if you prefer to remain with us, perhaps, as you are a shrewd youth, you may rise in the world without the help of your kinsman, Major Molineux."

Hawthorne has been blamed for failing to provide a "solution" and for not being optimistic as a good American should be, but it seems to me that here, as in *The Maypole*, he ends in reasonable, sober hopefulness for the future of life. Provided we recognize the facts and fully comprehend the positions, we can cope with it, if not master it, he implies. Declining to be, perhaps incapable of being, a naturalistic novelist, he was true to his best perceptions of his genius when he did the work of a dramatic poet, the interpreter and radical critic of the society which had produced him and for whose benefit he expressed his insight in a unique literature.[205]

II

. . . . .

There are few things more impressive in the history of the novel than the determination of the first great American novelists to find a non-naturalistic form for their work and to reject the English novelists' tradition of social comedy and melodrama, derived from the theater. Hawthorne was truly "empirical." He can be seen consciously trying, or somehow discovering for himself, the various possible techniques for his purpose: the märchen (*Young Goodman Brown*), the allegory of Bunyan (*The Celestial Railroad*), of Spenser and Milton, the romance, the morality play, the legend (*The Gray Champion* follows the widespread Holgar the Dane pattern), the myth, the masque, drama of various kinds in the light of Shakespeare, the panorama (*Main Street*), the pageant, the fable, the parable. As became a pioneer, Hawthorne instinctively kept close to the sources of literature. His stage is the platform stage of early drama, his settings of the traditional sort such as are provided for by a tree, an archway, a street, a public square, a forest clearing, the outside of a church, a fountain or well or pool. His stage noticeably differs from his equally dramatic successor's—in comparison, James's is seen to be the modern three-sided box. James took Hawthorne's drama indoors, or if not always into the drawing-room then onto the lawn or terrace of the country-house. Though both are equally concerned with the problems of a social life, they work at different levels. Over against Hawthorne's symbol of Young Goodman Brown James has, among many such, Pandora Day, a name so happily symbolic as to need no commentary. His American Artist is Roderick Hudson, his Old Moodie is Christopher Newman, he turns Westervelt (as Mr. Bewley has shown in *Scrutiny*) into Selah Tarrant. Instead of the problem [456] of the Snow-Image we have to decide what is the Lesson of the

Master. In sum, James's symbols belong to a later stage of civilization, but greater sophistication is not necessarily a proof of superiority in literature. It would have been impossible for James to create Hawthorne's rosebush and fruit and scaffold symbols, or to seize on Hawthorne's Maypole as the appropriate symbol for describing the conflict between the cultures of the old world and the new. James's drama has become secular, whereas Hawthorne's concern for his culture is positively religious and never gets out of touch with the sources of a religious drama. His folklore element is always notably more serious than Scott's, though he has nothing so picturesque as *Wandering Willie's Tale* and many of his attempts to write American folk-story are failures (like *Mr. Higginbotham's Catastrophe*) from poverty of the raw material. The apparent oddities of his writings are not due to incompetence but are inherent in their nature; he is fragmentary as are Shakespeare's *Winter's Tale* and the old Ballads.

This is the case it seems to me to urge against the argument that genius must be bulky and that Hawthorne did not write enough to be a major novelist. Hawthorne's claim does rest on a small body of work, but even ignoring his importance as a trail-blazer, an infector and literary ancestor, that work is sufficient. It is slight only in being tense, sensitive, elegant as a mathematical proof, sinewy, concentrated as a poem and incorruptibly relevant. Economy in art is not only a means but a test, a condition of significance. *The Europeans* has been dismissed as "slight," "a water-color" and insignificant because it is brief, but it is none the less demonstrably a major work of art and profoundly significant; [4] whereas the bulkiness of a Dreiser or a Thomas Wolfe is positively against him. As in *The Europeans* there is always in Hawthorne's best writings the sense of a deeply significant public drama being enacted [457] behind the deceptively simple apparent story. Looking back on his work, one's eye is inevitably caught and held by *The Scarlet Letter* with its structural symbols of the Scaffold and the Labyrinth, the Rose and the Black Flower, and one recalls Mr. C. N. Deedes's conclusion in his essay on that most ancient structure "The Labyrinth":

The Labyrinth was the centre of all the strongest emotions of the people—joy, fear and grief were there given the most intense forms of expression. These emotions were directed into certain channels, producing ritual and the earliest forms of art. The Labyrinth, as tomb and temple, fostered the development of all art and literature, activities which in those days possessed a religious and life-giving significance. [458]

⁴ *The Europeans* by F. R. Leavis, *Scrutiny*, Summer 1948.

APPENDICES

Nathaniel Hawthorne:
A Biographical Sketch

William Hathorne,[1] the earliest American ancestor of Nathaniel Hawthorne, migrated to Massachusetts in 1630, became a speaker in the House of Delegates and a major in the Salem militia. His figure haunted young Nathaniel Hawthorne who wrote of him in "The Custom House" (a prefatory section to *The Scarlet Letter*): "He was a soldier, legislator, judge; he was a ruler in the church; he had all the Puritanic traits, both good and evil. He was likewise a bitter persecutor, as witness the Quakers, who have remembered him in their histories, and relate an incident of his hard severity towards a woman of their sect, which will last longer, it is to be feared, than any record of his better deeds, although these were many." The son of William was John Hathorne, one of the three judges in the Salem witchcraft trials of 1692. The Hathorne prominence and fierceness faded in succeeding generations.

Nathaniel Hawthorne was born July 4, 1804, in Salem. His father, a sea captain, died of yellow fever in Dutch Guiana when Hawthorne was four. Thereafter, his mother, his two sisters, and Nathaniel lived together with four aunts and uncles. A lonely child, Hawthorne read much at night and went north in the summer to his uncle's house in Maine. In 1821 he entered Bowdoin College, where he enjoyed an undistinguished career, receiving his degree (eighteenth in a class of thirty-eight) in 1825. His lifelong friendships with Longfellow and Franklin Pierce were begun at Bowdoin.

After graduation from college Hawthorne returned to Salem determined to be a writer, and began his apprenticeship in the seclusion of his mother's house. In 1828 he published anonymously *Fanshawe, A Tale*, but was so dissatisfied with it that he attempted to reclaim all the copies. *Twice-Told Tales*, a collection of the stories that he had been writing for nine years, appeared in 1837. From 1836 to 1837 he tried editing and literary hackwork unsuccessfully, and even spent a brief time as a measurer in the Boston Custom House in 1839 to 1840. Endeavoring to achieve financial security, which he found impossible to get by his pen, he joined

[1] Hawthorne himself added the "w" to the spelling of the family name.

the Brook Farm experiment (1841), but soon became disillusioned with the farmer-philosophers. In 1842 he married Sophia Peabody, one of the "enlightened" Peabody sisters, settled at the Old Manse in Concord and was brought into close association with Emerson and Thoreau.

Poverty dogged him all his life, but a political appointment brought him the surveyorship in the Salem Custom House in 1846. When he lost his position there in 1849, he determined to devote his life to literature. A period of great literary fertility followed: *The Scarlet Letter*, in 1850; *The House of the Seven Gables* and *The Snow Image*, in 1851; *The Blithedale Romance* and a campaign biography of Franklin Pierce, in 1852. He began to be known as a man of letters but moved from Salem to Lenox where he formed his significant literary friendship with Melville. In 1853 he was appointed consul at Liverpool by President Pierce as a reward for his campaign assistance.

Hawthorne was in Liverpool for five years accumulating material for his notebooks and trying to achieve some financial independence. For two years after the Liverpool consulship, the Hawthornes (now with three children—Una, Julian, and Rose) lived in Italy. Here Hawthorne began *The Marble Faun*, which he finished in England. In 1860 Hawthorne returned to Concord and settled at the Wayside. For four years he tried unsuccessfully to complete another romance, working against the insuperable odds of failing health and failing creative energy. He died May 19, 1864, in Plymouth, New Hampshire, while on a trip for his health with Franklin Pierce. He was buried in Concord.

From *The American Notebooks of Nathaniel Hawthorne**

A life generally of a grave hue, may be said to be *embroidered* with occasional sports and fantasies.[165]

[165] Compare Bacon's essay, "Of Adversity": "We see in needleworks and embroideries, it is more pleasing to have a lively work upon a sad and solemn ground, than to have a dark and melancholy work upon a lightsome ground: judge therefore of the pleasure of the heart by the pleasure of the eye." In the *Italian Note-Books* (p. 214), Hawthorne adapts a phrase ("come home to everybody's business and bosom") from the Dedication of Bacon's *Essays*.

* Reprinted by permission of the publishers from Randall Stewart, editor, *The American Notebooks of Nathaniel Hawthorne*, Cambridge, Mass.: Harvard University Press, Copyright, 1932, 1960, by The President and Fellows of Harvard College. These entries were made between 1842 and 1845.

A Father Confessor—his reflections on character, and the contrast of the inward man with the outward, as he looks round on his congregation— all whose secret sins are known to him.[166]

A person with an ice-cold hand—his right hand; which people ever afterwards remember, when once they have grasped it [167]

A stove possessed by a Devil [168]

A physician for the cure of moral diseases.

Fancy pictures of familiar places, which one has never been in—as the greenroom of a theatre &c.

The famous characters of history—to imagine their spirits now extant on earth, in the guise of various public or private personages.

The case quoted in Combe's Physiology, from Pinel, of a young man of great talents and profound knowledge of chemistry, who had in view some new discovery of importance. In order to put his mind into the highest possible activity, he shut himself up, for several successive days, and used various methods of excitement; he had a singing girl with him; he drank spirits; smelled penetrating odors, sprinkled cologne-water round the room &c. &c. Eight days thus passed, when he was seized with a fit of frenzy, which terminated in mania.[169]

Flesh and Blood—a firm of butchers.

Miss Polly Syllable—a schoolmistress

Mankind are earthen jugs with spirit in them

Tender Love, Tough Love, which is better.

[166] Hawthorne's interest in the confessional is best evidenced in *The Marble Faun*, chap. xxxix, where Hilda tells her secret to a Father Confessor. According to Lowell, it had been part of Hawthorne's plan in *The Scarlet Letter* to make Dimmesdale confess to a Catholic priest. See Lowell's letter to Miss Norton, June 12, 1860, in *Letters of James Russell Lowell*, ed. Charles Eliot Norton (New York, 1894), I, 302. And Lowell was sorry that Hawthorne did not carry out the plan; he thought it would have been "psychologically admirable." It is clear that Hawthorne's interest in the subject steadily increased, and, gaining sufficient strength to overcome an inherited reluctance, found ultimate expression in *The Marble Faun*.

[167] Compare *The Scarlet Letter* (p. 228): ". . . Arthur Dimmesdale put forth his hand, chill as death. . . ." Other characters with cold hands in Hawthorne's fiction are Gervayse Hastings and the Virtuoso (*Mosses*, pp. 329, 559).

[168] In "Fire Worship," which appeared in the *Democratic Review*, XIII (December, 1843), 627–630, Hawthorne deprecates the substitution of the stove for the fireplace and describes the action of a stove as if it were diabolically possessed (*Mosses*, pp. 165, 166).

After this entry, one and one-half lines, constituting a separate paragraph, are blotted out.

[169] See Andrew Combe, *The Principles of Physiology* . . . (New York, 1836), pp. 233, 234. For the contribution of this passage to the development of "The Birthmark," see Introduction, p. *xxv*.

A spendthrift—in one sense he has his money's worth, by the purchase of large lots of repentance and other dolorous commodities.

Men's accidents are God's purposes. S.A.H.[170]

To sit at the gate of Heaven, and watch persons, as they apply for admittance, some gaining it, others being thrust away.

To point out the moral slavery of one who deems himself a freeman

A stray leaf from the book of Fate, picked up in the street.

The streak of sunshine journeying through the prisoner's cell; it may be considered as something sent from heaven to keep the soul alive and glad within him. And there is something equivalent to this sunbeam in the darkest circumstances; as flowers, which figuratively grew in Paradise, in the dusky room of a poor maiden in a great city; the child, with its sunny smile, is a cherub. God does not let us live [97] anywhere or anyhow on earth, without placing something of Heaven close at hand, by rightly using and considering which, the earthly darkness or trouble will vanish, and all be Heaven.

A moral philosopher to buy a slave, or otherwise get possession of a human being, and to use him for the sake of experiment, by trying the operation of a certain vice on him.[172]

When the reformation of the world is complete, a fire shall be made of the gallows; and the Hangman shall come and sit down by it, in solitude and despair. To him shall come the Last Thief, the Last Prostitute, the Last Drunkard, and other representatives of past crime and vice; and they shall hold a dismal merrymaking, quaffing the contents of the Drunkard's last Brandy Bottle.[173]

[170] This apothegm was inscribed on the glass of one of the windows of Hawthorne's study in the Old Manse with the signature, "Sophia A. Hawthorne 1843." In "Chiefly about War Matters" (1862), Hawthorne used this aphorism, adding an ironic footnote (Sketches, p. 332): "The author seems to imagine that he has compressed a great deal of meaning into these little, hard, dry pellets of aphoristic wisdom. We disagree with him. The counsels of wise and good men are often coincident with the purposes of Providence; and the present war promises to illustrate our remark."

[171] Mrs. Hawthorne cut out one-half of pp. [61, 62]. The excised portion of p. [61] contained the entries "Flesh and Blood . . ." through "A Spendthrift. . . ." The excised portion of p. [62] contained the paragraph beginning "The streak of sunshine. . . ." Mrs. Hawthorne copied these passages on the flyleaf at the back of the journal with the explanatory note: "Copy from a leaf cut out for the Chicago fair, April, 1865."

[172] Compare the case of Ethan Brand, who "wasted, absorbed, and perhaps annihilated" the soul of a young girl in the process of a "psychological experiment" (Snow Image, p. 489).

[173] In "Earth's Holocaust" (1844), the hangman, the last thief, the last murderer, and the last toper gather around the fire into which the gallows and many other objects have been cast by the reformers, and attempt to relieve their despondency by drinking out of the brandy bottle which the toper has rescued from the general destruction. See Mosses, p. 454.

The human Heart to be allegorized as a cavern; at the entrance there is sunshine, and flowers growing about it. You step within, but a short distance, and begin to find yourself surrounded with a terrible gloom, and monsters of divers kinds; it seems like Hell itself. You are bewildered, and wander long without hope. At last a light strikes upon you. You peep towards it, and find yourself in a region that seems, in some sort, to reproduce the flowers and sunny beauty of the entrance, but all perfect. These are the depths of the heart, or of human nature, bright and peaceful; the gloom and terror may lie deep; but deeper still is the eternal beauty.[174]

A man, in his progress through life, picks up various matters, time, care, habit, riches &c. until at last he staggers along under a heavy burthen.

To have a life-long desire for a certain object, which shall appear to be the one thing essential to happiness. At last that object is attained, but proves to be merely incidental to a more important affair; and that affair is the greatest evil fortune that can occur. For instance, all through the winter I had wished to sit in the dusk of evening, by the flickering firelight, with my wife, instead of beside a dismal stove. At last, this has come to pass; but it was owing to her illness, and our having no chamber with a stove, fit to receive her.

Generosity is the flower of Justice. S.A.H.

Madame Calderon de la B (in Life in Mexico) speaks of persons who have been inoculated with the venom of rattlesnakes, by pricking them in various places with the tooth. These persons are thus secured forever after against the bite of any venomous reptile. They have the power of calling snakes, and feel great pleasure in playing with and handling them. Their own bite becomes poisonous to people not inoculated in the same manner. Thus a part of the serpent's nature appears to be transfused into them.[175]

An Auction (perhaps in Vanity Fair) of offices, honors, and all sorts of things considered desirable by mankind; together with things eternally valuable, which shall be considered by most people as worthless lumber.[176]

---

[174] The figure comparing the human heart to a cavern occurs several times in stories and sketches which were published within a comparatively short period after this entry: in "The Christmas Banquet" (1844), ". . . the gloomy mysteries of the human heart, through which I have wandered like one astray in a dark cavern . . ."; in "Rappaccini's Daughter" (1844), ". . . he was startled at the horrible suspicions that rose, monster-like, out of the caverns of his heart . . ."; in "The Old Manse" (1846), "We have been standing on the greensward, but just within the cavern's mouth. . . ." See *Mosses*, pp. 322, 134, 44.

[175] See Mme C[alderon] de la B[arca], *Life in Mexico* . . . (Boston, 1843), II, 414. This passage suggests an analogy to "Rappaccini's Daughter" (1844), in which Beatrice, imbued with the poison of flowers, becomes poisonous to others.

[176] This suggestion was developed in "The Celestial Railroad," which was published in the *Democratic Review*, XII (May, 1843), 515-523. The passage

APPENDICES

328

An examination of wits and poets at a police-court; and they to be sentenced by [98] the Judge to various penalties, or fines, the house of correction, whipping &c. according to the worst offenses of which they were guilty.

A volume bound in cowhide. It should treat of breeding cattle, or some other coarse subject.

A young girl inherits a family grave-yard—that being all that remains of rich hereditary possessions.[177]

An interview between General Charles Lee, of the Revolution, and his sister, the Foundress and Mother of the sect of Shakers.[178]

For a child's sketch, perhaps, the life of a city Dove; or perhaps of a flock of doves, flying about the streets, and sometimes alighting on church steeples; on the eaves of lofty houses &c.

The greater picturesqueness and reality of back-yards, and everything appertaining to the rear of a house; as compared with the front, which is fitted up for the public eye. There is much to be learnt, always, by getting a glimpse at rears. When the direction of a road has been altered, so as to pass the rear of farm-houses, instead of the front, a very noticeable aspect is presented.[179]

A sketch—the devouring of the old country residences by the overgrown monster of a city. For instance, Mr. Beekman's ancestral residence was originally several miles from the city of New-York; but the pavements kept creeping nearer and nearer; till now the house is removed, and a street runs directly through what was once its hall.[180]

The print in blood of a naked foot to be traced through the street of a town.[181]

which is an expansion of this note is found in *Mosses*, pp. 227, 228. Hawthorne derived the idea of the note from Bunyan's description of Vanity Fair. See *The Pilgrim's Progress* (Everyman's Library), p. 104.

[177] The dwindling of hereditary possessions is a favorite idea with Hawthorne. See Introduction, pp. lxxvi–lxxix.

[178] Hawthorne was in error in supposing that Charles Lee (1731–82), who was a General in the American Revolutionary army, and Ann Lee (1736–84), who founded the sect of the Shakers, were brother and sister.

[179] This passage appears in a revised and expanded form in *Blithedale*, pp. 489, 490.

[180] In a letter to E. A. Duyckinck, dated Concord, November 26, 1843, Hawthorne wrote: "I am very sorry that your monster of a city has swallowed up Mr. Beekman's residence. He told me that there was peril of it, and it has often occurred to me since. Methinks it is a fit subject for a tale." (This letter is in the New York Public Library.) The letter, incidentally, supplies an approximate date for the entry.

[181] For a discussion of the relation of this entry to the development of *The Ancestral Footstep*, see A. Schönbach, "Beiträge zur charakteristik Nathaniel Hawthorne's," *Englische Studien*, VII (1884), 247 ff.

An essay on various kinds of death, together with the just-before and just-after.

The majesty of death to be exemplified in a beggar, who, after being seen, humble and cringing, in the streets of a city, for many years, at length, by some means or other, gets admittance into a rich man's mansion, and there dies—assuming state, and striking awe into the breasts of those who had looked down upon him.[182]

To write a dream, which shall resemble the real course of a dream, with all its inconsistency, its strange transformations, which are all taken as a matter of course, its eccentricities and aimlessness—with nevertheless a leading idea running through the whole. Up to this old age of the world, no such thing ever has been written.[183]

To allegorize life with a masquerade, and represent mankind generally as masquers. Here and there, a natural face may appear.

Sketch of a personage with the malignity of a witch, and doing the mischief attributed to one—but by natural means; breaking off love-affairs, teaching children vices, ruining men of wealth, &c.[99]

With an emblematical divining-rod to seek for emblematic gold—that is for Truth—for what of Heaven is left on earth.

A task for a subjugated fiend—to gather up all the fallen autumnal leaves of a forest, apart them, and affix each one to the twig where it originally grew.

A vision of Grub-street, forming an allegory of the literary world.

The emerging from their lurking-places of evil-characters, on some occasion suited to their action—they having been quite unknown to the world hitherto. For instance, the French Revolution brought out such wretches.

The advantages of a longer life than is allotted to mortals—the many things that might then be accomplished;—to which one life-time is inadequate, and for which the time spent is therefore lost; a successor being unable to take up the task when we drop it.[184]

George First had promised the Duchess of Kendall, his mistress, that, if possible, he would pay her a visit, after death. Accordingly, a large raven flew into the window of her villa at Isleworth. She believed it to

---

[182] The fundamental situation of a beggar in a rich man's house may have been suggested by *The Taming of the Shrew*. Hawthorne quotes one of Christopher Sly's speeches on page 78. See note 133.

[183] "The Celestial Railroad," which is told as a dream and ends with the awakening of the narrator, may have been Hawthorne's attempt to carry out the plan suggested here. Hawthorne had never read, perhaps, Chaucer's *Book of the Duchess*.

[184] Compare *Septimius Felton*, p. 238.

be his soul, and treated it ever after with all respect and tenderness, till either she or the bird died.—Walpole's Reminiscences [185]

The history of an Alms-House in a country village, from the eve of its foundation downward—a record of the remarkable occupants of it; and extracts from interesting portions of its annals. The rich of one generation might, in the next, seek for a home there, either in their own persons or those of their representatives. Perhaps the son and heir of the founder might have no better refuge. There should be occasional sunshine let into the story; for instance, the good fortune of some nameless infant, educated there, and discovered finally to be the child of wealthy parents.

Ladislaus, King of Naples, beseiging [sic] the city of Florence, agreed to show mercy, provided the inhabitants would deliver to him a certain virgin of famous beauty, the daughter of a physician of the city. When she was sent to the king—every one contributing something to adorn her in the richest manner—her father gave her a perfumed handkerchief, at that time a universal decoration, richly wrought. This handkerchief was poisoned with his utmost art; and in their first embrace, the poison being received into their pores, opened by heat,—it killed them both—"converting their warm sweat into a cold sweat, they presently died in one another's arms."—Cotton's Montaigne.[186]

Pearl—the English of Margaret—a pretty name for a girl in a story.[187]

The conversation of the steeples of a city, when the bells are ringing on Sunday—Calvinist, Episcopalian, Unitarian &c.[100]

Of a bitter satirist—of Swift, for instance—it might be said, that the person or thing, on which his satire fell, shrivelled up, as if the Devil had spit on it.[188]

---

[185] The passage which Hawthorne summarizes occurs in the "Reminiscences," chap. ii. See *Works of Horatio Walpole, Earl of Orford* (London, 1798), IV, 283.

The raven is included in "A Virtuoso's Collection" (*Mosses*, p. 541). It is not a part of the story as first printed in the *Boston Miscellany of Literature*, I (May, 1842), 193–200, inasmuch as the entry in the notebook was made after June 1, 1842; but the item was added before "A Virtuoso's Collection" was reprinted in *Mosses* in 1846. Other details which were entered in the notebook and added to the story after its first publication are the pen of Faust, Cellini's salamander, and Alexander's copy of the *Iliad* (*Mosses*, pp. 549, 550, 553).

[186] The incident is taken from the essay, "The Story of Spurina." See *Essays of Michael Seigneur de Montaigne new rendred into English by Charles Cotton Esq.* (London, 1686), II, 633, 634.

[187] The name was given about seven years later to the child of Hester Prynne in *The Scarlet Letter.*

[188] Hawthorne's views concerning the destructive power of satire are reflected further in a letter to Longfellow, written from Salem on June 5, 1849, in which he comments on the efforts of his political enemies to remove him from his office in the Salem Custom House:

"If they succeed in getting me out of office, I will surely immolate one or two

Allston's picture of Belshazzar's Feast—with reference to the advantages, or otherwise, of having life assured to us, till we could finish important tasks on which we were engaged.[189]

Visits to Castles in the Air—Chateaus en Espagne &c—with remarks on that sort of architecture.[190]

To consider a piece of gold as a sort of talisman—or as containing within itself all the forms of enjoyment that it can purchase—so that they might appear, by some fantastical chemical process, as visions.

To personify If—But—And—Though—&c.

The fount of Tears—a traveller to discover it, and other similar localities.

Benvenuto Cellini saw a salamander in the household fire. It was shown him by his father, in his childhood.[191]

---

of them. Not that poor monster of a Conolly, whom I desire only to bury in oblivion, far out of my remembrance. Nor any of the common political brawlers, who work on their own level, and can conceive of no higher ground than what they occupy. But if there be among them (as there must be, if they succeed) some men who claim a higher position, and ought to know better, I may perhaps select a victim, and let fall one little drop of venom on his heart, that shall make him writhe before the grin of the multitude for a considerable time to come. . . . If they will pay no reverence to the imaginative power when it causes herbs of grace and sweet-scented flowers to spring up along their pathway, then they should be taught what it can do in the way of producing nettles, skunk-cabbage, deadly night-shade, wolf's bane, dog-wood. If they will not be grateful for its works of beauty and beneficence, then let them dread it as a pervasive and penetrating mischief, that can reach them at their fire-sides and in their bedchambers, follow them to far countries, and make their very graves refuse to hide them. I have often thought that there must be a good deal of enjoyment in writing personal satire; but, never having felt the slightest ill will towards any human being, I have hitherto been debarred from this peculiar source of pleasure. I almost hope I shall be turned out, so as to have an opportunity of trying it. I cannot help smiling in anticipation of the astonishment of some of these local magnates here, who suppose themselves quite out of the reach of any retribution on my part." [This letter is in the possession of Mr. H. W. L. Dana.]

That Hawthorne had a real gift for personal satire is evidenced by numerous passages in his journals and letters. The most important writing of this kind in his fiction is the characterization of Judge Pyncheon in *The House of the Seven Gables.*

[189] Washington Allston (1779–1843) worked on this picture at intervals from 1817 until his death, July 9, 1843, leaving it unfinished. See Jared B. Flagg, *Life and Letters of Washington Allston* (New York, 1892), *passim.*

[190] "A Select Party," which appeared in the *Democratic Review,* XV (July, 1844), 33–50, gives an account of an entertainment at a castle in the air, with a description of the guests present and the architecture of the castle. See *Mosses,* pp. 70–88.

[191] The incident is related in Cellini's autobiography, Bk. I, chap. i (*The Life of Benvenuto Cellini . . .*, written by Himself; trans. Thomas Nugent [London, 1828], I, 8, 9). See note 185.

A man seeks for something excellent, and seeks it in the wrong way, and in a wrong spirit, and finds something horrible—as for instance, he seeks for treasure, and finds a dead body—for the gold that somebody has hidden, and brings to light his accumulated sins.

An auction of second hands—then moralizing how the fashion of this world passeth away.[192]

Noted people in a town:—as the town-crier—the old fruit-man—the constable—the oyster-seller—the fish-man—the scissors-grinder—&c &c &c

The Magic Play of Sunshine, for a child's story—the sunshine circling round through a prisoner's cell, from his high and narrow window. He keeps his soul alive and cheerful by means of it, it typifying [*sic*] cheerfulness; and when he is released, he takes up the ray of sunshine and carries it away with him; and it enables him to discover treasures all over the world, in places where nobody else would think of looking for any.

A young man finds a portion of the skeleton of a Mammoth; he begins by degrees to become interested in completing it; searches round the world for the means of doing so; spends youth and manhood in the pursuit; and in old age has nothing to show for his life, but this skeleton.

For the Virtuoso's Collection—the pen with which Faust signed away his salvation, with a drop of blood dried on it.[193]

For a child's sketch—a meeting with all the personages mentioned in Mother Goose's Melodies, and other juvenile stories.[101]

Great Expectation to be entertained in the allegorical Grub-street of the appearance of the great American writer. Or a search warrant to be sent thither to catch a poet. On the former supposition, he shall be discovered under some most unlikely form; or shall be supposed to have lived and died unrecognized.[194]

An old man to promise a youth a treasure of gold;—and to keep his promise by teaching him practically a Golden Rule.

A valuable jewel to be buried in the grave of a beloved person, or thrown over with a corpse at sea, or deposited under the foundation-stone of an edifice—and to be afterward met with by the former owner, in the possession of some one.[195]

In moods of heavy despondency, one feels as if it would be delightful to sink down in some quiet spot, and lie there forever, letting the

---

[192] Compare 1 Cor. 7.31.   [193] See note 185.

[194] In "A Select Party" is introduced the Master Genius of American literature who appears "with no insignia of rank or acknowledged eminence" and is as yet "unhonored among men." See *Mosses*, pp. 79, 80.

[195] In "The Antique Ring," which was published in *Sargent's New Monthly Magazine*, I (February, 1843), 80-86, a ring is buried in a tomb and is subsequently recovered. See *Sketches*, p. 61.

soil gradually accumulate and form a little hillock over us, and the grass and perhaps flowers gather over it. At such times, death is too much of an event to be wished for;—we have not spirits to encounter it; but choose to pass out of existence in this sluggish way.[196]

A noted gambler had acquired such self-command, that, in the most desperate circumstances of his game, no change of feature ever betrayed him;—only there was a slight scar upon his forehead, which, at such moments, assumed a deep blood-red hue. Thus, in playing at Brag, for instance, his antagonist could judge from this index, when he had a bad hand. At last, discovering what it was that betrayed him, he covered the scar with a green silk shade.

A dream, the other night, that the world had become dissatisfied with the inaccurate manner in which facts are reported, and had employed me, with a salary of a thousand dollars, to relate things of public importance exactly as they happen.

A person who has all the qualities of a friend, except that he invariably fails you at the pinch.[197]

. . . . .[102]

. . . . .

Saturday, August 9th, 1845.

Weight (ascertained at Portsmouth Navy Yard) 170 pounds—greater than at any former period. Una's 25 pounds.

In the eyes of a young child, or other innocent person, the image of a cherub or an angel to be seen peeping out;—in those of a vicious person, a devil.[236]

[196] Compare *The Scarlet Letter,* p. 226.

[197] Hawthorne undoubtedly had in mind his friend J. L. O'Sullivan, the editor of the *Democratic Review,* who was delinquent in paying for his contributions to that magazine.

The phrase "to fail you at the pinch" was a favorite one with Hawthorne and it indicates a shortcoming which cannot be imputed to him in his own relations with his friends. In a letter to Bridge, dated Concord, October 18, 1852, in which he refers to his reluctance to undertake the "Life of Franklin Pierce," Hawthorne wrote: ". . . after a friendship of thirty years, it was impossible to refuse my best efforts in his behalf at the great pinch of his life." (This letter is in the possession of Miss Marian Bridge Maurice.) In 1855, when Hawthorne was in Liverpool, Bridge wished to borrow three thousand dollars. Hawthorne wrote to Ticknor, who had advised against the loan (*Letters to Ticknor,* I, 73): "Shall I prove myself to be one of those persons who have every quality desirable in friendship except that they invariably fail you at the pinch?"

[236] Hester Prynne fancied that she beheld a fiend-like face in the small black mirror of Pearl's eye (*Scarlet Letter,* p. 122): "It was as if an evil spirit possessed the child, and had just then peeped forth in mockery."

October 11th, 1845.

In Boston, a man passing along Collonnade row grinding a barrel-organ, and attended by a monkey, dressed in frock and pantaloons, and with a tremendously thick tail appearing behind. While his master played on the organ, the monkey kept pulling off his hat, bowing and scraping to the spectators roundabout—sometimes, too, making a direct application to an in[di]vidual—by all this dumb show, beseeching them to remunerate the organ-player. Whenever a coin was thrown on the ground, the monkey picked it up, clambered on his master's shoulder, and gave it into his keeping; then descended, and recommenced his pantomimic entreaties for more. His little, old, ugly, wrinkled face had an earnestness that looked just as if it came from the love of money deep within his soul; he peered round, looking for filthy lucre on all sides. With his tail and all, he might be taken for the Mammon of copper coin —a symbol of covetousness of small gains, the lowest form of the love of money. Doubtless, many a man passed by, whose moral being was not unfairly represented by this monkey.

Una was with me, holding by my forefinger, and walking decorously along the pavement. She stopped to contemplate the monkey, and after a while, shocked by his horrible ugliness, began to cry.[237]

A disquisition—or a discussion between two or more persons—on the manner in which the Wandering Jew has spent his life. One period, perhaps, in wild carnal debauchery; then trying, over and over again, to grasp domestic happiness; then a soldier; then a statesman &c—at last, realizing some truth.

The most graceful way in which a man can signify he feels he is growing old, and acquiesces in it, is by adhering to the fashion of dress which chances to be in vogue when the conviction comes upon him; —thus, in a few years, he will find himself quietly apart from the crowd of young men.

The spells of witches have the power of producing "meats and viands, that have the appearance of a sumptuous feast, which the devil furnishes." But—"divine Providence seldom permits the meat to be good, but that it has generally some bad taste or smell, mostly wants salt, and the feast is often without bread." Cumberland's Observer, Vol. 11.[238]

---

[237] This passage was used in *The House of the Seven Gables* (pp. 197, 198), in the account of a similar performance which is observed by Phoebe and Clifford.

[238] See [Richard Cumberland] *The Observer*, XXIX (London, 1785), 288, 289. Compare *Blithedale* (p. 374): ". . . her [Zenobia's] gruel was very wretched stuff, with almost invariably the smell of pine smoke upon it, like the evil taste that is said to mix itself up with a witch's best concocted dainties."

It was believed by the Catholics that children might be begotten by intercourse between demons and witches. Luther was said to be a bastard of this hellish breed.[239]

Our most intimate friend is not he to whom we show the worst, but the best, of our nature.

Nothing comes amiss to Nature—all is fish that comes to her net. If there be a living form of perfect beauty instinct with soul—why, it is all very well, and suits Nature well enough. But she would just as lief have that same beautiful, soul-illumined body, to make worm's meat of, and to manure the earth with.[240]

Instances of two ladies, who vowed never again to see the light of the sun, on account of disappointments in love. Each of them kept their vow, living thenceforth, and dying after many years, in apartments closely shut up, and lighted by candles. One appears to have lived in total darkness.[241]

The infirmities, that come with old-age, are the interest on the debt of nature, which should have been more seasonably paid. Often, the interest is a heavier payment than the principal.

By a lord of the admiralty (in a speech in Parliament, during our revolution) the number of American sailors, employed in the British navy previously to the revolution, was estimated at 18000. (Annual Register, 1778.) [242]

[239] This paragraph is taken from the following passage in Cumberland's essay (*op. cit.*, p. 289):

"Though heretics have obstinately denied the copulation of wizards with the female daemons called Succubae; and of witches with the males, or Incubi, yet the whole authority of the Catholic Church with the Bull of Pope Innocent VIII expressly affirms it for a fact. . . . It is also an orthodox opinion, that children may be begotten by this diabolical commerce, and there is little doubt but that Luther was the son of an Incubus."

This idea was used in *The Scarlet Letter* (p. 124). Little Pearl was reported among the townspeople to be a demon offspring

". . . such as, ever since old Catholic times, had occasionally been seen on earth, through the agency of their mother's sin, and to promote some foul and wicked purpose. Luther, according to the scandal of his monkish enemies, was a brat of that hellish breed; nor was Pearl the only child to whom this inauspicious origin was assigned, among the New England Puritans."

[240] Compare *Blithedale*, pp. 595, 596.

[241] In "The Wives of the Dead" (1832) Hawthorne had treated a somewhat similar theme but had given the story a happy ending: the grief of the two wives changed to joy when their husbands, who had been reported dead, returned. See *Snow Image*, pp. 598–606.

[242] See "The History of Europe," *The Annual Register . . . for the Year 1778* (London, 1779), p. 201.

Some men have no right to perform great deeds, or think high thoughts
—and when they do so, it is a kind of humbug. They had better keep
within their own propriety.

In England, in 1761, a man and his wife, formerly in good circumstances, died very poor, and were buried at the expense of the parish.
This coming to the ears of the friends of their better days,[243] they had
the corpses taken out of their graves, and buried in a more genteel manner! [244]

In the Annual Register, Vol 4, for 1761, there is a letter from Cromwell
to Fleetwood, dated August 22, 1653—which Carlyle appears not to have
given. Also one, without date, to the Speaker of the House of Commons,
narrating the taking of Basing-House.[245]

Recently, in an old house which has been taken down at the corner of
Bulfinch street and Bowdoin square, a perfect and full-grown human
skeleton was discovered,[118] concealed between the ceiling and the
floor of a room in the upper story. Another skeleton was not long since
found, in similar circumstances.

An article on cemeteries, with fantastic ideas of monuments;—for instance a sundial;—a large, wide, carved stone chair, with some such
motto as 'Rest and think';—and others, between fun and seriousness.

In a garden, a pool of perfectly transparent water, the bed of which
should be paved with marble, or perhaps with mosaic-work—images, and
various figures, which, through the clear water, would look wondrously
beautiful.

. . . . .[119]

[243] Compare Fitz-Greene Halleck, "On the Death of Joseph Rodman Drake"
(1821):

"Green be the turf above thee
Friend of my better days . . ."

Hawthorne refers to Halleck in *Mosses*, p. 426.

[244] See "The Chronicle," April 2, *The Annual Register . . . for the Year 1761*
(London, 1762), pp. 95, 96. The phrase, "friends of their better days," does not
occur in *The Annual Register*.

[245] See "Characters," *The Annual Register . . . for the Year 1761* (London,
1762), pp. 49–51.

Selected Bibliography

BIBLIOGRAPHY

Blair, Walter, "Nathaniel Hawthorne," *Eight American Authors: A Review of Research and Criticism*, ed. Floyd Stovall (New York: Modern Language Association of America, 1956).

Thurston, Jarvis, *et al.*, *Short Fiction Criticism: A Checklist of Interpretation Since 1925 of Stories and Novelettes 1800–1958* (Denver: Alan Swallow, 1960).

WORKS

The Complete Works of Nathaniel Hawthorne, Riverside Edition (12 vols.; Boston: Houghton Mifflin Company, 1883).

The Complete Writings of Nathaniel Hawthorne, Old Manse Edition (22 vols.; Boston: Houghton Mifflin Company, 1900).

Nathaniel Hawthorne: The American Notebooks, ed. Randall Stewart (New Haven: Yale University Press, 1932).

BIOGRAPHY AND GENERAL CRITICISM

Arvin, Newton, *Hawthorne* (Boston: Little, Brown and Company, 1929).

Cantwell, Robert, *Nathaniel Hawthorne: The American Years* (New York: Rinehart & Company, Inc., 1948).

Gorman, Herbert, *Hawthorne: A Study in Solitude* (New York: George H. Doran Company, 1927).

James, Henry, *Hawthorne*, English Men of Letters Series (London: The Macmillan Company, 1879).

Hawthorne, Julian, *Nathaniel Hawthorne and His Wife* (2 vols.; Boston: J. R. Osgood, 1885).

———, *Hawthorne and His Circle* (New York: Harper & Brothers, 1903).

———, *Hawthorne Reading* (Cleveland: Rowfant Club, 1902).

Hoeltje, Hubert H., *Inward Sky: The Mind and Heart of Nathaniel Hawthorne* (Durham, N.C.: Duke University Press, 1962).

Lathrop, George Parsons, *A Study of Hawthorne* (Boston: J. R. Osgood, 1876).

Lathrop, Rose Hawthorne, *Memories of Hawthorne* (Boston: Houghton Mifflin Company, 1897).

Stewart, Randall, *Nathaniel Hawthorne: A Biography* (New Haven: Yale University Press, 1948).

Van Doren, Mark, *Nathaniel Hawthorne* (New York: William Sloane, Associates, Inc., 1949).

ANALYSIS, CRITICISM, AND SPECIAL STUDIES
Complete Works

Davidson, Edward H., *Hawthorne's Last Phase* (New Haven: Yale University Press, 1949).
Fick, Leonard J., *The Light Beyond: A Study of Hawthorne's Theology* (Westminster, Md.: The Newman Press, 1955).
Fogle, Richard H., *Hawthorne's Fiction: The Light and the Dark* (Norman, Okla.: University of Oklahoma Press, 1952).
Male, Roy H., *Hawthorne's Tragic Vision* (Austin: University of Texas Press, 1957).
Schubert, Leland, *Hawthorne, the Artist: Fine-Art Devices in Fiction* (Chapel Hill, N.C.: University of North Carolina Press, 1944).
Stein, William B., *Hawthorne's Faust: A Study of the Devil Archetype* (Gainesville, Fla.: University of Florida Press, 1953).
Turner, Arlin, *Nathaniel Hawthorne: An Introduction and Interpretation* (New York: Barnes & Noble, Inc., 1961).
Von Abele, Rudolph, *The Death of the Artist: A Study of Hawthorne's Disintegration* (The Hague: Nijhoff, 1955).
Waggoner, Hyatt H., *Hawthorne: A Critical Study* (Cambridge, Mass.: Harvard University Press, 1955).

Works containing Essays or Chapters on Hawthorne

Bewley, Marius, *The Complex Fate: Hawthorne, Henry James and Some Other American Writers* (London: Chatto & Windus, 1952).
———, *The Eccentric Design: Form in the Classic American Novel* (New York: Columbia University Press, 1959).
Chase, Richard, *The American Novel and Its Tradition* (Garden City, N.Y.: Doubleday-Anchor Books, 1957).
Feidelson, Charles, Jr., *Symbolism and American Literature* (Chicago: University of Chicago Press, 1953).
Fiedler, Leslie, *Love and Death in the American Novel* (New York: Criterion Books, 1960).
Hoffman, Daniel, *Form and Fable in American Fiction* (New York: Oxford University Press, 1961).
Levin, Harry, *The Power of Blackness: Hawthorne, Poe, Melville* (New York: Alfred A. Knopf, Inc., 1958).
Lewis, R. W. B., *The American Adam: Innocence, Tragedy, and Tradition in the Nineteenth Century* (Chicago: University of Chicago Press, 1955).

Matthiessen, F. O., *American Renaissance: Art and Expression in the Age of Emerson and Whitman* (New York: Oxford University Press, 1941).

Warren, Austin, *Rage for Order* (Chicago: University of Chicago Press, 1948).

Winters, Yvor, *In Defense of Reason* (Denver: University of Denver Press, 1947).

Criticism of Individual Stories

"The Haunted Mind"

Stein, W. B., *Hawthorne's Faust: A Study of the Devil Archetype* (Gainesville, Fla.: University of Florida Press, 1953), pp. 67–68.

Waggoner, Hyatt H., *Hawthorne: A Critical Study* (Cambridge, Mass.: The Belknap Press of Harvard University Press, 1955), pp. 9–11.

"Fancy's Show Box"

Doubleday, Neal F., "The Theme of Hawthorne's 'Fancy's Show Box,'" *American Literature*, X (November, 1938), 341–43.

Fairbanks, Henry G., "Sin, Free Will, and Pessimism in Hawthorne," *Publications of the Modern Language Association*, LXXI (December, 1956), 978–79, 986.

Waggoner, Hyatt H., *Hawthorne: A Critical Study* (Cambridge, Mass.: The Belknap Press of Harvard University Press, 1955), pp. 12–16.

"The Maypole of Merry Mount"

Fogle, Richard H., *Hawthorne's Fiction: The Light and the Dark*, pp. 59–69.

Hoffman, Daniel G., *Form and Fable in American Fiction* (New York: Oxford University Press, 1961), pp. 126–48.

Orians, G. Harrison, "Hawthorne and 'The Maypole of Merry Mount,'" *Modern Language Notes*, LIII (March, 1938), 159–67.

Vickery, John B., "The Golden Bough at Merry Mount," *Nineteenth Century Fiction*, XII (December, 1957), 203–14.

"The Minister's Black Veil"

Fogle, Richard H., "An Ambiguity of Sin or Sorrow," *New England Quarterly*, XXI (September, 1948), 342–49. Reprinted, revised, in Fogle, *Hawthorne's Fiction: The Light and the Dark* (Norman, Okla.: University of Oklahoma Press, 1952), pp. 33–40.

Stein, W. B., "The Parable of the Antichrist in 'The Minister's Black Veil,'" *American Literature*, XXVII (November, 1955), 386–92.

Voight, Gilbert P., "The Meaning of 'The Minister's Black Veil,'" *College English*, XIII (March, 1952), 337–38.

Walsh, T. P., "Hawthorne: Mr. Hooper's 'Affable Weakness,'" *Modern Language Notes*, LXXIV (May, 1959), 404–406.

"My Kinsman, Major Molineux"

Lesser, Simon O., "The Image of the Father," *Partisan Review*, XXII (Summer, 1955), 372–90.

Newman, Franklin, "'My Kinsman, Major Molineux': An Interpretation," *University of Kansas City Review*, XXI (March, 1955), 203–12.

Pearce, Roy Harvey, "Hawthorne and the Sense of the Past, or, the Immortality of Major Molineux," *English Literary History*, XXI (December, 1954), 327–49.

Stein, W. B., "Teaching Hawthorne's 'My Kinsman, Major Molineux,'" *College English*, XX (November, 1958), 83–86.

"Roger Malvin's Burial"

Adams, Richard, "Hawthorne's Provincial Tales," *New England Quarterly*, XXX (March, 1957), 39–57.

Birdsall, Virginia, "Hawthorne's Oak Tree Image," *Nineteenth Century Fiction*, XV (September, 1960), 181–85.

Donohue, Agnes McNeill, "'From Whose Bourn No Traveller Returns': A Reading of 'Roger Malvin's Burial,'" *Nineteenth Century Fiction*, XVIII (June, 1963), 1–19.

Orians, G. Harrison, "The Source of Hawthorne's 'Roger Malvin's Burial,'" *American Literature*, X (November, 1938), 313–18.

Thompson, W. R., "The Biblical Sources of Hawthorne's 'Roger Malvin's Burial,'" *Publications of the Modern Language Association*, LXXVII (March, 1962), 92–96.

"Wakefield"

Fairbanks, Henry G., "Sin, Free Will and Pessimism in Hawthorne," *Publications of the Modern Language Association*, LXXXI (December, 1956), 975–89.

"The Gentle Boy"

Dauner, Louise, "The 'Case' of Tobias Pearson," *American Literature*, XXI (January, 1950), 464–72.

Orians, G. Harrison, "The Sources and Themes of Hawthorne's 'The Gentle Boy,'" *New England Quarterly*, XIV (December, 1941), 664–78.

Male, Roy R., *Hawthorne's Tragic Vision* (Austin: University of Texas Press, 1957), pp. 45–48.

"The Birthmark"

Thompson, W. R., "Aminadab in Hawthorne's 'The Birthmark,'" *Modern Language Notes*, LXX (June, 1955), 413–15.

Male, Roy R., *Hawthorne's Tragic Vision*, (Austin: University of Texas Press, 1957), pp. 80–84.

"Young Goodman Brown"

Cherry, Fannye N., "The Source of Hawthorne's 'Young Goodman Brown,'" *American Literature*, V (January, 1934), 342–49.

Connolly, Thomas, "Hawthorne's 'Young Goodman Brown': An Attack on Puritanistic Calvinism," *American Literature*, XXVIII (November, 1956), 370–75.

McKeithan, D. M., "Hawthorne's 'Young Goodman Brown': An Interpretation," *Modern Language Notes*, LXVII (February, 1952), 93–96.

Ringe, Donald A., "Hawthorne's Psychology of the Head and the Heart," *Publications of the Modern Language Association*, LXV (March, 1950), 120–32.

Schroeder, John W., "'That Inward Sphere': Notes on Hawthorne's Heart Imagery and Symbolism," *Publications of the Modern Language Association*, LXV (March, 1950), 106–19.

Questions and Problems

I "The Haunted Mind"

1. Hawthorne seems to proceed from thought to thought by a process of free association. What relationship do the immediate sensory experiences have to his ideas?
2. How appropriate are the descriptions of the allegorical figures of Sorrow, Hope, Disappointment, Fatality, Shame and Remorse?
3. Trace the idea of death as it develops throughout the sketch.

II "Fancy's Show Box"

1. What meaning has the subtitle, "A Morality"?
2. What does Hawthorne mean by "Fancy"? What role does he give Fancy in human life?
3. At the beginning of the sketch, Hawthorne asks the question, "What is Guilt?" and answers it, "A stain upon the soul." Do any additional concepts of guilt develop throughout the sketch?
4. When Hawthorne says, "Mr. Smith, whose silver hair was the bright symbol of a life unstained, except by such spots as are inseparable from human nature," what view does he have of human nature?

III "The Maypole of Merry Mount"

1. Check a dictionary of folklore and legend for the symbolism of Comus and the maypole.
2. What does Hawthorne mean in the description of the dancing

bear—"His inferior nature rose halfway, to meet his companions as they stooped"?

3. Flower imagery plays a large part in the meaning of "The Maypole of Merry Mount." Consider the following flower references and all other allusions to flowers; then determine whether or not there is a progressive extension of meaning or symbolism.
   a. The garden flowers and "blossoms of the wilderness" on the maypole.
   b. The wreath of roses, "some that had been gathered in the sunniest spots of the forest, and others, of still richer blush, which the colonists had reared from English seed."
   c. "O, people of the Golden Age, the chief of your husbandry was to raise flowers!"
   d. The May couple wore roses in their hair and roses were scattered at their feet "or had sprung up spontaneously there."
   e. "The wreath of roses, that hung from the lowest green bough of the Maypole, had been twined for them, and would be thrown over both their heads, in symbol of their flowery union."
   f. When Edith is pensive, down comes "a little shower of withering rose leaves from the Maypole."
   g. Leaves and rosebuds are showered on Endicott by the falling maypole.
   h. "And Endicott . . . lifted the wreath of roses from the ruin of the Maypole, and threw it with his own gauntleted hand, over the heads of the Lord and Lady of the May."
4. What was the Puritan maypole?
5. Does Hawthorne take sides in the conflict between the Puritans and the votaries of the maypole? Draw your evidence from the text.

IV "The Minister's Black Veil"
   1. Does a parable mean the same thing to Hawthorne as a morality (see "Fancy's Show Box")?
   2. The Reverend Mr. Hooper is a very melancholy man. Why did he smile so often? What effects did his smiles produce? What did they mean? For example:
      a. When Elizabeth refused to marry him, he smiled.
      b. He smiled in death.
   3. Much of the final impression of ambiguity in a Hawthorne tale results from the varied and conflicting explanations of events within the story; the events are reported by observers whose authority is never established by Hawthorne. Indicate the explanations of the sexton, the parishioners, the doctor, etc., for

the minister's black veil. What does Elizabeth think of it? What does Mr. Hooper himself say of it? What is the effect of the black veil on Mr. Hooper, on Elizabeth, and on the parishioners? Finally, what do you think it means?

4. Why do you suppose that Mr. Hooper cannot bear to see himself in a mirror or in a well?

5. Comment on "that saddest of all prisons; his own heart."

V "My Kinsman, Major Molineux"

1. Is Robin really a "shrewd youth"? With what does Hawthorne equate shrewdness? What does Mr. Hoffman say about shrewdness and "the Yankee *naïf*"?

2. Is the gentleman who watches the parade with Robin a kind friend or a clinical observer?

3. Laughter echoes throughout the story. Trace the evolution of this laughter. Is it wholesome, evil, or what?

4. What does Hawthorne accomplish by having all of the characters encountered throughout the story reappear at the end?

5. Are there any advantages in reading the story on a dream level?

6. What does Mr. Gross mean by "history as moral adventure"?

7. Robin says to himself after his first encounter with the old gentleman and the laughter of the barbers, "You will be wiser in time, friend Robin." Does Robin become wiser?

8. "May not a man have several voices?" What does Hawthorne imply here? Is this part of Hawthorne's own technique?

9. Does Hawthorne's use of the terms "pity and terror" to describe Robin's final experience suggest Aristotle's idea of tragedy?

10. What is the meaning of Robin's half-dream of being excluded from his own home?

VI "Roger Malvin's Burial"

1. What is the importance of the source study in the interpretation of this story?

2. What is the symbolic meaning of the forest and the clearing? What happens in each place? Are the events in each similar or different?

3. Why does Reuben fail as a husbandman? Does he fail also as a father? Does Roger succeed as a father?

4. What is the real guilt of Reuben? What does Reuben think he has done?

5. What specific Biblical echoes do you find in this tale? Do they affect the over-all meaning?

6. What does Mr. Waggoner mean by the "triadic design"? What light does his discussion throw on the end of the story?

7. Can the end of the story—Reuben praying—be in any way construed as a solution to Reuben's problems?

VII "Wakefield"
1. What does Hawthorne mean by "the Outcast of the Universe"?
2. Why does Mr. Schiller say that we have to read Kafka, James, and Joyce before we can read Hawthorne?
3. Define allegory. What does Mr. Waggoner mean by "allegory in a new mode"?
4. Is "Wakefield" an anecdote or a story? Define your terms.
5. What does Hawthorne see as the real evil of isolation?
6. List all of the characteristics of Wakefield that Hawthorne indicates might have something to do with his eccentric behavior. What is meant by this statement, "In Wakefield, the magic of a single night has wrought a similar transformation, because, in that brief period, a great moral change has been effected. But this is a secret from himself."
7. Hawthorne says at the end of the story, "We will not follow our friend across the threshold. He has left us much food for thought, a portion of which shall lend its wisdom to a moral, and be shaped into a figure." What is the moral?

VIII "The Gentle Boy"
1. Define archetype, myth, symbol, and image; give examples of each from Hawthorne.
2. What are the basic tenets of the Puritans? the Quakers?
3. What light does the comparison of Tobias Pearson to the Biblical Tobias throw upon the story?
4. What is Hawthorne's purpose in introducing the character of the old Quaker?
5. What changes do the revisions of "The Gentle Boy" make in the tone of the story?
6. What seems to be Mr. Gross' concept of tragedy?
7. Distinguish sentiment and sentimentality. Has Hawthorne sentimentalized Ilbrahim?

IX "The Birthmark"
1. What extensions of meaning can you find in the title of the story?
2. Does Aylmer really love Georgiana? What does he want of her? Does he need her?
3. Is a religious imagery consonant with Hawthorne's view of science?
4. Who are the Furies? Why does Mr. Heilman say that Aylmer cannot see them?

5. Does Georgiana ever attain perfection? What does Aylmer mean by perfection? What does Hawthorne mean by perfection?

6. What is the symbolism of Georgiana's touching and blighting the plant which Aylmer gives her? How does Aylmer interpret this event?

7. Aylmer has assumed godlike qualities—creation, and eradication of evil—and he will accept Georgiana's idolatry if the experiment is successful. Yet Hawthorne describes the furnace of Aylmer's laboratory in terms suggesting hellfire. Is there a suggestion of Aylmer as a god in reverse—a devil, an anti-Christ?

X "Young Goodman Brown"

1. Is there any advantage to the circular structure of the story (clearing, to forest, to clearing)?

2. What are the dominant colors in the story? Do they contribute to the effectiveness of the tale?

3. Could Young Goodman Brown symbolize the Puritan religion (reread the last paragraph)? If so, what is the central meaning of Goodman Brown's experience?

4. Is there a basic disagreement in the interpretations of the story by Mr. Fogle and Mr. Hoffman? Discuss.

5. What is the reason for the dropping of Faith's pink ribbons? Does this touch add to, or detract from, the effectiveness of the story?

6. When Hawthorne says, "Goodman Brown cried out, and his cry was lost to his own ear by its unison with the cry of the desert," what does he mean by the desert? Is the desert distinguished from the forest?

7. Does Goodman Brown become a witch as Mr. Hoffman suggests? What are the sexual overtones that Hoffman sees in the story? Is there a relationship between sex and witchcraft?

Topics for Student Papers

Short Papers

1. A comparison of the criticism of James and Poe *or* Melville and Leavis *or* Lawrence and Matthiessen.

2. The evidences of Calvinism in the tales.

3. A summary of the given interpretations of any tale.

4. An interpretation of any one of the tales, taking into account the interpretations in the *Casebook*.
5. The importance of source studies of a tale.
6. An evaluation of the following devices in any story in the *Casebook*: Hawthorne's use of rhetorical questions; the conflicting explanations of events given by different characters.
7. A critique that compares and contrasts Robin and Ilbrahim.
8. A comparison of the journeys of Goodman Brown and Reuben Bourne.
9. A comparison of the quests of Robin and Aylmer.
10. Definitions and illustrations of Hawthorne's allegory, symbols, emblems, and "types."
11. Hawthorne's ministers.
12. The isolation of Wakefield and Goodman Brown.
13. Hawthorne's use of mirrors.

Longer Papers

1. Hawthorne and original sin.
2. Initiation into evil—a Hawthorne theme.
3. The "head and the heart" theme in Hawthorne.
4. The function of the symbolism in Hawthorne.
5. The color imagery in Hawthorne.
6. Hawthorne's use of crowds.
7. The symbolism of the forest and the clearing in Hawthorne.
8. Hawthorne's concept of isolation.
9. Hawthorne and secret guilt.
10. Hawthorne's concern with death and the grave.
11. Hawthorne's ambiguity—vice or virtue?
12. A detailed explication of: "The Haunted Mind" *or* "Fancy's Show Box" *or* "The Maypole of Merry Mount" *or* "The Minister's Black Veil."
13. Hawthorne and witchcraft.
14. The search for the father in Hawthorne.

Research Papers

1. Hawthorne's ideas of science in "Rappaccini's Daughter" and "The Birthmark."
2. The children in "The Gentle Boy" and in James's "The Turn of the Screw."
3. "Ethan Brand" and the "unpardonable sin."
4. The aesthetic ideal in "The Birthmark" and "The Artist of the Beautiful."
5. The clergy in "The Minister's Black Veil," "The Gentle Boy," and *The Scarlet Letter*.

6. The isolation of Clifford (*The House of the Seven Gables*) and Wakefield.

7. Witchcraft in *The Scarlet Letter* and "Young Goodman Brown."

8. Ideas of perfection in "The Birthmark" and *The Blithedale Romance*.

9. Secret guilt in "Roger Malvin's Burial" and *The Marble Faun*.

10. The idea of the quest in "My Kinsman, Major Molineux" and "Ethan Brand."

11. The reality of Hawthorne's good women: Dorcas, Georgiana, Faith, Dorothy Pearson, Mrs. Wakefield, Elizabeth, Phoebe (*The House of the Seven Gables*), Priscilla (*The Blithedale Romance*), and Hilda (*The Marble Faun*).

12. A detailed explication of any Hawthorne short story not in the *Casebook*.

13. Hawthorne's dark beauties: Catharine, Hester (*The Scarlet Letter*), Zenobia (*The Blithedale Romance*) and Miriam (*The Marble Faun*).

14. Comparison of a work by Poe *or* Melville *or* James *or* Lawrence with a work by Hawthorne.